CHALLENGING BIOLOGICAL PROBLEMS

CHALLENGING

THE AMERICAN INSTITUTE OF BIOLOGICAL SCIENCES

New York   **OXFORD UNIVERSITY PRESS**

BIOLOGICAL PROBLEMS

DIRECTIONS TOWARD THEIR SOLUTION

25th ANNIVERSARY VOLUME

JOHN A. BEHNKE, Editor
BioScience

EDITORIAL COMMITTEE

HARLYN O. HALVORSON
Rosenstiel Basic Medical Science Research Center
Brandeis University

CARL P. SWANSON
Department of Botany &
Institute for Man and His Environment
University of Massachusetts

WILLIAM G. VAN DER KLOOT
Department of Physiology and Biophysics
Health Sciences Center
State University of New York, Stony Brook

1972

Preface

Speculation has played a major role in the advancement of science. But its contribution is often not fully appreciated. Since the end results of scientific inquiry are generalizations based on accumulated facts, verified through applying rigid logical rules, publicly we are apt to downgrade the role of the inspired hunch, the imaginative approach to a problem. Those who know science well and daily play the game, however, understand that the best investigators progress by the use of fleet insight followed by step by step proof. It is the mark of a T. H. Morgan to see, perhaps in a flash, the possibility of finding an answer to heredity in the lowly fruit fly. It takes an Otto Loewi to dream of an experiment that will demonstrate the reality of the neurohumors.

On a lower Olympian plane, many scientists work largely on an observational and confirmation level, a less-demanding hill to climb. Team research and funds granted for rigidly defined objectives may be helping to accentuate the plodding, data-gathering side of science. Scientists know that the formal reports at meetings and in journals of hand over hand progress provide necessary information, but the hidden "seminars" in hotel rooms and corridors, on beaches and country campuses, and lonely brainstorming are where dreams are born.

With the value of such dreams or speculations in mind and a desire to bring them out where they could charge more brainstorms, the officers of the American Institute of Biological Sciences decided to celebrate its 25th Anniversary with a volume of perceptive speculations about ways to solve some of our most interesting and critical biological problems. Inventories of past developments and of the present status of such problems have become so numerous as to be commonplace. Looking backward may bring a glow of pride to those who were involved in the work remembered but is less likely to strike fire in those seeking new and exciting paths to explore. This book is designed to kindle such thought and to spark discovery.

When our intention was announced, some concluded that we were determined to promote a new genre of science fiction. This is a misinterpretation of our intent. In science fiction the author predicts that a certain sequence of discoveries *will be made* leading to a pre-determined result. The spirit and aim of the chapters that follow are quite different. Our authors, to varying degrees, have taken a "what would happen if we tried this or that?" approach to their respective problems. From a review of the salient points of their problems, they have attempted to predict directions and alternatives—not outcomes. The reader will find a galaxy of approaches, which, in themselves, are most stimulating.

Our first decision was not to organize the book around biological disciplines. There was neither space nor time to do them justice, and the excellent volume, "Biology and the Future of Man," edited by Philip Handler and prepared by distinguished panels of the National Academy of Sciences Survey Committee on the Life Sciences (Oxford University Press, 1970) had already analyzed future disciplinary directions in depth. We chose rather to center our attention on crucial problems, most of them at least partially interdisciplinary. But what problems and which authors?

The editor started by listing the problems identified in another NAS publication, "The Life Sciences." Nominations of problems and potential authors were solicited from the AIBS officers, the members of the *BioScience* Editorial Board and the members of the Editorial Committee chosen to work on the book. Personal letters were also written to a wide spectrum of prominent biologists. The result was a list of nearly 125 problems, some narrow, some broad, and many overlapping. These were grouped by related subjects and as primarily basic or applied.

The Editorial Committee then set to work to select the problems. The members agreed that rather than have separate sections devoted to theoretical and applied problems, we would encourage authors to treat their subjects both ways. In our invitations to participants, we emphasized this point. The 17 biological problems included were designed to be broad enough to allow a reasonable amount of latitude and not too broad to be handled in a concise chapter. The Committee also agreed on the importance of including the four chapters on biological communication; the ethical, social and economic climate for the life sciences (2); and graduate education.

The AIBS has always had a genuine interest in students at all levels. Those of us from the Institute involved in this project hope that these speculations will not only encourage students to choose careers in biology but also to find problems truly challenging for their research efforts.

To further stimulate their interest, we provided space for three chapters by students. We sent letters to 3000 life science departments asking them to invite their students to submit papers. The only stipulations were that they should be bonafide students not yet granted the doctorate. It would have been unrealistic to expect their papers to be speculative. A committee of judges, including Dr. Harold Finley, Howard University; Dr. Evelyn Hurlburt, Montgomery College and Dr. Gardner Lynn, Catholic University reviewed the entries and selected those included at the end of the book.

The Institute and I owe the authors of chapters a very special vote of thanks for producing outstanding contributions on an almost impossible schedule. We also deeply appreciate the creative thought and hard work of the Editorial Committee—Harlyn O. Halvorson, Carl P. Swanson, and William G. Van der Kloot. Anonymous critics of the various chapters made a constructive contribution, and the judges (already named) of the student papers performed an important task well.

The officers and the staff of the Institute not only offered valuable advice and encouragement but also wrote the "Introduction" and two important chapters ("The Integrative Approach to Biological Classification" and "The Regulation of Human Population"). I appreciated the help in the selection of problems and authors of the members of the Editorial Board of *BioScience* and many individuals—too many to list by name.

William C. Halpin and the staff at Oxford University Press have carried the production of the book through in excellent form and in record time. The advice and assistance of my "editor-teacher" wife helped beyond words in solving problems and providing unfailing encouragement. Finally, a very special "thank you" goes to my Secretary, Martha R. Kresheskey, for an inspired dedication to seeing the project through.

New York   J.A.B.
June 1972

Contents

ix

CHALLENGING BIOLOGICAL PROBLEMS

Introduction:
Future Challenges for the AIBS

JOHN R. OLIVE
AMERICAN INSTITUTE OF BIOLOGICAL SCIENCES

The American Institute of Biological Sciences was organized in 1947 to coordinate and promote scientific liaison between the different professional groups within biology and between biology and other sciences, such as chemistry and physics. By uniting the fragmented divisions of the biological sciences, the Institute was to be the spokesman for biology at large. "Now, 25 years later," states Dr. Detlev W. Bronk, one of the founders of the Institute, "the American Institute of Biological Sciences has a record of remarkable leadership and achievement. The schism between the zoological and botanical sciences is difficult to recall now that molecular biology comprises both and 'biology' has been broadened to 'the life sciences' which include the behavioral sciences too. . . . The AIBS is thus a heritage from them (the founders) to those who believe that knowledge cannot be contained within boundaries." We are confident that, in facing future challenges, the AIBS will continue to live up to its heritage, striving to communicate across boundaries not successfully crossed in the past.

A monument to AIBS involvement in the development of educational programs and improved communications among scientists exists in the Institute's past accomplishments and current contributions. In education, these include many valuable projects like the Biological Science Curriculum Study (BSCS), the AIBS Biological Sciences Film Series, and the

3

Visiting Lecturers' Program, all developed to meet the changing needs of students and to improve the quality of biology instruction.

The AIBS faces even greater challenges in the future if it is to be effective in serving the demands of modern biology. There is a tremendous need for revamping biological education throughout the United States. New methods must be developed to reach and involve high school students, college students, and parents. New approaches must be incorporated into educational programs to encourage participation in biology at various levels. An example of a current innovative program is Project BIOTECH which utilizes the modular approach in the development of teaching materials for training biotechnicians.

The information gap between biology and the physical sciences must be bridged. Currently, the BioInstrumentation Advisor Council (BIAC) of the AIBS facilitates information flow between biological and physical scientists by evaluating the current status of the application of the physical sciences to biological problems, initiating and supporting the development and dissemination of new techniques, and preparing surveys of the contemporary status of instrumentation for biologists. Considering the complexity and dynamic nature of today's scientific endeavors, there is an increased need for improved methods for interdisciplinary input and retrieval of information.

To participate in a viable democratic government, the public, too, must be informed. This outreach should be made in terms of all media, including national and international press, radio, and television. The AIBS can contribute by more effectively communicating the role of biology to the public, by insuring that information on public science programs is accurate, and by continuing its various education programs and initiating new ones as the needs arise.

As the public becomes more and more aware of the problems caused by pollution, overpopulation, and industrialization and as the government becomes more involved in regulating these areas, the advisory role of the AIBS becomes increasingly important. The impact of progress, such as highway construction, urbanization, and improved transportation, must be rationally assessed. If society's complex problems are to be approached from a scientific base rather than with hysteria, biologists must cooperate with economists, sociologists, engineers, physicists, and experts from other areas to make the facts available. The AIBS has the capability to provide the biological expertise to observe the problems objectively and to advise the federal agencies. The AIBS is officially represented in the Scientific Manpower Commission, Biological Science Information Services, American Association for the Advancement of Science, and United States National Committee for UNESCO, among others, and is regularly called upon to provide experts as individual consultants to various federal agencies, including the National Aeronautics and Space Administration, Office of Naval Research, U.S. Atomic Energy Commission, and the Department of Interior. The Special Science Programs of the AIBS afford biologists an opportunity to interact with the biological programs of federal agencies. The influence of the biologist is assured through AIBS participation in advisory panels, committees, and proposal review groups. In February of this year AIBS representatives met with the President's Science Advisor to review the President's budget and to offer suggestions and criticisms which would be useful to the White House staff and the policy planners in the Office of Science and Technology. This meeting was a major step forward for increasing the involvement of the Institute and marks the beginning of a new era in the relationship between the biological community and the government. The AIBS anticipates the necessity for expansion of this role in the future.

The official journal of the Institute, *BioScience,* also faces an expanded role in providing information to biologists. To better inform the biological community, the journal must emphasize its news and views component, offer increased information about legislation or governmental policies directly affecting the biological sciences, and effectively voice the many problems facing contemporary biologists.

Meetings present another challenge for improving communications among biologists and keeping the biological community abreast of the latest advances and discoveries in the scientific field. In recent years, a plenary session for all attendees has been a feature of the Annual AIBS Meeting, directing the attention of both the participating biologists and the public to the vital role biology must play if the serious problems which confront mankind are to be solved. In cooperation with other organizations, the Institute also sponsors national biological congresses to help create a better public understanding of science, and international conferences to discuss research opportunities and to exchange information.

The Institute foresees greater emphasis on international scientific cooperation and is seeking contact with comparable agencies in other countries. It recognizes that greater involvement with developing countries is also essential. In a time of supersonic transport and communication via satellite, the problems we face are world problems, and their solutions require international approaches.

For AIBS to fulfill its role effectively, it is essential that it have the active participation of all biologists. Its relationship with biologists is symbiotic, for they need an organization which can unify the fragmented disciplines and speak forcefully for them as a whole. The unification of biologists remains one of the Institute's greatest challenges. Dr. David Davis, past president of the AIBS suggests: "Science is integrating but organizations are disintegrating. . . . One promising approach [to this problem] is to apply to biological societies the same systems approach that we apply to ecological communities. How can we maximize energy, i.e. research funds, in the biological disciplines? How can we increase the efficiency of use of these resources by decreasing infant mortality, i.e. fruitless ideas? How can diversity, i.e. disciplines, serve to stabilize the community? Another approach to this problem is to increase the awareness that biology is an entity which relies on all aspects for its advancement. And still another approach is to recognize the need for population control of organizational units."

In the next few years, the AIBS anticipates an even greater involvement in its role as intermediary between the biological science community and the major events about which biologists need to be aware and to which they should contribute their expertise. Practically all the major problems in the future have biology at their base, and this leaves biologists with a compelling obligation to participate and share their knowledge. Solving the problems of the environment, population, industrialization, space exploration, and other problems facing our dynamic society will require total cooperation and dedication on the part of all biologists. Interaction with the sister sciences and the interested public will be highly essential. More than ever, solutions to the problems will have to be sought through a team approach, with engineers, physicists, biologists, chemists, and social scientists cooperating and sharing a unity of purpose.

In facing the future, all biologists must think in terms of innovation, and they must be aware of other interacting disciplines. They must be alert to changing needs of the biological community and to the role of biologists in a changing world. The American Institute of Biological Sciences is dedicated to serving the interests of biology and biologists in meeting these challenges.

1 Biological Innovation and Genetic Intervention

JOSHUA LEDERBERG
DEPARTMENT OF GENETICS
Stanford University
PROGRAM ON SCIENCE, TECHNOLOGY AND SOCIETY
Center for Advanced Study in the Behavioral Sciences
Stanford, California

This volume is intended to be a glimpse of the future as a way of celebrating the history of an exciting era in biological science. The hazards of prophecy (not least to the prophets) are well known. Still, it would be a relatively simple task to post lookouts at the frontiers of contemporary insight and knowledge in fields like genetics and molecular biology. If, mercifully, our range is confined to the next 25 years, shrewd observers may miss no more than half of the significant questions that will unpredictably emerge and may score even better in outlining the solutions to some of the major problems that are clearly recognized—like the structure and development of the nervous system, immunity, or neoplasia. We should, however, be uneasy (or delighted, according to one's temperament) about the prevalent mood that tells that most of the really exciting fundamental questions have been answered—for history teaches that this often foretells a new scientific revolution that could shake our beliefs to their very roots.

This purview is based on an autonomous model of science that has uncertain durability. Perceived ignorance (or error) is postulated to be

The latter portion of this essay has been adapted from a presentation to the Jubilee Symposium of Hoffman-LaRoche & Co., Ltd., held at Basel, Switzerland in September 1971, and is used here with their kind permission.

7

the main orienting influence in scientific activity. Paradoxically, the more we know, the better we perceive what we do not; hence, the process is inherently autocatalytic. We should, then, be able to judge the main directions of scientific development as the exploration of the *known unknown*. The main uncertainty is the liability of all autocatalytic processes to burgeon unexpectedly in scale, or in direction, in response to imperceptible fluctuations.

A glance at the national research budget over the last five years is enough to deflate the political plausibility of this model. The overall growth of science is clearly not autocatalytic, and, increasingly, other issues of political and social choice override the opportunity presented by perceived ignorance as determinants of investment and support.

On the one hand, the central flow and apportionment of research funds is increasingly tied to specific technological missions, like cleaning up the environment or curing cancer. On the other, the autonomy of the research laboratory is increasingly caught up in irresistible pressures at the periphery for social goals that are orthogonal to scientific knowledge: equal opportunity in education and employment for minority groups and women, amenities for the local community, and the ideals of participatory democracy. (The laboratory, of course, did serve other masters in the past—viz., the ego-aggrandizement of the chief Forscher, or the central motifs of the industrial-capitalist culture.) Specific research projects are also under increasingly severe scrutiny by polarized cults of critics on issues like the exploitation of human subjects, relevance (intended by the investigator or not) to the military capability of the country, or potential abuse in conflicts over welfare assistance and population policy.

These pressures are bound to impinge on the conduct of science through their influence on institutional support but, of equal importance, on the recruitment of students and perhaps, above all, on the morale of the investigators themselves.

It follows, then, that the future course of biological research will be influenced only in limited measure by its technical opportunities, even as far as they can be observed from the existing frontier. The prophet must also foresee the outcome of complexly interwoven trends in the ethics, politics, economics, and social structure of the entire culture in which science is embedded. No contingency more dreadful than large scale nuclear warfare can be imagined. If even this can hardly be dismissed with the confidence of a logically-rigorous demonstration, how much more precarious are our predictions that bypass many other tempests.

I am scarcely qualified to enlarge the reader's previsions of the larger scene. What is manifest is that scientists will be less and less indulged as innocents, that they will be increasingly bewildered if they do not attend to the social forces that rive our milieu. Indeed, we may have to take a more positive role in leading the culture through the religious crisis that scientific skepticism has done much to edify. To understand how "society" will deal with science demands a deeper understanding of how science is perceived by the public, and how scientific progress influences the welfare of everyman. The noisiest grievances about science (or technology) have to do with weaponry and with environmental ravagement. An even more durable complaint may be the Luddites'—that new machines deprive men of a sense of worth in their work by unregulated technical progress that outpaces human adaptability.

Scientists should also seek a deeper understanding of their own profession—what inspiration and discovery really consist of and the forces that mold the choice of researchworthy problems. They may then be more likely to face up to the rationalization of their work (even in ways that may lead to their own technological displacement); for example, through more efficient dissemination of research literature or through the development of computers to undertake lower level "cerebral" functions (Feigenbaum et al., 1971). Can we believe that we have an ideal understanding of the innate talents and learned skills required for most effective performance in different fields or that the disciplines themselves are most effectively and adaptively organized?

This preamble may be summarized with a presumptuous assertion that limits to the development of scientific knowledge of life are no longer technical ones. The elucidation of the "secret" of heredity, the replication of DNA, leaves no doubt that the basic principles of many other mysteries of biology are also tractable by similar methods. We have no need to invoke an *élan vital,* other than sheer complexity of organization, to account for the special attributes of life. (That complexity remains, however, an effective and formidable guardian of the freedom of the individual will in any practical test.) It follows that further advances in biology will be dictated by the problems that biologists choose to attack; this, in turn, will be enforced by social policy to a far greater degree than in the past. An inevitable corollary is exposure to the crossfires of political conflict over the definition of the social good. There are many signs to justify Aron's (1968) prediction that the fundamental conflict may be between relative-egalitarian versus absolute-efficient conceptions of ethical utilities. (Which is preferable: to live in a levelled society free of disparity or a stratified one, whose pyramid may rise from a higher base?) Biologists, as imputed experts on the diversity of organisms, will face many dilemmas over this social conflict of equality and efficiency (Lederberg, 1972).

The long run possibilities of biological technology are unbounded—even mortality may become a matter of definition of the rate of change of memory and personality (converging, then, with the consoling reassurances of the great religions), as we contemplate the gradual but increasingly foreplanned replacement of outworn molecules. But, in the short run, everyone still dies, and too many die prematurely according to any ethical standard. Futuristic pretensions about genetic engineering are a mockery to a mother who has delivered a trisomic child. And we are still unable to tell the offspring of a Huntington's choreic whether he will transmit the disease to his children or, indeed, whether he will in some few years succumb himself. This disparity between present-day reality and eventual potentiality may arouse deep-seated resentments against that rosier future and even against contemporary scientists who are not quite able to bring it off—in time. Perhaps this is an argument against advertising the future, but too much indispensable planning hangs on clarifying the picture the best we can. The remainder of this essay will, however, focus on the challenges and horizons of the more recent future.

According to popular legend, "anything possible will be done" if the technologists get their hands on it. Anyone who is trying to do anything substantial knows that the opposite is usually true. Absent the incentives of military applications, the more sophisticated the science the greater is the distance between its conceptual opportunities and reduction to practice. One of the most egregious gaps between scientific potential and human needs is in agriculture. Formidable technical competence and human importance attach to the new introductions of dwarf wheat and rice which have promoted the green revolution. Nevertheless, the scientific foundations of these breeding ventures go little beyond the rediscovery of mendelism in 1900. Shrewd agronomic insight, and meticulous attention to detail in the selection of parent stocks and intermediate hybrid lines, rather than innovational genetic theory, were the roots of these successes.

It is likely that many more opportunities await the intelligent application of the most straightforward techniques of plant breeding. They will, in fact, be indispensable, merely to retain our present position in the face of the evolution of parasites adapted to new and homogeneous genotypes.

In principle, the cell- and molecular-genetics developed in the last 25 years could make even more incisive contributions, but it has yet to make any significant impact. Some of the fault must be laid at the door of the agricultural research establishment. But the USDA must, in turn, be responsive to a community that now puts increased crop efficiency very low on its list of priorities, since bumper crops prove to be economic disasters. We are, then, relatively backward in fundamental biochemical and genetic investigations of the development of seed proteins compared to their importance in human nutrition. Until recently, the NIH would have been hard put to justify research grants on the amino acid sequence of zeins in different varieties of corn. But if we had information of this kind, to the depth of, say, our knowledge of human hemoglobins, we should be much further along in designing more efficacious sources of plant protein.

This remark does too little credit to the empirical development (IAEA Panel, 1969) of hi-lysine corn. The nutritional advantage of these mutants, which have visibly-altered seeds, evidently depends on the diminution of zein content and substitution by other proteins. However, the developmental mechanisms involved are still poorly understood, and we are still very far from a rational design of a seed protein optimized for human nutrition. With a more detailed analysis of gene-controlled protein sequences, we would have a firm basis for the stepwise accumulation of point mutations or recombinants towards that optimum. The substitution of threonine for serine, or of lysine for arginine, in a seed protein would be expected to have little impact on its function for the plant compared to its utility for man. Plant breeding is, of course, burdened with logistic problems of assessing intact seedlings as the units of genic expression and with the traditional problems of diploid inheritance (need for back-crosses and multiple progeny tests). These might be averted by more attention to artificial haploids and to the manipulation of plant cells in culture, including cell fusion. Similar techniques have greatly advanced our knowledge of the genetics of a species, man, which few would have expected to outstrip maize two decades ago.

Viruses (as an exemplification of plasmagenes) may also play a role.

(Indeed, they already do; for example, in the control of male fertility for the production of hybrid corn). An example of genetic engineering of a virus that may eventually be important for improving the quality of plant protein is suggested by the claim of Rogers and Pfuderer (1968) of the engineering of a tobacco mosaic virus variant to which poly-A was appended, with the concomitant production of excess polylysine. Well defined clones of such variant viruses have not, however, been reported.

A control long-run objective for molecular agrobiology is the maximization of protein yield at the expense of polysaccharides. The plant will have to be engineered into a kind of lactating organ in which just enough structural cellulose is invested to sustain the primary utility of protein synthesis. The dwarf varieties, indeed, exhibit this very principle.

Human consumption of photosynthetic product amounts to about 300 M (3×10^8) tons of fixed carbon per year. This is only about 5% of the total crop yield, most of this being waste tillage. Crops, in turn, make up only 10% of land-cover photosynthesis; it will be at least as difficult to expand this ratio as to improve the efficiency of already cultivated lands. A rising population will have few alternatives more palatable than the use of chemically recycled cellulose or fossil carbon for human, as well as industrial, fuel.

The salvage of the world food resources is by all odds a mixed blessing, according to well-known Malthusian reasoning. It is difficult to see how striving countries will be induced to limit their population growth so long as the weight of numbers is a political, and even a military, weapon in interstate competition. The technical means of contraception are improvable, but scarcely lacking now. We have little basis for optimism except the hope that world order and economic modernization may advance in spite of the population drag, and that these factors will encourage a demographic reversal. The natural and man-made disasters that have afflicted Bengal are visions of the alternate paths.

Another crushing affliction of most of the world is infestation with animal parasites, especially malaria, blood flukes, and worms. Environmental sanitation, directed at vector control, has been the most effective public health measure to mitigate these debilitations, but tropical countries are likely to remain burdened with them for many years nevertheless. The well defined life cycle of these parasites should make them biologically fascinating, as well as humanely rewarding, targets for more profound study with modern methods. The attenuated mutant already plays a central role in prophylaxis against virus infection by vaccination

without the benefit of deep insight into the mechanism by which the parasitism is frustrated. With the flukes and worms, well defined morphogenetic stages are involved in the progress of an infestation, and with the
malaria plasmodia, it should be even easier to superimpose biochemical
analyses of the critically altered stages of attenuated mutants which could
confer analogous benefits in the form of virus vaccines for the control of
corresponding diseases. The genetic engineering of Plasmodium falci-
parum vies with that of Oryza sativa as a further target of molecular
genetics.

From the standpoint of scientific and technical accessibility and of
clarity of ethical consequence, parasites and domesticated animals and
plants are clearly the most attractive targets for genetic design. However,
utopian aspirations for the "biological improvement" of man were appended to the development of genetics even before its emergence as a
rigorous experimental discipline. The eugenic aspiration, of course, con-
flicted headon with theological doctrines of the origin of man in original
sin and alternative recipes for salvation. It is refueled today by doctrines
of the inevitability of evil in human nature that are fallacious deductions
from ethological research.

The most telling argument for eugenics is the fear that the existing
human species is doomed to self-destruction. But a culture that cannot
evolve the political machinery to contain its weapons will hardly improve
its competence for survival by adding biological engineering to its repertoire.

Like many other messianic visions, eugenics is faulted by a confusion
between the needs of an abstract *mankind* and those of individual men
and women. In many arenas, utopian aims for the ordering of human
affairs might be achieved at the sacrifice of individual liberties. In the
economic sphere, "from each according to his abilities" is a plausible
humanitarian ideal, but it can be enforced only with the apparatus of a
police state and an arbitrary determination of what each has to contribute. Apart from the already fatal obstacles of political implementation,
genetic planning faces frustrations analogous to the failures of planned
economies, both with respect to technique and to the validation of consensual purposes. In the real world, social movements will continue to
have much more incisive effects on the human gene pool than any conceivable technical advances that could be labelled as "tampering with
the genes."

Geneticists, in the main, have been so critical of large-scale eugenics that they may forget that the allegation of seeking to breed Supermen will be renewed in every popular discussion. Some of my own efforts to outline the difficulties and paradoxes of genetic design have, for example, been misquoted (Ramsey, 1970) as advocacy. I will plead guilty to withholding categorical anathema on issues that are amenable to deeper exploration, both technically and morally. Social attitudes on questions like contraception and abortion have changed too dramatically in one or two generations to reinforce the posture of sempiternity of our ethical pronouncements, above all in human biology. This is no assurance of ever-increasing permissiveness—the history of the tides of moral fervor shows more displacement than dissipation, and they may return once again to now-abandoned shores.

Let it be clearly posited, nevertheless, that the remaking of man is an illusionary goal for the application of genetics in a liberal society.

The principal task of genetics is scientific understanding; the principal target for its applications to man is the alleviation of individual distress—which the physician cannot repudiate no matter what the general state of the world. In pursuing his goals, it should go without saying that the geneticist is bound by the same set of ethical restraints that apply to other innovative branches of medicine. The surgeon does not use his scalpel by whim, and even in the chase after potential knowledge, he is, above all, accountable by law and ethical tradition to the needs of his patient.

Table I catalogs a number of potential techniques that may relate to the prevention or therapy of genetic disease or which may influence genetic constitution. This is not a well-bounded arena, for all of medicine —indeed, all of culture—is potentially euphenic and eugenic. That is, they may: 1) ameliorate the actual development and expression of genetic predisposition, and 2) thereby, indirectly influence the relative frequency of different genes in the population.

The boundaries of what should be called "genetic" disease are also uncertain, for every pathology must have both a genetic and an environmental component. Many common diseases, as well as overall longevity, have a significant heritability. About 5% of overall morbidity can be related to specific genetic defects with a relatively simple basis; if we also take account of the heritable component of prevalent diseases, like schizophrenia, diabetes, cardiovascular disease, and so on, at least a fourth of total morbidity (in medically advanced communities) must be attributed to genetic imperfections.

Genetic Load, Mutagenesis, and Environmental Hygiene

The genetic load is, therefore, a formidable part of the problems that must be faced by medical practitioners and their patients. Plainly, preventive measures should have a high priority, if we could, thereby, prevent the intrusion of genetic defects in the first instance. This may not always be possible—an unknown part of the genetic load is "segregational"; it derives from heterosis; i.e., an advantage of the heterozygote over either homozygote. Natural selection, then, tends to keep both of the alternative alleles in the population, notwithstanding the inevitable quota of impaired homozygotes that must recur at every generation.

Heterosis is important to framing reasonable expectations for genetic improvement since no freely-breeding population can then be composed exclusively of the healthiest (heterozygous) phenotypes. The production of high-yielding corn is based on the careful nurturing of a number of rather weakly, highly-inbred strains as parent stocks which are then crossed to produce vigorous hybrids. The farmer who tries to use these, in turn, as seed corn courts disaster—a fact hardly in keeping with racist mythology or with the naiver forms of eugenicism.

Furthermore, the heritability of different diseases gives no assurance that a single optimum genotype can exist. Susceptibility to cancer may reflect a low excitability of the immune mechanism; allergy the converse. Total freedom, both from cancer and allergy, may be physiologically unattainable. We have only provocative data about mutual exclusions in predisposition to disease, but we can still be fairly sure that we have more choice about how, rather than whether, to die.

These aspects of disease genetics are relatively independent of the mutation rate, responding mainly to natural selection. They offer some room for genetic insight, short of total amelioration, since the existing gene pool has evolved in a historical context of medical and other cultural determinants that have changed far more rapidly than gene frequencies can have responded. Furthermore, Darwinian fitness, or reproductivity, is becoming less and less congruent with the standards of somatic quality by which we judge ourselves and our peers.

However, the "mutational" part of the genetic load must be considerable, and this is related to the rate of mutation (informational deterioration) in the genetic material. A certain level of mutation is an inevitable

TABLE I. *Potential Technologies of Eugenics and Euphenics (Not Confined to Man)* *

A. *Selective mating:*
  1) By phenotype of parents (assisted by biochemical and cytological assay)
     a) negative—distracting, discouraging, or sterilizing the "unfit"
     b) positive—
         i) encouraging select pairs
        ii) with artificial insemination, donor ("rational germinal choice")
       iii) with oval or ovarian transplant
        iv) both ii and iii, or fertilization *in vitro,* followed by implantation
         v) extracorporeal gestation (test tube baby)—*see also* euphenics
        (i–v are not very different in their *genetic* consequences)
  2) By genotype of parents—as above, with deeper analysis of parental consti-
     tution. Except for specific aberrations, very little can be said at present
     about genetics of *desirable* traits.
  3) By relationship of parents
     a) inbreeding—The main impact is to expose recessive, usually deleterious,
        genes; increase phenotypic variability of F_1; decrease the genotypic
        variability of later generations.
     b) outbreeding—antithesis of a). Most cultures strongly encourage out-
        breeding.
  4) By age of parents—to forfend accumulation of deleterious mutations and
     chromosome anomalies which increase with parental age
  5) By phenotype or genotype of the zygote or of the fetus (antenatal diag-
     nosis and voluntary abortion)—Earlier selections would avoid the trauma
     of aborting an established fetus.
  6) By genotype of the gametes; e.g., separation of X from Y or normal from
     defect-bearing sperm
  7) With sperm of other species (compare 1) b) iv))—Nothing is known of
     the consequences among primate species (possibly *in vitro*). All con-
     temporary races of man appear to be freely infertile. Cross-pollination is,
     of course, a crucial technique in plant breeding.

B. *Innovations in Zygote Biology*—Vegetative (asexual) propagation. Cloning.
   (Almost universal among plant spp.)
  1) Parthenogenesis—development of an unfertilized egg. (This might be
     genetically identical to the mother, or might be a product of meiosis,
     which would be an intense form of inbreeding.)
  2) Regeneration—development of a whole individual from somatic tissues (as
     in some plants and lower animals like earthworms)
  3) Differentiation of gametes from somatic tissues previously subject to ex-
     tensive genetic manipulation

  * From Lederberg, 1971b; *see also* Davis, 1970.

TABLE I. (*Cont.*)

4) Somatic reduction in gamete-forming cells in culture (somatic inbreeding) —would allow predictable outcome of further matings from a given parent which is not now assured.
5) Nuclear transplantation—renucleation of a fertilized enucleated egg. Genetically equivalent to cloning from the source of the nucleus
6) Embryo—splitting to produce twins or multiplets. Not to be confused with multiple ovulation (occasionally induced by fertility-promoting drugs). About ⅓ of spontaneous twins are monozygotic, i.e., arise from the splitting of one embryo.
Note also the opposite phenomenon.
7) Embryo fusion (chimerism)—so that one individual comprises two or more genotypes. This grades into tissue transplantation at later stages. It should allow different genotypes a new latitude for mutual complementation, *e.g., mens sana in corpore sano.* Somewhat less than 1/1000 live births are spontaneous chimeras, but some of these arise by other mechanisms.

C. *Adjuncts from somatic cell biology*—For eugenic applications, these would be coupled with procedures like B. 5). For euphenic effects, altered cells can be grafted back to a host or some manipulations done directly on his tissues.
1) Algeny—directed alterations of genes
a) controversial claims of effects of DNA uptake in mammalian cells following a long tradition of genetic work with DNA in bacteria
b) incorporation of viruses
i) experimental tumor viruses
ii) use of specially modified viruses
1) vaccination to induce immunity to viruses
2) virogenic therapy to replace missing genes
3) virogenic enhancement for superior performance—if we but knew the biochemistry thereof
c) incorporation of chromosome fragments transmitted by cell fusion
d) specifically induced mutations—No plausible approaches are now apparent.
2) Random mutation and specific selection of cells with altered properties— has full precedent in strain selection in microbes. Many uncertainties relating to possible cancer potential of such implants
3) Cell fusion to form somatic hybrids—These cells may then lose various chromosomes to give many new forms. Extends scope of 2). Can be readily applied to fuse cells from "distant" species, e.g., fish and human
4) Development of symbiotic strains of lower species, with habitats that grade from the external world (e.g., crops) to internal to intracellular— Parasitic worms in man have evolved in this direction with the help of adaptations to thwart immunological rejection. In principle, they might be domesticated. So also might algae be trained to an intracellular habitat in man where they might photosynthesize essential nutrients, if not bulk calories, as they already do in primitive animals.

byproduct of molecular accidents in cell metabolism. However, if we argue from the relative incidence of environmental, compared with intrinsic, carcinogenesis, which may be parallel phenomena, we may judge that four fifths of our ambient mutation rate is of environmental origin and could be eliminated by environmental hygiene (relating to drugs, food additives, and possibly some natural foods, water, and air pollutants, certain virus infections). About 10% of that quota can be attributed to the natural radiation background, which is essentially not avoidable, and an equal proportion to artificial radiation. At one point, nuclear power development appeared to be the main source of increasing environmental radiation, but the newly adopted standards of the AEC promise to keep this to a negligible proportion of the background. The major source of artificial radiation today, by far, is diagnostic X-rays which approximate half or more of the natural background. Our increasing sensitivity to genetic hygiene will raise agonizing issues of the costs and benefits of medical X-rays. These can hardly be answered by pointing to the overall benefit which is irrefutable. They do demand an examination of the dispensable margin, be this 10 or 80% of the total level of manrads now dispensed. Many physicians believe that "defensive medicine," that is, the anticipation of lawsuits for malpractice, is responsible for a needless volume of cautionary X-rays. The present legal framework compensates the single patient who might have been benefited by a routine X-ray that was negligently withheld. It does nothing for the 10,000 others or their progeny who must eventually pay some price for having been X-rayed with unimportant results. Our skills at matching these costs and benefits can only be sharpened if we are first educated to asking such questions in economic, rather than diabolic, terms.

The same issues confront us in the formulation of policy about chemical additives to the environment—solvents, drugs, food additives, and so forth. It is not very useful to assert that a compound is mutagenic without proceeding to a more quantitative evaluation of its impact, and our data on human response to chemicals is even more fragmentary than to radiation. Before joining the bandwagon against synthetics, the geneticist must caution that natural foods need a similar examination. The first authentic publication about chemical mutagenesis (Auerbach and Robson, 1944) concerned allyl isothiocyanate, a constituent of horseradish and mustard. (This compound has, moreover, been found to induce skin tumors after local application in mice.) Mustard has not, however, been subjected to the rigors of evaluation according to the Delaney Amendment, perhaps for fear that this would overturn our simplistic approaches to a problem that is as complex biologically as it is vulnerable to the bias of vested interests. Environmental hygiene may be the most fruitful area of application of more sophisticated molecular genetic analysis.

Options for Genetic Therapy

Among these options, a few stand out for offering the most realistic opportunities for health benefits. They include:

ANTENATAL DIAGNOSIS

An increasing number of diseases will be reliably diagnosed by cytological and biochemical studies on cell cultures derived by amniocentesis (Dorfman, 1972). We already have exciting advances in the understanding of several neurochemical disorders which rely upon the identification of specific enzyme defects. The techniques of cell-fusion and of chromosome identification with fluorescent stains will strengthen our ability to trace mutant genes, and similar methods will also help identify high-risk parents. We can visualize more direct assays for specific information content of DNA with techniques for the isolation of specific messenger RNA and, then, the homologous genes. The DNA segments can then, in principle, be tested in cell-free systems for protein synthesis or, perhaps, even subjected to direct analysis of their nucleotide sequences.

This level of sophistication in the analysis of gene effects should, in many cases, lead to deeper understanding of the disease and may provoke explicit therapies. Meanwhile, our main recourse is voluntary abortion of the impaired fetuses to allow a mother the best chance available to her of delivering a child free of malignant defect.

Our experience with the antenatal diagnosis of sex should help correct overanxious predictions about the anticipated misuse of "genetic engineering." This has allowed a reliable method of voluntary control of the sex of offspring for some years. Whether the sex of the fetus has ever been a controlling factor in a decision about abortion, without more persuasive indications, simply has not surfaced as a significant social problem to warrant any special regulatory controls. The common-sense and patient-oriented values of the medical profession remain the most effective bulwark against nonsensical distortions of its tools.

Actually, voluntary control of the sex of offspring might encourage a limitation of family size (e.g., one boy, one girl) consistent with the social interest in overall moderation of population growth. Then, a balanced sex ratio could be maintained even under voluntary choice.

TRANSPLANTATION

Many genetic defects involve cell populations as metabolic units that could be supplanted or restored by transplantation. For example, complete transfusion plays an important part in the therapy of Rh-hemolytic anemia (but is associated with a danger of graft- vs host-immune disease when applied to the fetus). The scope of tissue transplantation should not be judged by its present limited application which is constrained by the hazard of graft-rejection. Specific ways of mitigating rejection are bound to appear as a fruit of immunobiological and immunogenetic research. We will then have a simple, practical way, for example, to deal with sickle-hemoglobin disease—namely, by transplantation of normal erythropoietic marrow to the newborn or, perhaps, the fetus. We will also surely find that many other diseases, genetic or not, are amenable to relief by tissue and organ transplants—e.g., hepatocytes for PKU and for galactosemia, or insulin-secreting cells for diabetes. The last example illustrates the opportunities for therapy even where the transplanted organ may not be the primary seat of action of a defect.

The growing popularity of transplantation of hair (auto- today; homo- tomorrow; hetero- yesterday [the obsolete fur coat]) attests to the same principle.

Transplanted immunocytes are also likely to play a key role in the treatment of auto-immune disease (perhaps, after systemic elimination of offending cells) and in the prevention and treatment of neoplasms.

In cell biology research, we have just begun to move into the arena of systematic work on the genetics of somatic cells. The discovery by Henry Harris (1970) of Oxford of powerful methods to induce the fusion of cells has attracted enormous interest in the consequences of mixing chromosomes of different genotypes and species and in their reassortment in various combinations. The way is, then, open to genetic analysis (and genetic engineering) of mammalian and human cells in a way that would have been technically and ethically impossible otherwise. We can also expect that domesticated lines of somatic cells will be important inputs to therapeutic applications of transplants.

Vaccination and Virogenic Therapy

Since 1798, vaccination has constituted an important medical application of the genetic modification of somatic cells by viruses, though its practitioners to this day are often oblivious to its mechanism. Jenner found that inoculation with infectious lymph caused a mild disease, cowpox, immunity to which also protected against the dangerous smallpox.

Many aspects of vaccination are still scientifically obscure, but we can now describe the process in terms of molecular genetics. The DNA of the cowpox virus is purposely introduced into certain cells which adopt the genetic information contained therein. These cells thereupon produce new gene products, encoded by the viral DNA, which stimulate other body cells to produce antibodies against them. The cross-immunity is then a byproduct of the virogenic alteration of some cells of the host.

Live viruses are now widely used for vaccination against many other diseases, including polio, measles, and—in special cases or in the near future—rubella, mumps, rabies, and so on.

Vaccination can be regarded as if it were a therapy to replace the functions of hypothetical genes not normally present in the human organism, those that would endogenously stimulate the formation of antibodies. This idea can be extended, in principle, to other gene products, for example, enzymes that may be missing in certain gene-defect diseases like phenylketonuria and perhaps diabetes. Laboratory models for this kind of virogenic therapy are being perfected and rational trials for human disease can be anticipated shortly (Rogers, 1970). Although basic genetic principles underlie this technique and the genetic apparatus of somatic cells is altered, it is classified as euphenic because the germ cells are left unchanged, and there should be no effects in future generations. This is a matter of empirical observation rather than necessary principle in biology, and it is quite conceivable that some inoculated virogenes might also be inherited, as has already been postulated for certain tumor viruses in rodents. This reservation applies with equal force to vaccination against infectious diseases about which we have little information in proportion to the enormous numbers of children involved.

The recent discovery of "reverse transcriptases," which copy RNA information back to DNA, promises to simplify some of the technical problems of developing virogenic agents. Differentiated cells should, under certain conditions, produce multiple copies of active messenger RNA molecules, and it will be easier to purify and test these than to attempt to dig out a single DNA gene from the complete chromosome set. (In due course, however, this should also be facilitated by knowing the chemical signals that distinguish the active from the inactive genes in a given cell.) Reverse transcription would then allow the recoding of the RNA message into DNA which would then be spliced to a virus for facilitated re-integration into chromosomes.

Virogeny will be in competition with cell transplants for the replacement therapy for genetic defects, but each may have special advantages in particular cases. For example, the transplantation of neurones is not likely to be very helpful except at the earlier stages of development.

Proposals for virogenic therapy reawaken many other questions about the use of live virus vaccines for mass prophylaxis—a public health measure that involves most of the world's population in contrast to the few subjects of experimental approaches to gene therapy. Inevitably, live viruses will carry a residual hazard of atypical reactions, and of passenger contaminants although these could be mitigated by more attentive research. On the other hand, the assumption that public smallpox vaccination can be safely abandoned is based on experience with the management of breakthroughs under almost optimum conditions. The notion that smallpox will be finally eradicated within the decade is hindered by serious geopolitical obstacles, and we do not know what would happen if the virus should be reintroduced: 1) in unusually virulent form; 2) into populations who are immunologically relatively naive with respect to other infections as well as smallpox; and 3) under contingencies of breakdown of public health services. The 1972 epidemic may be a fortunate tocsin.

Viruses used for prophylaxis in man have been developed and monitored with scarcely more sophistication than that available to Jenner. The molecular biologist should insist that the highest standards of chemical and biological purity and characterization available in the research laboratory be applied to these agents. This will not be possible without a recognition that cheap vaccines will be worth what we pay. The drug companies cannot be faulted if higher standards are not imposed uniformly on their competitors.

Renucleation (Cloning)

From the work of Briggs and King (1952) and of Gurdon (1968), we know that an activated egg may be renucleated with a nucleus taken from a somatic cell of an existing frog. From a genetic standpoint, the new embryo is like a cutting, or clone, of a rose plant.

The question of renucleation of human eggs was first introduced (Lederberg, 1966) to make a rhetorical point. Many speculations had been put forward about the possibilities of "genetic surgery"—of a kind that would require fantastic innovations in our knowledge of molecular genetics. Renucleation in frogs had, however, been demonstrated long before, and it was also very plain that it would be available in man as a necessary prerequisite to more incisive techniques of genetic manipulation. It follows that, *if* one wishes to agonize about the likelier directions of futuristic change, he should attend to renucleation rather than genetic surgery.

My erstwhile remarks that mice and men should not differ from frogs in amenability to renucleation may have been naive. Chromosome-inactivation, exemplified by the inactivation of one X in normal female cells, may play an even more important role in tissue differentiation in mammals compared to amphibia (Di Berardino and Hoffner, 1970). In that event, renucleation may not be technically possible until long after the achievement of other aspects of ontogenetic control which, in turn, may make renucleation relatively less useful for any practical problem.

We may still discuss "cloning" if only as a speculative exercise.

If it could be done today, it is hard to see where renucleation would have very important applications, but this is precisely the kind of anticipatory study that needs to be done. On the positive side, it may give some, otherwise sterile, mates the opportunity of parenthood. An anovulatory woman might borrow an otherwise wasted egg cell, renucleate it with one of her own, or her husband's somatic cells, and have it reimplanted into her own uterus. Or a fertile wife might offer an intact egg for microsurgical fertilization with a haploid spermatocyte nucleus from her azoospermic husband.

We can properly understand the moral objections and justifications of such procedures only if we explore the whole continuum of technical interventions in human reproduction. Ever since primitive man discovered the connection between sexual intercourse and conception, human reproduction has entailed deliberate exercise of purpose and intelligence, an unavoidable power and responsibility for the next generation. The guarding of such responsibilities against external intrusions is the essence of personal freedom. It goes without saying that we would abhor state-enforced reproduction of any kind. Conversely, to what extent should individual patients be deprived of the possibility of using technical devices they, and their professional counselors, believe to be in their own and their offspring's interest?

Many unanswered questions remain on the ethical or technical merits of renucleation. Popular discussion of cloning has probably overemphasized the significance of a common genotype: Monozygotic twins are not copies of an identical personality, especially if they have been reared separately. They do resemble one another more closely than other relatives, to be sure, and renucleation could be a means of avoiding certain genetic defects that arise from segregation. If, for other valid reasons, renucleation is ever practiccd, we can clear up many uncertainties about the interplay of heredity and environment; and students of human nature will not want to waste such opportunities. So many developmental hazards may be associated with renucleation that very extensive animal studies would be the minimum prerequisite to ethically justifiable trials in man, and the interval gives us ample time to ponder the values in balance.

Our consensual standards of an ethical medical experiment require that it serve a reasonable humanitarian purpose and that it have the informed consent of the individuals concerned. The problem of renucleation sets into relief the general problem of parenthood. Who else can speak for the welfare of the individual not yet in being? Should parents be held in contempt if they procreate despite the knowledge that they are risking a significant deformity in their offspring? Should they be encouraged to undertake artificial measures that will give their young an easier start? And where is the boundary-line between the responsibility of the parent and of the community for manipulating a child's development—the socialization or education that predestines him to function as a particular kind of human being?

These questions are properly applied to the destinies of particular individuals born day by day. Gloomy predictions about the long-range future of the species might be substantiated as a side effect of medical care and other welfare measures that avert the pain of natural selection. However, the pace of discovery in genetics is so rapid, compared to that of biological evolution, that we can afford to wait another 50 or 100 years before we tackle the species problem. We will then have sharper tools and, at least, as much wisdom about how to use them. Meanwhile, we have enough to do in trying to minimize the enormous burden of personal distress and anxiety that attends our genetic load as it is manifest birth by birth, death by death. Indeed, it is hard to see how we can make better substantial progress towards an ideal of human improvement than by freeing individual families of the anxiety and the burden of known defects. The general questions of human improvement (Lederberg, 1971a) apply with equal force to policies of education and even to the standards of health and nutrition promulgated by pediatricians.

Summary

Advances in molecular biology promise to enlarge our technical capacity to intervene in genetic problems. Social and ethical factors are, therefore, likely to play an increasingly important role in determining the application of new scientific advances in man. This is no cause for great alarm, for the same principle already applies to the use of surgery and of other medical interventions that could, in theory, also be applied for extraordinary "renovations" of human nature.

The evolution of wise policies for the use of genetic advances, and the surveillance of existing practices for compliance with consensual ethical standards, and for the anticipation of social injury, of course, requires a widely disseminated understanding of the probable potentialities of various types of genetic intervention.

The most important influences on the genetic composition of the human species are likely to remain side effects of other global policies: the movement of populations, transportation technology, the effects of war and of discrepancies in economic development and attention to preventive genetic hygiene, especially through the identification and elimination of principal environmental sources of gene mutation.

Specific options for genetic therapy include the rapidly developing field of antenatal diagnosis (coupled with elective abortion of threatened fetuses); cell and organ transplantation; and virogenic therapy. The last would entail the introduction of desired DNA segments into domesticated strains of viruses; these would then serve for the vaccination of patients lacking a critical metabolic function which would then be restored under the influence of the added DNA.

The renucleation of eggs (cloning) is also a theoretical possibility, likely to be of more metaphorical, than pragmatic, interest. The discussion of cloning may help to illuminate the ethical problem of parenthood, generally: What is the responsibility of each generation for the biological and educational predetermination of its successors?

In any event, the central responsibility of the geneticist, *qua* physician, is to the welfare of his individual patients.

References

I could not pretend to have mastered all of the works that would have to be cited in a comprehensive bibliography of the subjects of this paper. Indeed, the central issues might be obscured more than clarified by too detailed an elaboration.

A comprehensive bibliography on *bioethics* is maintained by Kennedy Center for Bioethics, Georgetown University, Washington, D.C.

Further references may be found in the bibliographies of the papers cited here and by using these, in turn, as keys for a citation-index search of current literature. This list of references has been limited to secondary sources and to a few titles essential for the clarity of the text. The most secure prediction that can be made about the near future is the early obsolescence of this bibliography.

Aron, R. 1968. *Progress and Disillusion—the Dialectics of Modern Society.* Signet (N.A.L.), New York.

Auerbach, C. and J. M. Robson. 1944. Production of mutations by allyl iso-thiocyanate. *Nature,* **154**: 81-82.

Briggs, R. and T. J. King. 1952. Transplantation of living nuclei from blastula cells into enucleated frogs eggs. *Proc. Nat. Acad. Sci., Washington,* **38**: 455-463.

Davis, B. D. 1970. Prospects for genetic intervention in man. *Science,* **170**: 1279-1283.

Di Berardino, M. A. and N. Hoffner. 1970. Origin of chromosomal abnormalities in nuclear transplants—a reevaluation of nuclear differentiation and nuclear equivalence in amphibians. *Dev. Biol.,* **23**: 185-209.

Dorfman, A. (ed.). 1972. *Antenatal Diagnosis.* University of Chicago Press, Chicago.

Feigenbaum, E. A., B. G. Buchanan, and J. Lederberg. 1971. On generality and problem solving: A case study using the DENDRAL program. *Machine Intelligence, 6*: 165-190.

Gurdon, J. B. 1968. Transplanted nuclei and cell differentiation. *Science, 219*: 24-36.

Harris, H. 1970. *Cell Fusion*. Harvard University Press, Cambridge, Mass.

IAEA Panel, 1969. New Approaches to breeding for improved plant protein. International Atomic Energy Agency, Vienna.

Lederberg, J., 1966. Experimental genetics and human evolution. *Amer. Nat., 100*: 519-531.

―――. 1971a. Orthobiosis: the perfection of man. *In*: A. Tiselius and S. Nilsson (eds.). *The Place of Value in a World of Facts*. Nobel Symposium XIV. Wiley Interscience, New York. p. 29-58.

―――. 1971b. Biomedical frontiers: genetics. In: *The Challenge of Life*. Roche Jubilee Symposium, Basle, Switzerland.

―――. 1972. The freedoms and the control of science: notes from the ivory tower. *So. Cal. Law Rev., 45*: 569-614.

Ramsey, P. 1970. *Fabricated Man—the Ethics of Genetic Control*. Yale University Press, New Haven, Conn.

Rogers, S., 1970. Skills for genetic engineers. *New Scient., 45*: 194-196.

――― and P. Pfuderer. 1968. Use of viruses as carriers of added genetic information. *Nature, 219*: 749.

2 Cellular Mechanisms of Learning

I. KUPFERMANN
NEW YORK UNIVERSITY SCHOOL OF MEDICINE AND
PUBLIC HEALTH RESEARCH INSTITUTE OF THE CITY OF NEW YORK

A central problem in neurobiology is the cellular basis of learning. Learning is a very general feature of behavior, and aspects of learning enter into practically every area of neurobiological interest, including sensory processing, motor function, and motivation and drives. As well as being pivotal for the understanding of diverse behavioral functions, the cellular mechanisms of learning are of great current interest because the problem is well defined and great progress seems possible in the near future. Unlike complex functions such as speech or consciousness, behavioral modification is a feature of the behavior of all organisms, including very simple invertebrates. Consequently it has been possible to utilize a variety of powerful analytical methods that cannot be employed in studying other more complex behavioral processes that are limited to higher vertebrates.

Fundamental to an understanding of the cellular basis of learning is the concept of plasticity. A persistent modification of behavior is likely to be represented by a persistent modification, or plastic change, in the functional properties of some of the neurons that mediate the behavior. The study of these plastic changes is the core of cellular studies of learning.

Studies of the author supported by PHS grant NB-07621 and Career Development Award KL-MH 12240.

Some of the questions that can be asked about the plastic changes underlying learning include: 1) Where in the brain do they occur? 2) How are they formed, and once formed, how are they maintained? 3) What is the nature of the changes; that is, are they electrical, chemical, structural, etc.? 4) How do given neural alterations result in modified behavior? At the present time, we have very few answers to these questions. The questions, however, have been clearly formulated, and techniques are on hand to begin to find answers.

History

The history of research on the cellular basis of learning is surprisingly contemporary. For heuristic purposes, it is convenient to divide the research into three periods encompassing the decades of the 1950s, 1960s and 1970s.

During the decade of the 50s, much of the foundation of neurophysiology was established. Basic insights into the mechanisms of the action potential and synaptic transmission were obtained, and the integrative role of inhibitory and excitatory synaptic potentials was established. It was on this solid foundation that all of further cellular neurophysiology was built.

During the decade of the 60s, investigators began to explore the ways in which the fundamental functional properties of neurons could be altered. Most studies concentrated on mechanisms of *synaptic* plasticity since synaptic transmission is a particularly labile feature of neural function. During this period, investigators described a variety of types of synaptic plasticity, including either increased or decreased synaptic efficacy for a period following intense synaptic use (post-tetanic potentiation or depression), as well as increased or decreased synaptic efficacy following stimulation of pathways that appeared to make presynaptic or axo-axonic connections on the plastic synapse (presynaptic facilitation, presynaptic inhibition). During this period, it was not established that any of these plastic changes mediated learning.

A characteristic feature of studies done in the late 60s to the present has been an attempt to relate the plastic properties of the nervous system to alterations in behavior and to begin to limit the study of plasticity to those changes that are of functional or behavioral significance. In the years ahead, it is this trend that will probably constitute the main thrust

of research on cellular mechanisms of learning. The remainder of this
essay will discuss three areas in which there should be progress. First,
there will be a continued development of specialized biological preparations that can be used as tools for the study of the cellular basis of behavior and learning. Second, these preparations should make possible the
elucidation of the mechanisms of forms of neural plasticity that underlie
simple types of behavioral modifications in both invertebrates and vertebrates, and there is likely to be progress in establishing the generality of
the mechanisms described in specific preparations. Finally, because of
increased knowledge of the cellular basis of learning, we are likely to
begin to see substantial progress toward the solution of a number of
controversial issues in the psychology of learning.

Development of Invertebrate Neurophysiological Preparations

To study the mechanisms for plasticity that underlie the modification of
a behavior, it is first necessary to understand the neuronal circuitry underlying the behavior. Not all workers in neurobiology subscribe to the
thesis that the most effective way to study the nervous system is by a
single cell analysis. But the incredible specificity of the interconnections
of brain circuits suggests that, ultimately, such crude methods as biochemical analysis of whole-brain homogenates, ablation of large masses
of neural tissue and recording of gross electrical potentials will have to be
supplanted by an analysis of single neurons. In order to study the neuronal circuit controlling a behavior, all the individual relevant neurons
must be accessible for electrophysiological and biochemical study. Since
at the present time these conditions are extremely difficult to meet in the
vertebrate nervous system, there has been increasing use of invertebrate
preparations to study the cellular basis of learning and behavior.

One of the hopes of the neurobiologists who study a particular invertebrate preparation is that it will provide a model system that can be
used to study various general aspects of neurobiology. The animal itself
often is of no special interest; it is utilized as a tool for the study of problems that are common to many different species. This approach is in the
biological tradition of selecting organisms with advantageous properties
for the study of specific problems. A neurophysiological analysis of behavior ideally requires a preparation that has good behavioral as well as
neurophysiological features. By and large, preparations that are advan-

tageous because of behavioral features do not have ideal neurophysiological features. It is unlikely that any *one* preparation will be ideal for studying the cellular basis of learning, but in the years ahead, there should be a narrowing of interest to a relatively few preparations with advantageous features. We will soon obtain substantial descriptions of the neural organization of simple reflexes in the crayfish (and similar crustaceans such as the lobster), *Aplysia* (and similar gastropod molluscs such as *Tritonia*), and the leech.

Crustaceans have been utilized primarily because of the ease of stimulating and recording action potentials extracellularly from individual neurons whose axons can be dissected from nerves and connectives (e.g., Wiersma, 1961). The behavior of crustaceans is rich and easy to study. It is relatively easy to obtain intracellular recordings from muscle in these animals. However, the neuronal cell bodies in these organisms are distant from the regions of synaptic input, and it is very difficult to record synaptic potentials from their central neurons. Nevertheless, in recent years there has been increasing use of intracellular recordings from identified neurons in crustaceans.

The difficulty of obtaining intracellular recordings from neurons in crustaceans is also true for other arthropods. This may account in part for the disappointing progress in analyzing the mechanism of learning in the cockroach. Ten years ago Horridge (1962) developed a technique to operantly condition restrained cockroaches. An animal learned to keep a leg raised if it received an electric shock whenever the leg was extended. The conditioning occurred even when the head of the animal was removed, suggesting that the relevant plastic changes could be localized to a limited portion of the nervous system (ganglia in the ventral cord). Aside from some unconfirmed reports of biochemical changes in the cockroach nervous system during learning, little has been learned about the mechanisms underlying operant conditioning in the roach. One reason for this lack of progress may be that the difficulty of working with the cockroach nervous system may have dissuaded many workers from making any serious systematic attempts at analysis. Nevertheless, a cellular analysis of behavioral modification in the cockroach remains as an attractive research possibility.

In the leech it is possible to obtain intracellular recordings of synaptic potentials from either muscle or central neurons. Compared to what is known about its nervous system, there is very little known about the behavior of the leech. This limitation is easy to rectify, and in future years, the gap between neurophysiological and behavioral knowledge in the leech will close.

Neurons in the nervous systems of gastropod molluscs are easily studied by intracellular techniques. Many neurons are 50 to 100μ in diameter, and some are up to 500μ. Similar to the leech, there is relatively little known about the behavior of these animals, and it is sometimes claimed that gastropod molluscs do very little or that their behavior only consists of simple reflexes. However, evidence is beginning to accumulate that indicates that the behavior of gastropod molluscs has some of the subtlety and complexity seen in higher animals. For example, gill withdrawal in the sea hare *Aplysia* (Kupfermann and Kandel, 1969) can occur as a simple reflex in response to a tactile stimulus but also can occur as a preprogrammed response pattern that is triggered by external stimuli. The triggered response does not bear any fixed relationship to the exact time or intensity of the triggering stimulus. It is preprogrammed in the sense that the long behavioral sequence runs off without the necessity of any sensory feedback from outside of the nervous system. In addition, gill withdrawal in *Aplysia* can occur spontaneously, with no obvious external triggering factor. Another complex motor response in gastropod molluscs involves control of the buccal muscles during feeding responses. Within the last year, workers have begun to analyze buccal control in *Pleurobranchea* (Davis and Mpitsos, 1971), *Aplysia* (Kupfermann and Cohen, 1971), *Navanax* (Spira and Bennett, 1972), and *Heliosoma* (Kater et al., 1971). This concentration of attention on a single type of behavior in different, but relatively closely related, species should result in the rapid accumulation of knowledge about the control of the delicate sequencing of buccal muscle contractions during feeding. Studies of buccal muscle control may provide principles applicable to complex motor systems in general and may set a background for a powerful analysis of the neural basis of modifications of a type of motivated behavior such as feeding.

Parallel with the attempts to develop a simple preparation for the neuronal study of behavior has been an attempt to find a simple form of behavioral modification that has properties shared by behavioral modification in general. One such behavioral model is habituation which is often considered to be one of the simplest forms of learning. Habituation refers to reflex response decrement following repeated stimulation. The term is typically restricted to reflex decrement due to some relatively long-lasting neuronal process rather than sensory adaptation of muscular fatigue. Similar to more complex forms of learning, habituation can be retained for a period of days or weeks following the initial training.

The gastropod mollusc *Aplysia* has been recently used to study the neural mechanisms underlying short-term habituation (for review, *see* Kandel et al., 1970). Because of the advantageous features of the nervous system of *Aplysia,* it was possible for the first time to show that synaptic plasticity mediates a type of behavioral modification. When a tactile stimulus is applied to the region of skin surrounding the external gill of the animal, the gill withdraws. If the tactile stimulus is repeatedly presented, the gill withdrawal reflex ceases to occur or becomes much weaker (habituation). A strong tactile stimulus to the head could immediately restore responsiveness (dishabituation). The response decrement was found to be associated with a decrease of the size of the excitatory synaptic potentials (increased synaptic efficacy) produced by mechanoreceptor cells that synapse on the motor neurons that innervate the gill. Restoration of behavioral responsiveness following a strong stimulus was due to an increase of the synaptic potentials at the same synapses that showed decreased efficacy. Thus, a given sensory to motor-neuron synapse shows profound decrement in efficacy when repeatedly activated and shows facilitation following stimulation of other sensory neurons. The facilitation may be the result of presynaptic facilitation, either by means of one sensory neuron on the synaptic terminal of another or by means of one or more interneurons that synapse presynaptically on the sensory neurons. There is evidence that synaptic plasticity of the primary sensory neurons may underlie simple forms of short-term behavioral modification in the crayfish (Zucker et al., 1971) and cockroach (Callec et al., 1971) as well as in *Aplysia*. Recent studies have shown that habituation in *Aplysia* (Carew et al., 1972), as well as other animals, can be retained for a period of weeks. It is not yet known whether these long-term behavioral modifications are mediated by the same synaptic changes that underly the examples of short-term habituation that have been studied. The continued study of the mechanisms of habituation and dishabituation in invertebrates should yield important insights into the ways in which the nervous system stores elementary forms of information.

Vertebrate Preparations

One approach to the problem of the complexity of the vertebrate nervous system has been to study simplified vertebrate preparations. This approach has been most successfully employed in the analysis of habituation of the flexion reflex which is mediated by the isolated spinal cord. There is evidence that the plastic changes underlying habituation of the flexion reflex are occurring at interneurons in the circuit rather than at the final motor neurons or at the terminals of primary sensory fibers (Groves and Thompson, 1970; Spencer et al., 1966), but even for this simple reflex, we do not know the detailed neuronal circuitry involved, and consequently, it has not been possible to specify the nature of the plastic changes that mediate modification of the reflex. In future years there undoubtedly will be progress in understanding the cellular basis of habituation of the flexion reflex; and a comparison of the mechanisms mediating modification of this reflex with the mechanisms mediating modification of reflexes in invertebrates should provide important insights into the generality of the findings coming out of invertebrate studies. Direct comparison between vertebrates and invertebrates will not be the only means of assessing the generality of findings from invertebrates. It will be of interest to see whether or not the mechanisms of plasticity described for a given reflex in one species also apply to modification of other reflexes in the same species or for other reflexes in different species of invertebrates. Thus, without ever directly characterizing mechanisms of plasticity in vertebrates, we will be in a position to know whether behavioral modifications are mediated by just a few cellular mechanisms or by a wide variety.

Lower vertebrates, such as fish and salamanders, offer some of the advantages of invertebrates and may prove useful for bridging studies between invertebrates and higher vertebrates. Some of the neurons in lower vertebrates are extremely large and can be identified as unique individuals, as is the case for identified cells in invertebrates. In addition, in contrast to warm-blooded vertebrates, the nervous system of cold-blooded vertebrates can often survive rather drastic experimental manipulation of the ionic content of the bathing fluids, and this permits analytic studies not otherwise possible.

Habituation, like complex learning, involves the storage of information regarding environmental events. However, complex learning, unlike habituation, typically is contingent upon an association between two stimuli, or between a stimulus and response. Compared to habituation, associative learning is not readily demonstrated in simple invertebrates or simplified vertebrate preparations. However, even the simplest forms of non-associative behavioral modification, such as habituation, have complex behavioral parametric features that could provide a foundation on which more complex associative forms may have developed. For example, the magnitude and retention of habituation is affected by the pattern and spacing of the trials, the total number of trials, and the strength of the habituatory stimulus. These variables suggest that the rate of habituation may also be dependent upon the temporal relations or association between pairs of stimuli. The detailed exploration of how such temporal factors affect the cellular mechanisms of simple forms of non-associative information storage should provide insights into more complex learning. In addition, a number of suggestive studies indicate that within a short time several simple preparations will be developed for the direct study of the cellular basis of associative conditioning.

Associative conditioning is most readily demonstrated in higher vertebrates with relatively intact nervous systems. To study mechanisms of learning mediated by complex nervous systems, investigators have often been forced to utilize a variety of methods that only indirectly reflect the function of individual neurons. For example, gross metal electrodes have been used to record the average electrical activity (evoked response, EEG) of the neurons and glia in a large mass of neural tissue. In an attempt to make sense of such recordings, increasingly sophisticated techniques of data analysis have been employed. This trend will continue, but it is not clear that it will ever yield results that are sufficiently unambiguous to determine cellular mechanisms.

Several workers have applied single-unit recording techniques to the analysis of the intact nervous system of vertebrates. The most complete analysis of neural circuitry has been done for the cerebellum (Eccles et al., 1967). There have been no systematic attempts to study behavioral modifications mediated by the cerebellum, perhaps because its behavioral functions are so poorly understood. However, with increasing knowledge of cerebellar function, the cerebellum may provide a good model system for the cellular study of behavioral modification in vertebrates.

Similar to the cerebellum, the hippocampus has an anatomically simple organization that greatly facilitates the study of its functional neuronal circuitry. Clinical data in humans suggest that the hippocampus is critically involved in short-term memory functions. For example, patients who have had their hippocampus surgically removed for the treatment of epilepsy are almost totally incapable of learning anything new, although memories of experiences obtained before the hippocampal removal are relatively unaffected. An intensive effort at a cellular analysis of the hippocampus should yield rich rewards in understanding learning.

Mechanisms of Neuronal Plasticity

Although at the present time it is known that simple forms of short-term behavioral modifiability in invertebrates are due to synaptic plasticity, the precise mechanisms of the synaptic alterations are not known. For example, is the synaptic decrement that explains habituation in *Aplysia* due to a decrease of the amount of transmitter released per presynaptic spike, or is it due to a decreased responsiveness of the postsynaptic receptor?

The future analysis of the mechanisms of synaptic plasticity that mediate simple forms of behavioral modifications will rely upon the application of powerful electrophysiological techniques that were primarily developed to analyze synaptic function at the squid giant synapse or at peripheral neuromuscular synapses that are accessible for microelectrode study. A major problem in the study of central synapses is that they are located in a complex neuropil and cannot be readily explored with microelectrodes. Therefore, the techniques developed for peripheral synapses cannot be directly applied to central synapses but will have to be creatively adapted and improved upon. Studies at peripheral synapses have shown that alterations of synaptic efficacy are due to alterations in the amount of transmitter released rather than in responsiveness of the postsynaptic neuron, and it seems likely that this will be the case for at least some of the synaptic modifications that underlie behavioral modifications and learning.

Whether due to presynaptic or postsynaptic mechanisms, long-lasting modifications of synaptic function will probably involve long-lasting modifications in the biochemical function of neurons, and some of the most interesting and exciting developments in the cellular analysis of learning will come from the biochemical analysis of neuronal plasticity.

At the present time, biochemical knowledge of neuronal plasticity is at a level similar to electrophysiological knowledge. A number of biochemical mechanisms that could conceivably underly learning have been studied in specialized preparations but which, if any, of these mechanisms are operative during learning is not known. For example, there is evidence that neurotransmitters can alter a number of biosynthetic mechanisms in neurons. Acetylcholine can affect the turnover of phosphatidyl choline (e.g., Hokin et al., 1960) and norepinephrine, serotonin and dopamine can affect the level of cyclic AMP (e.g., Kebabian and Greengard, 1971). There is also suggestive evidence that synaptic activity can affect the nature and amount of RNA in neurons. These mechanisms offer a means whereby the presynaptic neuron could produce biochemical effects on the postsynaptic neuron and modify its responsiveness to synaptic input. Other data suggest possible ways in which activity of a presynaptic neuron could affect its own ability to synthesize neurotransmitter substance (e.g., Weiner and Rabadjija, 1968). It is conceivable that processes such as habituation or sensitization might be due to a chronic decrease or increase of the activity of the enzymes that synthesize the transmitter agents in neurons in the reflex pathway.

In simple systems, such as *Aplysia,* it should prove possible to compare enzyme activity before and after habituation or sensitization training. Since individual identifiable neurons can now be injected with various markers or other substances (e.g., Koike et al., 1972), it is likely that measurements can be made of the biochemical activity of those neurons specifically involved in mediating behavioral changes. It is likely that at least part of the biochemical mechanisms that underlie learning have already been studied in *in vitro* systems. As studies progress to actual neurobehavioral systems that are capable of showing behavioral modifications, we should be able to concentrate attention on those mechanisms that are of functional significance.

The development of preparations in which it is possible to study the detailed cellular mechanisms underlying behavioral modification will permit a direct approach to a number of biochemical hypotheses that have been suggested entirely on the basis of indirect data. For example, there is evidence that substances that inhibit protein synthesis can interfere with the retention of learned tasks. From such studies, it has been claimed that protein synthesis is necessary for the retention of long-lasting learning. However, it is not clear whether inhibition of protein synthesis directly interferes with the formation of plastic changes in the nervous system or whether the inhibition somehow interferes with the readout or expression of plastic changes. When systems are developed in which plastic changes can be localized to given synapses or neurons, it will become possible to see exactly what the effect is of inhibition of the synthesis of proteins or other macromolecules. Furthermore, we will be able to study the precise effects of psychoactive drugs and hormones. On the basis of poorly controlled experiments involving the injection of substances extracted from the brains of trained animals, it has been suggested that specific forms of learning are mediated by specific macromolecules. This is a fascinating hypothesis with far reaching implications. Unfortunately, support of the hypothesis comes largely from poorly controlled experiments which often cannot be replicated. It seems highly unlikely that every item of information storage in the brain is represented by a unique macromolecule. Nevertheless, certain general classes of behavior are affected by circulating substances such as hormones, and the elucidation of the mode of action of such systemic substances should provide a foundation for the development of a rational technology of behavioral modification in the future.

In future years there will be increasing use of genetic approaches toward studying the possible neural mechanisms of plasticity and learning. A number of researchers in molecular genetics have recently turned their attention to problems in neurobiology. These workers bring with them the techniques that resulted in a revolution in our thinking about mechanisms of gene action, and such techniques may be particularly useful in studying the basis of the development of the brain. The problems associated with how individual neurons make appropriate connections and how they develop appropriate biophysical and biochemical properties are similar to the more general problems of cellular differentiation. How does a liver cell become a liver cell, and how does it stay that way once formed? How do neurons acquire new functional properties during learning, and how do they retain those properties, often for the lifetime of the organism? As we begin to obtain knowledge about mechanisms of cellular differentiation in general, we will most certainly achieve new insights into the mechanisms of neuronal development and plasticity.

One approach toward using genetic techniques to study the nervous system involves a search for behavioral or neural mutants in an organism with a nervous system that is simple enough to permit cellular analysis.

An understanding of the genetic basis of developmental mutations will help to decipher the biochemical steps that account for normal development.

A rapidly developing tool for utilizing genetic techniques is tissue culture of neuroblastoma cells and neurons. Colonies of such cells can be grown and treated like colonies of bacteria. In such systems it should be possible to study the cellular control mechanisms that determine the specific properties of a neuron as it differentiates. For example, what determines that a neuron synthesizes one transmitter agent rather than another and seeks connections with certain neurons but not others? The cellular mechanisms controlling neuronal development are undoubtedly more complex than those controlling bacterial development, and it is difficult to predict the rate of progress of this approach. The genetic approach to the nervous system, however, represents a powerful method in the hands of several highly competent researchers and will most likely provide some substantial insights into the functioning of the nervous system.

The development of the nervous system will continue to be fruitfully studied by more traditional methods. For example, contrary to traditional beliefs, there is growing evidence that under the right circumstances, the nervous system of mammals is capable of limited but significant regeneration or functional reorganization (e.g., Raisman, 1969) following damage. In future years there should be increasing dependence upon studies of regeneration and axonal sprouting in the mammalian brain. Regeneration following damage represents a type of development that occurs in a fully developed nervous system. There are no *a-priori* reasons why regeneration in the mammalian nervous system cannot be as exquisitely specific as it is in cold-blooded vertebrates. As understanding of the factors that limit the extent of regeneration in the central nervous system of mammals develops, we will not only gain insights into mechanisms of neuronal plasticity but also will begin to lay the foundations for the application of neurophysiological knowledge to clinical problems of recovery of function following neurological damage due to trauma or aging. It is not beyond the realm of possibility that within the next 25 years methods will be developed which will permit the brain to grow appropriate new connections where the original connections have become damaged or are inappropriately and inefficiently connected because of a genetic or developmental anomaly.

Solution of Controversies in Behavioral Sciences

One exciting outcome of cellular studies of learning will be the development of insights into some of the persistent problems of psychology: What is the relationship between operant and classical conditioning? Does learning proceed in distinct stages of short-term and long-term memory? What is the relationship between non-specific or non-associative forms of behavioral modification and associative forms? Is reinforcement necessary for learning, and what is the role of motivational factors?

A number of behavioral scientists have pointed out that although the methods used to produce classical and operant (or instrumental) conditioning appear quite different, the behavioral laws described for these two types of conditioning are surprisingly similar. In principle, it is possible to construct simple neurophysiological models that can generate either operant or classical conditioning, utilizing a single type of neuronal plasticity (Kupfermann and Pinsker, 1969). It remains to be seen whether such models have any biological reality.

One feature of neurophysiological models of learning is that by means of appropriate neuronal circuitry they can generate associative conditioning, utilizing mechanisms of neuronal plasticity that are not inherently different from those that provide models of non-associative conditioning (sensitization or pseudoconditioning). The prevalence of non-associative forms of behavioral modification in lower animals suggests that associative forms of modification were an evolutionary development that built on non-associative forms. Investigators are just beginning to obtain data about the mechanisms of non-associative forms of behavioral modifications such as habituation and pseudoconditioning, but it does not seem unlikely that, within the decade, we will be able to compare the mechanisms of non-associative modifications with simple types of associative conditioning.

Some of the most difficult problems to solve in the cellular study of learning involve questions of the nature of reinforcement and motivation. For example, why is a given reinforcing stimulus effective only when the animal is in a certain motivational state? The problem of reinforcement can be conceptualized as one of specifying the nature of the neuronal pathways that permit stimuli to produce plastic changes under some conditions, but not others. The solution of questions concerning reinforcement will require a general understanding of the nature of motivation at the cellular level. Motivation has been conceived of in terms of an analogy to the physical concept of energy. Something within the organism is said to energize behavior. When the energy is depleted, the organism ceases to perform. An understanding of motivation will require specification of the physiological basis of the concept of energy in behavior. The energy concept may turn out to have some physical counterpart, such as the activity level of electrogenic ion pumps in endogenously active neurons. On the other hand, the physiological correlates of energy may bear little relation to any physical concepts of energy. Thus, for example, the waning of a reflex that is repeatedly evoked could be seen as being mediated by the depletion of a central energy store that drives the reflex. A period of rest restores the energy, and the reflex reappears in full strength. The organism can be conceived of as a type of automobile with a slow and constant source of gasoline. If it is driven too much, it uses up its supply of energy and ceases to function. We now know that such a formulation is misleading, at least for some cases of reflex habituation studied in invertebrates. The examples that have been analyzed indicate that response decrement is due to a decrease of excitatory synaptic efficacy from sensory units onto motor units. There is no change in the inherent capacity of the motor units to discharge spikes. It is not as if the car is out of gas; rather, the starter button is no longer functional.

There is evidence that the behavior of simple invertebrates is under the control of many of the same motivational variables that control vertebrate behavior. The cellular analysis of motivation in invertebrates with favorable nervous systems has just begun. Such studies will undoubtedly provide data relevant to the problems of the cellular mechanisms underlying reinforcement and complex forms of learning.

Many problems in psychology of learning are basically physiological in nature, but for years, neurophysiology has had little to offer toward their solution. In the past, premature attempts to utilize neurophysiological concepts to deal with behavioral problems resulted in controversies that at the time could not be resolved, and psychologists argued that the science of behavior should be restricted to behavioral experiments and data. However, as we obtain a more fundamental understanding of the nervous system, we will find that many problems in psychology can be resolved only by physiological studies. Over the coming years we will see the application of techniques of cellular neurophysiology to progressively more complex problems in the behavioral sciences.

Acknowledgement

I thank Eric R. Kandel for his comments on the manuscript.

References

Callec, J. J., J. C. Guillet, Y. Pichon, and J. Boistel. 1971. Further studies on synaptic transmission in insects. II. Relations between sensory information and its synaptic integration at the level of a single giant axon in the cockroach. *J. Exp. Biol.,* **55**: 123-149.

Carew, T. J., H. M. Pinsker, and E. R. Kandel. 1972. Long-term habituation of a defensive withdrawal reflex in *Aplysia. Science,* **175**: 451-454.

Davis, W. J. and G. J. Mpitsos. 1971. Behavioral choice and habituation in the marine mollusk *Pleurobranchea californica* MacFarland (Gastropoda, Opisthobranchia). *Z. Verg. Physiologie,* **75**: 207-232.

Eccles, J. C., M. Ito, and J. Szentagothai. 1967. *The Cerebellum.* Springer-Verlag, Berlin, Heidelberg, New York.

Groves, P. H. and R. F. Thompson. 1970. Habituation: A dual-process theory. *Psychol. Rev.,* **77**: 419-450.

Hokin, M. R., L. E. Hokin, and W. D. Shelp. 1960. Effects of acetylcholine on the turnover of phosphatidic acid and phosphoinositide in sympathetic ganglia, and in various parts of the central nervous system *in vitro. J. Gen. Physiol.,* **44**: 217.

Horridge, G. A. 1962. Learning leg position by ventral nerve cord in headless insects. *Proc. Roy. Soc. B.,* **157**: 33-52.

Kandel, E. R., V. Castellucci, H. Pinsker, and I. Kupfermann. 1970. The role of synaptic plasticity in the short-term modification of behavior. *In*: G. Horn and R. A. Hinde (eds.). *Short-term Changes in Neural Activity and Behavior.* Cambridge University Press, London.

Kater, S. B., C. Heyer, and J. P. Hegmann. 1971. Neuromuscular transmission in the gastropod mollusc *Helisoma trivolvis*: Identification of motoneurons. *Z. Vergl. Physiol.,* **74**: 127-139.

Kebabian, J. W. and P. Greengard. 1971. Dopamine-sensitive adenyl cyclase: Possible role in synaptic transmission. *Science,* **174**: 1346-1349.

Koike, H., M. Eisenstadt, and J. H. Schwartz. 1972. Axonal transport of newly synthesized acetycholine in an identified neuron. *Brain Res.,* **37**: 75-81.

Kupfermann, I. and J. Cohen. 1971. The control of feeding by identified neurons in the buccal ganglion of *Aplysia. Amer. Zool.,* **11**: 667.

―――― and E. R. Kandel. 1969. Neural controls of a behavioral response mediated by the abdominal ganglion of *Aplysia. Science,* **164**: 847-850.

―――― and H. M. Pinsker. 1969. Plasticity in *Aplysia* neurons and some simple neuronal models of learning. *In*: J. Tapp (ed.). *Reinforcement and Behavior*. Academic Press, New York.

Raisman, G. 1969. Neuronal plasticity in septal nuclei of adult rat. *Brain Res.*, **14**: 25-48.

Spencer, W. A., R. F. Thompson, and D. R. Neilson, Jr. 1966. Decrement of ventral root electrotonus and intracellularly recorded PSPs produced by iterated cutaneous afferent volleys. *J. Neurophysio.*, **29**: 253-274.

Spira, M. E. and M. V. L. Bennett. 1972. Synaptic control of electronic coupling between neurons. *Brain Res.*, **32**: 294-300.

Weiner, N. and M. Rabadjija. 1968. The regulation of norepinephrine synthesis. Effect of puromycin on the accelerated synthesis of norepinephrine associated with nerve stimulation. *J. Pharmacol. Exp. Ther.*, **164**: 103-114.

Wiersma, C. A. G. 1961. Reflexes and the central nervous system. *In*: T. H. Waterman (ed.). *The Physiology of Crustacea*, 2: 241-279. Academic Press, New York.

Zucker, R. S., D. Kennedy, and A. I. Selverston. 1971. Neuronal circuit mediating escape responses in crayfish. *Science*, **173**: 645-650.

3 Abnormal Growth—
The Challenge of Diversity

VAN RENSSELAER POTTER
THE McARDLE LABORATORY
University of Wisconsin Medical Center

Introduction

Of all the adversary positions in the cancer field, none has been more prolonged than the contest between the advocates of a viral etiology and those who believe in the somatic mutation theory of cancer causation. As we look toward the next 25 years of increasing environmental complexity, we need to develop theoretical principles and practical methods for recognizing chemical carcinogens without waiting until there has been prolonged exposure of target populations. Facing these chemical hazards, it seems desirable to pursue at least four variants of the controversy between the somatic mutation theory and the virus theory of cancer etiology. These are: 1) somatic mutations can cause cancer without the involvement of any factor resembling a virus; 2) appropriate viruses can cause cancer without affecting the genetic apparatus; 3) cancer-producing viruses act by interacting with the genetic apparatus of somatic cells, yielding what could justifiably be called somatic mutations; and 4) normal cells can be transformed to cancer cells with neither somatic mutations nor virus involvement, assuming that the normal repertory of gene capabilities is so vast and programmed karyotypic instability so widespread in normal differentiating mammalian cells that occasional spontaneous bizarre dislocations and recombinations of available subprograms inevitably result in clones that are operationally recognized as

cancer, with certain chemicals and viruses merely increasing the probability of program disruption.

All of these possibilities should be examined without the assumption
of anything but the broadest kind of a unitary hypothesis into which all
cancers must fall in terms of one or another theoretical subset. If we
take it as probable that various types of cancer may arise by different
mechanisms, we can enlarge the scope of the problem to include other
forms of abnormal growth or development that may have much in common with some, but not all, types of cancer. These other forms of pathology could include psoriasis, xeroderma pigmentosum, hereditary polypo-
sis, and the hereditary persistence of fetal hemoglobin (PHF). Some of
these conditions will be briefly discussed later in this paper.

Peyton Rous, Oncologist

There is probably no one whose career was so closely connected for so
many years with both chemical carcinogenesis and viral carcinogenesis
as Peyton Rous's. Born in 1879, he discovered the Rous sarcoma virus in
1911, received the Nobel Prize for this and related studies on cancer in
1966, and died in 1970 at the age of 90. In the interim he carried out important studies on chemical carcinogenesis and coined the words *initiation* and *promotion* to describe the phenomena that he observed. It is instructive to read his final pronouncements on the cancer problem (Rous,
1959, 1965, 1967), and we should realize that the first two commen-
taries came before his long-delayed recognition, whereas the last paper
was his Nobel address. We are indebted to a close friend of his (Huggins,
1970) for a record of some correspondence which shows how this wonderful man felt about many things, including the somatic mutation theory,
which, after all, seemed to him the only obstacle between the virus theory
and the solution to the cancer problem. The dates of the letters quoted
provide an interesting between-the-lines commentary related to the chro-
nology of the three papers cited above.

Peyton Rous in 1959 was tremendously piqued by reports emanating
from the International Cancer Congress in London in 1958. He was
particularly upset by the suggestion that cancer might be the result of spontaneous mutations. He was well aware of the existence of tumor induction by chemicals, but he seemed to regard "authentic" somatic mutations as something that occurred in cells that were non-proliferating by

definition. Thus: "One can readily understand why somatic cells that have undergone authentic mutations such as those thus far reported should rarely manifest themselves. Their lack of any increased ability to proliferate must result in their virtual imprisonment within the normal tissue context, unless indeed they have mutated early in the development of the organism to which they belong." And elsewhere: "The cutaneous cells [in a mosaic] give no sign of increased ability to proliferate, much less to do so independently of the organism. Here lies the crucial difference between neoplastic cells and those that have undergone somatic mutations of the kinds thus far recognized." After considering and rejecting what he called the "reconciling assumption" that neoplastic viruses might produce a special kind of somatic mutation, Rous noted that this was "less than necessary." He ended by concluding: "At the time of writing, the somatic mutation hypothesis, after more than half a century, remains an analogy . . . it has resulted in no good thing as concerns the cancer problem, but in much that is bad. . . . Most serious of all . . . has been its effect on research workers. It acts as a tranquilizer on those who believe in it, and this at a time when every worker should feel goaded now and again by his ignorance of what cancer is." (Rous, 1959).

Six years later, in his masterful paper (at age 87), "Viruses and Tumour Causation. An Appraisal of Present Knowledge" (Rous, 1965), he did not mention the somatic mutation hypothesis and did not refer to his 1959 "blast" against it (Huggins, 1970). At this time we have a note to a friend: "New virus deeds incessantly reported keep me as watchful as a shooter standing at a butt in England while beaters are making the pheasants fly over. There's an urgency to my task which is exhilarating." (Huggins, 1970).

Finally, in his Nobel address entitled: "The Challenge to Man of the Neoplastic Cell" (Rous, 1967), he takes a broader view. Referring to the experiments by Yamigiwa and Ichikawa as early as 1918, he commented: "This opened an era of rewarding search for other chemical agents—and physical as well—which are oncogenic. . . . All such oncogens are initiating in character, and some can be dangerous promoters too, if the exposure to them is long. The wider and closer one looks the more closely does one see that chemical and physical agents start off nearly all human tumors and that these latter are occupational diseases resulting from the exceedingly hazardous occupation of living out a life in this world." But again, as in 1959, he rejected the somatic mutation hypothesis, asking: "What can be the nature of the generality of neoplastic changes, the reasons for their persistence, their irreversibility, and the discontinuous, step-like alterations that they frequently undergo?" and answering: "A favorite explanation has been that oncogens cause alterations in the genes of the ordinary cells of the body, as distinct from the generative somatic mutations as these are termed. But numerous facts, when taken together, decisively exclude this supposition," here referring to his 1959 paper without further discussion.

I have dealt at some length with Peyton Rous and his views, partly because he epitomizes the dichotomy of an era that may have ended with his death. As we look forward to the next 25 years of biological research, we can build on the foundation laid by Peyton Rous without being limited by the views he held in 1959. Even as he wrote, events were moving toward the "reconciling assumption" that to him was unacceptable. Perhaps the era of the dichotomy has ended, and we can think in terms of a spectrum of properties in tumor cells and other forms of pathology considered to be outside the normal range, with the changes brought about sometimes by viruses alone, sometimes by viruses plus other agents, sometimes by other agents without virus involvement, and sometimes spontaneously, with neither outside agents nor virus involvement.

Somatic Mutations and Virus Insertion:
The Reconciling Assumption

Peyton Rous died on February 16, 1970, unaware of the excitement that was about to stir the field of cancer virology as a result of new experiments with the Rous sarcoma virus (RSV). Although Howard Temin had advanced the idea of RNA-directed DNA synthesis as early as 1964, it was not until May 1970 that he reported experiments describing this activity in RSV particles (Temin and Mizutani, 1970). The earlier supporting evidence was not discussed by Rous in the papers cited above. Temin's finding was independently confirmed by David Baltimore (1970) and within weeks by other laboratories. Although a number of years must pass before the full significance of Temin's discovery can be fully assessed, a recent article in *Scientific American* concluded with the statement:

Probably the most important implication of this discovery for the understanding of cancer in man has been the removal of the dichotomy between viral and genetic theories of the origin of cancer. At a time when genes were thought to consist of DNA alterable only by mutation, and when most of the known cancer-causing animal viruses were of the RNA type, it was hard to imagine common features of genetic and viral theories. Now that we have uncovered evidence that cancer-causing RNA viruses can produce a DNA transcript of the viral RNA, one can readily formulate hypotheses in which elements related to viral RNA are attached to the genome of the cell and transmitted genetically to become activated at some future time and cause "spontaneous" cancer. Experiments designed to test this idea are now in progress in a number of laboratories around the world. (Temin, 1972).

It now appears that the transformation of normal cells to cancer cells by the Rous sarcoma virus requires the insertion of a DNA transcript of the viral information into the host genome and the expression of at least some of this DNA in each subsequent cell cycle. This statement appears to apply also to the DNA oncogenic viruses. It has been stated that oncogenic viruses have from 7 to 50 genes but that only a few of these are required for transformation (Allen and Cole, 1972). Whether the transformation involves a single insertion or whether multiple insertions occur, leading to genetically diverse lines of cancer cells, appear to be problems for the future, but it is now clear from studies with rat cells (Temin, 1972) that the subsequent production of free virus particles is not a necessary concomitant of the transformation. Thus, it appears that transformed cells have been produced in which the cells can be regarded as having an "altered genome" rather than as being "infected" by virus particles. This situation was precisely the idea that Rous dismissed when he rejected the "reconciling assumption."

Evidence showing karyotypic changes in transformed cells is provided by a study of the chromosomes of 50 primary rat sarcomas induced by the Rous chicken sarcoma virus, strain Schmidt-Ruppin (RSV-SR) (Mitelman, 1971). About 80% of the sarcomas had a normal-appearing diploid stemline, but half of these had one or more side lines, defined as 10% or more of the cells showing a distinctive karyotype. Among the 10 sidelines that were earliest to appear, 8 had an identical karyotype, deviating from the normal by the addition of one t chromosome. Out of a total of 58 deviating populations, 43 displayed this same feature of one or more extra t chromosomes. Mitelman concluded that his findings were compatible with an origin from a single mutant cell followed by further changes that promote karyological instability (Ohno, 1971). It seems likely that if the virally induced tumors were to be transplanted, some of the lines would be stable enough to permit reproducible experiments on their biochemical properties, as in the case of the Morris hepatomas (Potter and Watanabe, 1968), and no doubt the biochemical diversity would be just as great. Unfortunately, there seems to be little inclination on the part of virologists or biochemists to carry out such experiments.

It is only a slight extension of the "altered genome" concept to regard chemically induced carcinogenesis as some kind of an accessory to viral carcinogenesis. Stich et al. (1971) have reported that hamster cell cultures exposed to 4-nitroquinoline 1-oxide (4NQO) develop many DNA lesions and engage in repair synthesis of DNA. Under certain conditions the affected cells enter into DNA replication in the S phase without completing repair synthesis, presumably leading to the formation of mutant cells. It seems likely that a prolonged production of mutations could lead to a heterogeneous cell population from which selection would produce neoplastic cells having various combinations of mutations and disrupted programs for the expression of existing genes. This concept of cancer is one way to explain the great phenotypic diversity seen among various lines of cancer cells. But apparently certain viruses have a special capability for neoplastic transformation, and it is, therefore, of great interest to find that Stich et al. (1971) reported that the unrepaired breaks in DNA in cells exposed to 4NQO appear to provide openings for increased probability of virus insertion. Hamster cell cultures exposed to 4NQO before the addition of oncogenic simian adenoma (SA-7) virus showed at least a 20-fold increase in transformation frequency compared with cultures infected with SA-7 alone. But there is as yet no evidence that chemically transformed cells have been produced with the help of some other unidentified virus. The demonstration that there is a high correlation between the occurrence of DNA breaks and the oncogenicity of a series of 4NQO derivatives is quite compatible with the idea that transformation is a result of multiple mutations. It is reasonable to propose that in a population of dividing cells in which many breaks are produced, not all will be repaired, and some copy errors will be made. Thus there should be a correlation between the total number of breaks and the final number of mutations.

Carcinogens as Mutagens

During the lifetime of Peyton Rous, there were many attempts to correlate carcinogenicity with mutagenicity, with confusing results, which led
him to write that some carcinogens induce somatic mutations whereas
others do not, that some mutagenic agents fail to be carcinogenic, and
that many substances closely related chemically to agents of both sorts do
neither (Rous, 1959). More recently it has become clear that many compounds that produce cancer are not of themselves carcinogenic; they have
to undergo metabolism by living systems or be chemically converted to
the active carcinogens. This discovery had to be made before the confusing data on carcinogenicity and mutagenicity could begin to make
sense, and it is now clear that the discovery of N-hydroxylation of the
carcinogen 2-acetylaminofluorene (AAF) was a milestone in the unraveling of the mystery (Cramer et al., 1960). Thus, it was highly significant that AAF is carcinogenic in the rat but not in the guinea pig,
when it could also be shown that the N-hydroxylation occurred in the rat
but not in the guinea pig. Moreover, N-hydroxy AAF could be shown to
produce cancer in both species. Additional studies revealed the further
metabolism to an ester of N-hydroxy AAF which could be shown to exert
a direct chemical attack on the guanine moiety of guanosine or deoxy-
guanosine. Present evidence suggests that N-hydroxylation occurs in the
case of a number of aromatic amine and amide carcinogens and that the
sulfuric acid ester of N-hydroxy AAF is an ultimate reactive and carcinogenic derivative of AAF in rat liver. A consideration of these and many
additional findings led Miller (1970) to suggest that most and perhaps
all of the chemical carcinogens either are strong electrophilic reactants as
administered (Boutwell et al., 1969) or are converted *in vivo* into potent
electrophilic reactants in the species in which they are carcinogenic (cf.
Miller and Miller, 1971; Selkirk et al., 1971). With this concept the relationship between carcinogenesis and mutagenesis could be reinvestigated,
and it was found that the esters of N-hydroxy AAF were mutagenic for a
DNA transformation system in *B. subtilis* whereas the parent carcinogens
or the N-hydroxy derivatives were not mutagenic (Maher et al., 1968;
see also studies on mutagenicity of epoxides by Huberman et al., 1971).
Similar studies have now been carried out with demonstrations of DNA
breaks and various levels of repair synthesis in cultured human xeroderma

pigmentosum cells as affected by N-acetoxy AAF but virtually not at all by the parent compound (Stich et al., 1972; Setlow and Regan, 1972).

The knowledge that the ultimate chemical carcinogens are strong electrophilic reactants provides a springboard for many new studies in the future (Miller, 1970). These include research on attempts to (a) inhibit or prevent the generation *in vivo* of these active forms, (b) neutralize or inactivate the strong electrophiles *in vivo* with low molecular weight non-toxic nucleophiles, and (c) predict carcinogenicity of foreign molecules (e.g., drugs, food additives, pollutants, and deliberately disseminated chemicals) from measures of their conversion to reactive electrophiles by one biological system (e.g., liver) and subsequent mutagenicity in another test system (e.g., bacterial or mammalian cell culture). Good test systems are already available, e.g., in prostate cells (Chen and Heidelberger, 1969) for studying carcinogenesis in mammalian cells in tissue culture.

Carcinogenesis in vitro: The Study of Blocked Differentiation in Cultures

We may anticipate that within the next few years there will be successful attempts to maintain normal liver cells in tissue culture and to study chemical carcinogenesis in these cultures. It will be highly desirable to obtain stable clones of transformed cells, which can be used to inoculate numbers of inbred animals so that the neoplastic and biochemical behavior of the cells *in vivo* can be characterized in reproducible experiments. We may anticipate that such experiments would lead to demonstrations of diversity as great as the diversity already noted in the widely-studied Morris hepatomas, which occur as more than 40 different transplantable lines, no two of which are karyotypically and biochemically alike (Potter and Watanabe, 1968). The availability of the cell lines in tissue culture would facilitate the comparison of the behavior of neoplastic cells in the presence of factors that convert normal hepatocytes from the fetal state to the adult state and vice versa.

One of the threads of unity in the biochemical diversity that we presently witness is the indication that hepatoma cells are unable to respond to the organismic controls that direct the programmatic conversion of immature normal hepatocytes to the adult pattern of response (Walker and Potter, 1972). This phenomenon has been referred to as "oncogeny is blocked ontogeny" (Potter, 1969) and is historically related to many early comparisons between cancer tissues and normal tissues from embryonic and newborn rats (e.g., Potter et al., 1945). However, the recent studies have been greatly advanced by a growing knowledge of isozymes in fetal and adult tissues, as well as the wide availability of the Morris hepatomas (Walker and Potter, 1972). It is expected that a programmed set of responses in a developing hepatocyte could involve the sequential induction, repression, or modulation of successive sets of gene activities, and that an adult hepatocyte could revert back to the replicating state without invoking a permanent change (mutation) in the genome. It is also reasonable to try to explain the neoplastic transformation as a permanent change (mutation) in one or more of the genes that are transiently active in the normal progress of development, i.e., to assume a "blocked ontogeny." Hypotheses in terms of mutation, integrated viral genomes, or non-genetic mechanisms could be tested if we had normal liver cells that could be reversibly shifted from fetal to adult enzymatic phenotypes in tissue culture by appropriate manipulations of the culture medium (e.g., *see* Parsa et al., 1972) and hepatoma cells that could or could not undergo similar shifts. We could apply similar protocols to various lines of hepatomas in the tissue culture system and establish whether they were "locked in," i.e., whether they would respond to measures that were effective for normal cells or whether "heroic" measures would break through an apparent block. (*See,* for example, studies *in vivo* by Potter et al., 1970 in which a hepatoma that seemed non-responsive to a particular enzyme induction responded when conditions were altered.) Such experiments could be subjected to much more rigorous controls *in vitro* than *in vivo*. Depending on the nature of the controlling factors in the normal systems and the responses obtained in the neoplastic lines, it might be possible to deduce the nature of the defects in the latter. Presumably, sequence differences in regulating proteins or nucleic acids could be shown if a gene mutation had occurred.

Hereditary Non-malignant Blocked Ontogeny

A possible model for the blocked ontogeny hypothesis of cancer formation may be available in the case of several non-malignant diseases. One of these is hereditary persistence of fetal hemoglobin or PHF (*see* Kabat,

1972). Hemoglobin is a tetrameric protein containing two α chains and two β chains in the normal adult ($\alpha\alpha\beta\beta$). In the early embryo the β chains are not found, but instead there are two ϵ chains ($\alpha\alpha\epsilon\epsilon$) which are soon replaced by γ chains in the fetus ($\alpha\alpha\gamma\gamma$). Soon after birth the γ chains are replaced by β chains and to a very slight extent by δ chains. In the condition known as PHF, the γ chains continue to be synthesized throughout the adult life, and the β and ϵ chains are never formed. One might look upon the persistence of fetal hemoglobin, i.e., persistence of γ-chain formation and failure to progress to β-chain formation as a "blocked ontogeny" in which there is a hereditary failure to respond to the signals to repress γ-chain formation and derepress β-chain formation. Similarly, in the blocked ontogeny that is proposed to explain neoplasia, there would be a "persistent" formation of certain fetal enzyme systems that are required for cell replication, owing to a failure to respond to the signals that call for their repression. Again we must ask whether the failure is in a gene that is unable to respond to the chemical signals or in a cell component that causes interference with signal transmission; for example, a plasma membrane that excludes or fails to respond to the exogenous chemical that signals repression.

Another disease that should be considered as a possible case of nonmalignant blocked ontogeny is psoriasis. This condition is somewhat like a benign tumor since it consists of a replicating cell population but does not invade or metastasize. Cell division is excessive (Weinstein and Frost, 1968), but the cells simply shed into the environment. Voorhees et al. (1972) have described psoriasis as a condition in which the epidermis exhibits three characteristic features—accelerated proliferation, incomplete differentiation, and glycogen storage—and have proposed that cyclic AMP may be needed to maintain the stability of the differentiated state in normal epidermis. They reported significant decreases in cyclic AMP in psoriatic epidermis. The incomplete differentiation and excessive cell proliferation in psoriasis may well be another example of blocked ontogeny or persistent activity of certain fetal genes. Since this disease afflicts some 6 million Americans, has many morphological variants, and is widely recognized as having a hereditary basis coupled with unknown environmental factors (*see* Baker, 1971), it might be a useful model for studying abnormal growth involving a combination of genetic and environmental factors.

Cumulative Mutations, Hereditary plus Somatic

One of the ways to explain the vast diversity (Potter and Watanabe, 1968) of enzymatic phenotypes in neoplasia under the somatic mutation hypothesis is to assume that each neoplastic cell line had accumulated random hits until a sufficient combination of "essential" hits had occurred. Diversity in such a case would be inevitable, because it would be impossible to acquire the right "essential" hits without also acquiring a number of non-essential hits, and the list of these would vary from one cell line to another. Moreover, there could be more than one "sufficient combination." Ashley (1969) has reviewed the "two-hit" and "multiple-hit" theories of carcinogenesis and concluded that, for gastric cancer in women in England and Wales, the multiple-stage theory provided a better fit to the data. He recognized that in a multiple hit theory the genetic diversity of the population at risk could play an important role. Thus, there could be certain individuals in the population with genotypes which already contained one or more inherited mutations and which, therefore, caused them to develop cancer after fewer additional changes in this or that cell type than would be needed in the average individual. This proposition was advanced by Burch (1962) in terms of the proposition (a) that where the etiology of a given neoplasm involves somatic nuclear gene mutations, individual tumors of this type will be found in which inherited mutations have substituted for somatic; and the converse proposition (b) that where Mendelian inheritance of a neoplasm can be demonstrated, somatic mutation should also contribute to its genesis. He adduced support for these ideas mainly in terms of human leukemias. An extensive review of hereditary factors in neoplasia is available (Lynch, 1967). Most recently, Knudson (1971) has published a study of retinoblastoma, a malignant neoplasm in children. This disease has long been considered to have a hereditary component, but Knudson has been able to take the analysis further. Based on a review of 48 cases, he developed the hypothesis that retinoblastoma is a cancer caused by two mutational events: in the dominantly inherited form, one mutation is inherited via the germinal cells, and the second occurs in somatic cells; in the non-hereditary form of the same disease, he proposed that both mutations occur in somatic cells.

One of the most exciting examples of the production of cancer by the combined action of hereditary mutations and somatic mutations is seen in the case of xeroderma pigmentosum, a form of skin cancer characterized by extraordinary sensitivity to sunlight, with dozens of lesions occurring on every surface reached by the sun. The hereditary nature of the disease has been known for many years (Lynch, 1967). The mutation-producing ability of the ultraviolet rays in sunlight is also well known. The explanation of at least one kind of multiple-mutation cancer came when it was discovered that enzymes capable of repairing UV-induced lesions in DNA were present in mammalian cells and could be demonstrated in cell cultures (Rasmussen and Painter, 1966): when cells taken from the skin of patients afflicted with xeroderma pigmentosum were placed in cell culture and treated with UV light, the lesions were produced but the repair enzyme systems were ineffective (Cleaver, 1968). In this case the first mutation, genetically inherited, was the inability to bring about repair of DNA mutations. Against this background, sunlight could be deadly and could simply pile up somatic mutations in skin cells until a combination sufficient for neoplasia was attained. There is no reason to assume a unique minimum number any more than in the case of the Morris hepatomas, and no reason to assume that every neoplasm would have the same enzymatic phenotype or the same combination of altered or activated genes. As documented in the case of the Morris hepatomas (Potter and Watanabe, 1968), each tumor could be a unique combination of essential and non-essential changes in the enzymatic phenotype.

As one looks at the human cancer problem in the perspective of retinoblastoma and xeroderma pigmentosum, we realize that the genetics of cancer cells in man is made more difficult to systematize by a world that is rapidly changing with respect to the number and complexity and the absolute levels of foreign chemicals and harmful radiations that are in many cases deliberately introduced into the environment. We realize that the demonstration of a genetic component would be much easier in an environment saturated with the factors necessary to produce cancer in every single individual that was genetically vulnerable. But the case of xeroderma pigmentosum shows that cells taken from non-cancerous areas of skin can be placed in culture and diagnosed by exposure to sunlight followed by a test for DNA repair synthesis. Clearly, the way is open for the testing of cells from the population at large prior to any overt signs of cancer under conditions that may reveal inherited differences in terms of increased susceptibility or increased resistance to carcinogens.

In the case of animal systems, one would predict that, if multiple hits are required, the difference between genetic susceptibility and genetic resistance might be merely a matter of dose level. Increasing the dose would simply override the resistance and produce cancer in all the animals, and this is generally the case, although data are not plentiful and protocols seldom ideal. The assumption of genetic components could go far toward explaining why some heavy smokers escape lung cancer, whereas some moderate smokers develop lung cancer. No one has proposed a tissue culture system for spotting the genetically liable individuals, but such a system can readily be imagined. However, the magnitude of the problem in all its dimensions is so great that prudence and common sense seem to call for anti-smoking campaigns and a general effort to clean up the environment.

One of the difficulties in proving a causal relationship is the long lag between exposure to the carcinogen and the appearance of the actual cancer. The case of xeroderma pigmentosum was relatively simple since the implication of sunlight and heredity was quite straightforward owing to the clear and rather prompt reaction to sunlight. The case of cigarette smoking was less clear-cut, and the presence of other environmental carcinogens complicated the relationship so that any statement concerning a genetic relationship at this time can only be speculative. Even more complicated is the case of transplacental carcinogenesis which has been alleged to have been demonstrated in the case of 8 young women with clear-cell adenocarcinoma of the vagina 14 to 22 years after their mothers had been treated with stilbestrol (*see* Miller, 1971).

Cancer Diversity

From the standpoint of the future of cancer research, it would seem to make sense to put more effort into understanding the nature and extent of cancer diversity. As of this writing there is no clear evidence that there are ever two primary neoplasms that are exactly alike in their enzymological phenotypic expression, and even in the case of transplanted neoplasms carried in the inbred animals of tumor origin, one cannot assume that the tumors will remain constant from one transplant generation to the next. Diversity extends even to the *tendency* of a tumor line to diversify, with some lines remaining fairly constant in their properties for many transplant generations. We need to extend the knowledge of tumor diversity for three good reasons. First, this type of information is necessary for fundamental knowledge having to do with the nature of the cancer phenomenon itself. There must be basic explanations for the fact that normal tissues of an organism are usually able to display a certain limited spectrum of phenotypic responses to the environment for many decades, while a neoplastic clone is not a new pattern of stability, but a new pattern of instability. We need to examine the widest pattern of diversity in order to seek the common thread of neoplastic escape from the warp and woof of normal development and to define the "minimum deviation" that can trigger the process. It is doubtful whether assiduous attention to a *single* example can produce a single key for a labyrinth that has many entrances. We need intensive parallel studies in close communication and operating concurrently on several model systems.

Second, we need to extend the knowledge of tumor diversity in order to achieve a better grasp of the measures required for cancer prevention, as we learn about the combining action of various genetic and environmental factors in the phenomena of initiation, promotion, and progression.

Third, we need to extend the knowledge of tumor diversity in order to understand the magnitude of the problem of cancer therapy and to be able to explain to an impatient public the extent of the uncharted areas and the reasons for their continued existence.

Perhaps a fourth reason for extending the knowledge of the nature and extent of cancer diversity is a moral or ethical one. Perhaps it would tend to instill some humility into those who imply that money will buy an era of genetic engineering that will restore health to shattered bodies or to corpses stored in liquid nitrogen—without creating any Frankensteins. We can do much to prevent cancer, to prolong useful lives, and to alleviate suffering even today, and we will do more, but we cannot eliminate the fundamental variability that makes life possible and death inevitable, and we should not eliminate the fundamental variability of life even if we could.

As of today we can propose a "diversity hypothesis" and suggest experiments to test the hypothesis. We can suggest *that diverse neoplasms and non-malignant developmental aberrations may result from diverse environmental insults superimposed upon diverse genetic capabilities.* Experiments designed to test this hypothesis could pay enormous dividends in the health sciences in general, not merely in the area of cancer. The testing of the hypothesis has in the past been fraught with almost insuperable difficulties and painfully slow accumulation of data when the approach was limited to the methods of epidemiology, natural history, and population genetics. Today we are on the verge of developing techniques that would permit the study of carcinogenesis *in vitro* and blocked development *in vitro* using hundreds of tissue cultures from a single bit of tissue obtained from appropriate human subjects at no risk or inconvenience to them. Each of these cell lines would represent a unique human genome and in the early phases ought to be established by using cells from individuals having a family history of low or high incidence of some form of cancer or some non-malignant disease such as psoriasis. Having any desired number of replicate cultures available from selected individuals, a laboratory could superimpose any desired dosage of a variety of known or suspected carcinogens, and determine whether cell lines from individuals with a family history of cancer are more readily transformed to malignant clones by strong electrophiles in general or in particular, while cell lines from certain other individuals tended to be less susceptible to transformation by critical doses of the same carcinogens. With improvements in technique, it would be possible to characterize each cell line in terms of the critical dose level that would produce a given percentage of cell transformations for a wide spectrum of known and suspected carcinogens, including viruses. This information would uncover the existence of cancer-prone individuals or family lines if the diversity hypothesis is correct.

To undertake such studies we need to achieve certain goals above the present level of sophistication in the field of tissue culture. For example, we need to be able to maintain cell replication in cells that are capable of differentiation and then shift from replication to differentiation by a change in culture conditions, and to establish the boundary conditions that will permit non-replicating differentiated cells to stop producing their special phenotypic products and resume replication. These goals are being approached by a number of laboratories today. Having arrived at the required technical level, the studies on tissue cultures should be undertaken on a rather massive scale with careful selection of cell donors. Within a relatively few years, it might be established that for nearly every type of cancer the probability of occurrence is strongly influenced by genetic variation in the human population with environmental factors superimposed on genetic susceptibility.

This idea may be politically less attractive than the idea that cancer is something analogous to poliomyelitis and can be conquered by similar methods, because even in a complex world, people still want simple answers. However, the world does not operate according to our simplistic wishes but only as it can.

References

Allen, D. W. and P. Cole. 1972. Viruses and human cancer. *New England Med. J.*, **286**: 70-82.

Ashley, D. J. B. 1969. The two "hit" and multiple "hit" theories of carcinogenesis. *Brit. J. Cancer*, **23**: 313-328.

Baker, H. 1971. Psoriasis—clinical features. *Brit. Med. J.*, **3**: 231-239. July 24.

Baltimore, D. 1970. RNA-dependent DNA polymerase in virions of RNA tumour viruses. *Nature*, **226**: 1209-1211.

Boutwell, R. K., N. H. Colburn, and C. C. Muckerman. 1969. *Ann. N. Y. Acad. Sci.*, **163**: 751-763.

Burch, P. R. J. 1962. A biological principle and its converse: Some implications for carcinogenesis. *Nature*, **195**: 241-243.

Cleaver, J. E. 1968. Defective repair replication of DNA in xeroderma pigmentosum. *Nature*, **218**: 652-656.

Chen, T. T. and C. Heidelberger. 1969. Quantitative studies on the malignant transformation of mouse prostate cells by carcinogenic hydrocarbons *in vitro. Int. J. Cancer*, **4**: 166-178.

Cramer, J. W., J. A. Miller, and E. C. Miller. 1960. N-hydroxylation: A new metabolic reaction observed in the rat with the carcinogen 2-acetyl-aminofluorene. *J. Biol. Chem.*, **235**: 885-888.

Huberman, E., L. Aspiras, C. Heidelberger, P. L. Grover, and P. Sims. 1971. Mutagenicity to mammalian cells of epoxides and other derivatives of polycyclic hydrocarbons. *Proc. Nat. Acad. Sci., U.S.A.*, **68**: 3195-3199.

Huggins, C. 1970. Peyton Rous: In memoriam. *Perspect. Biol. Med.*, **13**: 465-468.

Kabat, D. 1972. Gene selection in hemoglobin and in antibody-synthesizing cells. *Science*, **175**: 134-140.

Knudson, A. G., Jr. 1971. Mutation and cancer: Statistical study of retinoblastoma. *Proc. Nat. Acad. Sci., U. S. A.*, **68**: 820-823.

Lynch, H. T. 1967. Hereditary factors in carcinoma. *Recent Results in Cancer Research*, Vol. 12. Springer-Verlag, New York.

Maher, V. M., E. C. Miller, J. A. Miller, and W. Szybalski. 1968. Mutations and decreases in density of transforming DNA produced by derivatives of the carcinogens 2-acetylaminofluorene and N-methyl-4-aminoazobenzene. *Mol. Pharmacol.*, **4**: 411-426.

Miller, J. A. 1970. Carcinogenesis by chemicals: An overview—G. H. A. Clowes memorial lecture. *Cancer Res.*, **30**: 559-576.

————— and E. C. Miller. 1971. Guest editorial. Chemical carcinogenesis: Mechanisms and approaches to its control. *J. Nat. Cancer Inst.*, **47**: v-xiv.

Miller, R. W. 1971. Editorial: Transplacental chemical carcinogenesis in man. *J. Nat. Cancer Inst.*, **47**: 1169-1171.

Mitelman, F. 1971. The chromosomes of fifty primary Rous rat sarcomas. *Hereditas*, **69**: 155-186.

Ohno, S. 1971. Genetic implication of karyological instability of malignant somatic cells. *Physiol. Rev.*, **51**: 496-526.

Parsa, I., W. H. Marsh, and P. J. Fitzgerald. 1972. Pancreas acinar cell differentiation. VI. Effects of methyl donors and homocysteine. *Fed. Proc.*, **31**: 166-175.

Potter, V. R. 1969. Recent trends in cancer biochemistry: The importance of studies on fetal tissue. *Can. Cancer Conf.*, **8**: 9-30.

—————, R. D. Reynolds, M. Watanabe, H. C. Pitot, and H. P. Morris. 1970. Induction of a previously non-inducible enzyme in Morris hepatoma 9618A. *Advan. Enzyme Regulation*, **8**: 299-310.

—————, W. C. Schneider, and G. J. Liebl. 1945. Enzyme changes during growth and differentiation in the tissues of the newborn rat. *Cancer Res.*, **5**: 21-24.

————— and M. Watanabe. 1968. Some biochemical essentials of malignancy: The challenge of diversity. *In*: C. J. D. Zarafonetis (ed.). *International Symposium on Leukemia-Lymphoma*, p. 33-45. Lea and Febiger, Philadelphia.

Rasmussen, R. E. and R. B. Painter. 1966. Radiation-stimulated DNA synthesis in cultured mammalian cells. *J. Cell Biol.*, **29**: 11-19.

Rous, P. 1959. Surmise and fact on the nature of cancer. *Nature*, **183**: 1357-1361.

—————. 1965. Viruses and tumour causation. An appraisal of present knowledge. *Nature*, **207**: 457-463.

—————. 1967. The challenge to man of the neoplastic cell. *Science*, **157**: 24-28.

Selkirk, J. K., E. Huberman, and C. Heidelberger. 1971. An epoxide is an intermediate in the microsomal metabolism of the chemical carcinogen dibenz(a,h)anthracene. *Biochem. Biophys. Res. Comm.*, **43**: 1010-1016.

Setlow, R. B. and J. D. Regan. 1972. Defective repair of N-acetoxy-2-acetylaminofluorene-induced lesions in the DNA of xeroderma pigmentosum cells. *Biochem. Biophys. Res. Comm.*, **46**: 1019-1024.

Stich, H. F., R. H. C. San, J. A. Miller, and E. C. Miller. 1972. Various levels of DNA repair synthesis in xeroderma pigmentosum cells exposed to the carcinogens N-hydroxy- and N-acetoxy-2-acetylaminofluorene. (Manuscript submitted.)

————, R. H. C. San, and Y. Kawazoe. 1971. DNA repair synthesis in mammalian cells exposed to a series of oncogenic and non-oncogenic derivatives of 4-nitroquinoline l-oxide. *Nature,* **229**: 416-419.

Temin, H. 1972. RNA-directed DNA synthesis. *Sci. Amer.,* **226**(1): 25-33.

———— and S. Mizutani. 1970. RNA-dependent DNA polymerase in virions of Rous sarcoma viruses. *Nature,* **226**: 1211-1213.

Voorhees, John J., E. A. Duell, L. J. Bass, J. A. Powell, and E. R. Harrell. 1972. Decreased cyclic AMP in the epidermis of lesions of psoriasis. *Arch. Dermatol.* (In press.)

Walker, P. R. and V. R. Potter. 1972. Isozyme studies on adult, regenerating, precancerous, and developing liver in relation to findings in hepatomas. *Advan. Enzyme Regulation,* **10**: 231-256.

Weinstein, G. D. and P. Frost. 1968. Abnormal cell proliferation in psoriasis. *J. Invest. Dermatol.,* **50**: 254-259.

4 How Membrane Permeabilities Change

HAROLD LECAR
LABORATORY OF BIOPHYSICS
National Institute of Neurological Diseases and Stroke
National Institutes of Health

Membranes regulate the flux of materials into and out of all cells, but the membranes of the excitable cells of the nervous system are able to change their ion permeabilities drastically, milliseconds after receiving a stimulus. A prime example is the generation of a nerve impulse for which a small change in transmembrane electrical potential, of the order of 10mV, serves as a stimulus for a thousand-fold increase of the membrane permeability to sodium ions, occurring within half a millisecond.

Such rapid changes in ion permeability give rise to the electrical impulses which are transmitted along nerve axons. The resting cell membrane is selectively permeable to admit potassium ions. Since the interior of the cell has a higher concentration of potassium than the surrounding body fluid, an electrical potential of -70 millivolts, inside to outside, exists across the membrane of the resting cell. Sodium ions are concentrated mainly outside the cell, and when the permeability to sodium increases, the battery potential across the membrane reverses its polarity to a value of about (plus) 50 millivolts. This sudden 120 millivolt reversal, followed by a relatively slower recovery, is called the nerve action potential.

Other membrane excitations entail similarly-rapid permeability changes in response to other stimuli. Synapses, such as the neuromuscular junction, are activated when transmitter substances released by the action of nerve impulses reaching the presynaptic nerve endings diffuse across the space between two cells and cause permeability changes in the post-synaptic membrane.

In an analogous way, the membranes of sensory receptor cells act as transducers, able to transform various forms of energy—light, mechanical, or chemical—into electrical signals by means of permeability changes. Muscles also have an action potential. The initiation of muscle contraction involves the propagation of electrical signals by changes in membrane permeability. Recent studies have shown that a similar sequence of ion-permeability changes at the cell membrane is responsible for the regulation of the ciliary motion of protozoa (Eckert, 1972).

Many of the characteristics of the ion permeability changes in the nerve axon and in the neuromuscular junction are now known in great detail (Katz, 1966; Cole, 1968; Hodgkin, 1964; Katz, 1970). Much is also known about permeability changes in sensory receptors (Hagins, 1972; Case, 1966) and neuronal synapses (Katz, 1966; Eccles, 1964; Bennett, 1967). The knowledge gained has given investigators new insights into the information-processing methods of the nervous system and has clarified the mode of action of various neural drugs.

In this article, we will survey some recent attempts to understand the changes that occur in the membrane at the molecular level to produce the sharp permeability changes of excitation. This aspect of the field is still quite speculative; only recently has reliable information on the molecular structure of any kind of membranes become available. We will first consider in detail one particular excitation phenomenon, the voltage-sensitive ionic permeability changes of the nerve axon because the axon is probably the most studied and best understood of all excitable membranes (Hodgkin, 1964; Cole, 1968; Adelman, 1971). However, all of the permeability phenomena underlying the various kinds of excitations have features in common. Which of these are common to all membranes and what molecular mechanisms are involved are the main questions investigators seek to answer.

The information needed for a molecular understanding of permeability change will come from several different disciplines, each of which employs its own characteristic language. Physiologists studying membrane transport use a vocabulary of functional entities, such as carriers and pores; biochemists, attempting to isolate the relevant membrane constituents, use enzymatic terms such as permeases, transferases, and transportases; biophysicists studying excitable cells write in terms of current-voltage curves and electrical transients to describe membranes by equivalent electrical circuits, but they are all considering different aspects of the same phenomena.

Signal Transmission Along Nerve Axons

The nerve axon is a cable for transmitting electrical impulses within the nervous system. The stimulating currents—in nature, the result of permeability changes in the post-synaptic region—cause a voltage drop across a portion of the axon membrane.

The voltage drop is small ($\sim$ 100 mV), but because voltage equals field times distance and cell membranes are remarkably thin ($\sim$ 50 to 75 A.U.), the electric field generated within the membrane by the voltage drop is enormous ($\sim$ 100,000 V/cm.). This large field can cause dielectric breakdown in many insulating materials. The permeability changes which characterize nerve firing result from some structural change within the membrane under the stress of the transmembrane electric field.

Much of what has been learned about axon excitation is a result of research on giant axons. These huge cylindrical structures (as large as 1 mm in diameter) have been studied by the voltage clamp, a device which permits the experimenter to control the potential across the membrane by electrical feedback. The sheer size of the giant axon makes it the most promising preparation for voltage clamp experiments entailing the impalement of the axon by several rather large electrodes. The giant axon is also uniquely suited to other sophisticated experiments, such as the measurement of ion fluxes by radioactive tracers and experiments in which the cytoplasmic contents of the cell are altered by internal perfusion.

In addition to making life convenient for experimenters, giant axons also serve a valuable function for the animals which have them. Nerve conduction speed increases with increasing axon diameter, and giant axons are an evolved specialization for fast transmission of the signals triggering the animal's escape reflexes. Creatures with giant axons—squids, polychaete worms, etc.—although quick, are not particularly clever. Cleverness requires having many nerves, and giant axons take up too much space. For the higher animals, a more efficient kind of nerve evolved, the myelinated nerve, possessing a specialized cable geometry for rapid conduction without such large diameters. At the membrane level, however, the mechanisms of excitation are identical in myelinated nerves and giant axons; only the geometrical arrangement in which the excitable membrane is employed is different (Cole, 1968).

The current biophysical picture of the generation of a nerve impulse is as follows: There are two processes—a transient, large (10^3 to 10^4 fold) increase of the nerve membrane permeability to sodium, driving the system towards the equilibrium potential for the sodium battery (120 mV above rest), followed by a delayed increase of the potassium permeability which makes the nerve once again function as a potassium battery and, thereby, hastens the return of the membrane potential to its resting value.

Synapses and sensory receptors possess membrane structures which modify ionic permeabilities when other forms of energy are received at the membrane. Because of the imbalance of ion concentrations between the inside and outside of the cell, currents flow and potentials change in response to the permeability changes. Thus, electrical disturbances are the currency of information processing. The ion permeability structures in the synapses and receptors, however, are not as sensitive to electrical stimulation as are those in the axon. If they were, all of the signals in the nervous system would be self-regenerative and a single sensory input would reverberate everywhere. The synapses and receptors provide the small stimulating currents needed to trigger axonal excitation. Since synaptic regions, axonal regions, and specialized receptor regions often coexist in the same cell membrane, membranes must be extremely heterogeneous. Is the heterogeneity caused by regional variations in the overall membrane structure or does the diversity of function indicate the existence of specialized permeability sites within the membrane? A great deal of evidence presently points to the latter possibility—that the membrane contains many different types of specialized transport structures (Ehrenstein and Lecar, 1972; Kotyk and Janacek, 1970). If this is in fact the case, one is then prompted to ask what structural features do all these membrane sites have in order to be ion transport sites and what variations do they show in order to be activated by such a diversity of stimuli? The major focus of membrane research in the near future will be to isolate and to describe the properties of these permeability structures.

Although the elements in the membrane which are responsible for ion permeability may be able to function independently of each other, membrane excitation in one part of a cell can have consequences elsewhere because of the electric currents generated. A stimulus which alters the membrane ionic permeability can also alter the transmembrane electrical potential. In the axon, a cycle ensues in which changing potential alters permeability, and permeability further alters potential. At the sodium equilibrium potential, the cycle stops because the voltage can no longer change by increasing sodium permeability. The electric currents generated in this way stimulate a similar cycle a little bit further down the axon, and the excitation spreads.

Interactions between changing permeabilities and voltages also travel from cell to cell. A voltage change at the presynaptic nerve ending effects the release of transmitter substances which diffuse across the synaptic gap and cause permeability changes in cell membranes of the next neuron in line.* These permeability changes generate small currents. If a sufficient number of such small electrical disturbances occur within a short time, they can add together to act as a stimulus to propagate a nerve impulse in the next axon. In this way, information progresses by electrical telegraph signals along the axon cable and by chemical transmission at the synaptic switchboard.

The effects of permeability changes can be more indirect than the simple transmission of signals. Nerve impulses can also trigger the release of the contents of secretory cells, which then act as transmitters, diffusing through the body and causing permeability changes at any cells possessing the appropriate membrane receptors. The complexity of these interrelated permeability changes can sometimes be seen when a drug or a genetic disease interferes with the production of a single transmitter substance and causes a recognizable syndrome with extensive bodily manifestations (Rosenberg, 1969).

Active and Passive Transport

It is important to remember that the ion currents which flow when a nerve fires and the ion fluxes which charge the cell battery are different

---

* Not all synapses are chemical, however. Some seem to be low impedance spots where the membranes of two cells are fused. These "tight junctions" also occur extensively in epithelial tissues. How normally resistive membranes can fuse to form a low impedance junction remains a mystery at this point (Lowenstein, 1970).

transport processes. The currents which flow during excitation are passive in the sense that they derive their driving force from the ion concentration gradient and do not require an additional metabolic source of energy. During a nerve action potential, a sodium selective pathway opens in the membrane, and sodium ions flow into the cell passively along their electrochemical gradient.

The active transport of sodium out of the cell is carried out by some mechanism which has been called the sodium pump. The pump operates even when the cell is at rest and is not directly involved in nerve firings. For giant axons, internal perfusion and metabolic poisons have been used to show that nerves can fire indefinitely after the cell metabolism has been destroyed, provided the ionic concentration differences are maintained (Hodgkin, 1964). Active transport may be more intimately involved in the functioning of smaller cells. In a small nerve terminal, the ion transfers of just a few action potentials may alter the composition of the cytoplasm, thereby draining the battery. Metabolic energy is needed to recharge the battery, and thus, active transport is required for the recovery of the nerve after a burst of impulses. This is an example of the intricate way in which many kinds of membrane processes are linked in the information processing of the nervous system.

For our discussion, the sodium pump is also important because it is an example of the active accumulation of materials which is carried on by all cell membranes. Not only ions, but sugars and amino acids, must be accumulated against their concentration gradients. The salient characteristic of active transport is its substrate specificity. Some of the amino-acid transport systems of microorganisms transport only a single substrate. Such specificity can only be possessed by protein-binding sites. Much has been learned about the chemical reactions at several transport sites, and these chemical affinities can be exploited in the isolation of the actual proteins involved in the various active transport systems. The major mystery of active transport is how the energy of the metabolic reaction at the membrane is employed to move the binding site from one side of the membrane to the other in order to transport the substrate against a gradient (Kotyk and Janacek, 1970).

Active transport and excitation, although distinctly different processes, have at least one feature in common. In both cases, an external form of energy alters some characteristic of the permeability site. In the case of active transport, a chemical interaction somehow causes the transport site to move molecules across the membrane. In the case of excitation, the external energy causes the site to increase or alter its permeability, but the flow through the activated site is driven by the cell's own electrochemical battery.

We can summarize the important features about axon excitation briefly. Experiment has shown that the two conducting processes of nerve impulses, the transient Na conductance and the delayed K conductance, seem to be independent of each other. This independence was demonstrated by a kind of chemical dissection (Hille, 1970). There are drugs which can abolish one component of the current without affecting the other. Tetrodotoxin, the puffer fish poison, and saxitoxin, a shellfish poison, both knock out the transient sodium current without affecting the potassium current, whereas tetraethyl ammonium ions block the delayed potassium current without greatly affecting the early sodium flow. Such experiments not only demonstrate the integrity of the two pathways but can also be used to show the asymmetry of the membrane. Tetrodotoxin is only effective from outside the cell and not when injected internally; tetraethyl ammonium is far more effective when injected internally. Furthermore, the sodium pathway can be blocked from different sides of the membrane by different drugs (Ehrenstein and Lecar, 1972).

Neurotoxins which are able to bind selectively to a particular membrane permeability site show promise as "markers" for locating and isolating the sites. An example in current use is the polypeptide α-bungarotoxin, isolated from a snake venom, which binds to acetylcholine receptors and blocks the postsynaptic response; radioactively labeled α-bungarotoxin has been used to estimate the density of postsynaptic receptors (Miledi and Potter, 1971).

Selectivity

The different conducting pathways in the axon are distinguished by their different patterns of ionic selectivity. The two processes involved in excitation are not perfectly selective. The sodium pathway cannot distinguish between Na and Li and will also transport, albeit less efficiently, a sequence of other cations including K (about $1/10$ the permeability of Na). The potassium channel has its own characteristic sequence of preferences. The selectivity sequence is one of the many ways in which the excitation channels differ from the sodium pump. Unlike the Na excitation pathway, the pump *can* distinguish between Na and Li. There are other excitation processes, such as those in certain muscles, which have a voltage-dependent activation selective to Ca instead of Na. Such pathways are not blocked by tetrodotoxin.

The ability of membranes to recognize subtle distinctions among the substances to be transported provides a set of indirect molecular fingerprints for learning about the transport structures. Recently, it has been discovered that the sequence of ionic preferences of the Na channel are quantitatively the same in the nerves of animals in different phyla (Hille, 1971a). Thus, we may deduce that the Na channel in an axon is a rather stable entity and not a membrane property which can be readily modified.

As was mentioned in connection with active transport, some membrane transport sites seem to be very selective indeed. An example is the system responsible for the uptake of sugars in erythrocytes. Experiments have shown that sugars which penetrate the membrane will interfere with the uptake of other sugars as if the molecules were competing for sites within the membrane. The pyranose ring of sugar molecules can exist in two conformations, "chairs" and "boats," and the membrane can distinguish between these forms (Stein, 1967).

The problem of ion selectivity is a bit different than that of non-electrolytes (Diamond and Wright, 1969; Eisenman et al., 1967). The major attraction between electrically charged particles is the enormous electrostatic force. The geometry of a binding site within the membrane will assume much different significance depending upon whether or not that site is charged. A negatively charged site within a membrane will associate itself preferentially with positively charged ions. The major principles governing preference among various positive ions have been deduced theoretically. A positive ion is strongly attracted to the negative binding site. However, ions in solution always travel with a coterie of water molecules bound to them by electrostatic forces. Ion selectivity is determined by the interplay of these forces; in order to approach the binding site, an ion must divest itself of some of its water molecules. Some of the potent neurotoxins, such as tetrodotoxin, have ionic groups which can infiltrate the site; the molecular structure of the toxin also includes side groups which act to clog the transport channel. Recent experiments have determined the selectivity sequence of the sodium channels for various organic cations which differ from each other in steric details (Hille, 1971b). Such experiments probe the internal structure of the permeability site.

Phenomenological Theories of Permeability Change

The two major attributes of the permeability changes during excitation are the ion selectivity and the trigger process or gate which allows the permeability changes to occur. During a nerve impulse, the gating process manifests itself as an explosive change in conductance. Axons normally respond to electrical stimuli in a discontinuous all-or-none manner. However, voltage-clamp experiments (in which ion currents can be measured in response to a fixed step of voltage) demonstrate that the membrane process which determines the discontinuous behavior during excitation is a smoothly-varying voltage-dependent conductance. This voltage-dependent ion conductance follows changes in applied voltage with a characteristic time course which has been summarized in the Hodgkin-Huxley equations (Hodgkin, 1964). All of the thresholds and other distinctive features of the action potential can be explained in terms of these equations. The molecular origin of the conductance changes, however, is not yet understood. The membrane conductance, plotted as a function of the transmembrane potential, follows a sigmoid curve reminiscent of a magnetization curve. Following the analogy to magnetization, one might speculate that the electric field activates groups within the membrane, and that the conductance curve represents the statistical distribution of activated groups. Other explanations have been proposed as well, and the nature of the voltage-dependent conductance is an open question. The critical feature of the conductance curve, a feature which is necessary for excitation, is the sensitivity to voltage. At the foot of the conductance curve, a 5 millivolt change in voltage will produce a 2 to 3 fold change in conductance. Even allowing for the enormous transmembrane electric field, such a sensitive activation requires something special—either a large amount of energy for a single molecular channel to change its configuration or cooperation between a number of subunits.

Although most workers on axons would agree that the major unsolved problems of excitation are the unraveling of the nature of the transport site and the molecular basis for permeability change, it is interesting to dwell for a moment on the success of the Hodgkin-Huxley phenomenological theory. The theory uses a set of differential equations to describe the response of an axon in terms of electrical equivalent circuits. These equations are able to predict all of the axon phenomena of classical neurophysiology. Knowledge of synaptic transmission is fast approaching the same level of quantitative understanding. Thus, for the purpose of understanding how the "components" of the nervous system function, the equivalent circuit pictures play the same role as the equivalent circuit pictures of ordinary electronic devices. It is quite possible that a science of neural modeling and neural circuit analysis will arise independent of the molecular understanding of the membrane permeability changes.

Such quantitative phenomenological theories as the Hodgkin-Huxley theory form a convenient middle ground. The theory provides a set of "quasi first principles" for predicting more complicated phenomena. On the other hand, a physical explanation for the behavior described by the equation stands as a goal of investigations into the molecular nature of permeability change.

Carriers and Channels

Let us return to the distinction between the active Na pump and the passive excitation currents in the axon in order to contrast two types of transport mechanisms found in membranes. We have already seen that one requires metabolic energy and the other does not, but there are further differences (Baker, 1968).

First of all, the two processes transport Na ions at different rates. The conducting units of the sodium pathway, activated during excitation, can handle 10^{16} ions/cm^2 per sec, and this sodium flux shows no sign of saturating. The sodium pump, on the other hand, cannot move more than $1/1000$ of this amount and obeys a form of saturation kinetics, as if some constituent of the membrane needed for transport could be overtaxed. This kinetic difference is highlighted when the temperature is lowered. There is a decrease in the rate at which the conducting units become activated, but the maximum rate of ion transport does not change with temperature. However, the ability of the pump to transport is severely altered—even inhibited altogether—by decreasing temperature.

These criteria can be used to distinguish between two types of transport mechanisms, sometimes called channels and carriers (Hille, 1970; Eigen and DeMaeyer, 1971; Ehrenstein and Lecar, 1972). A channel is a continuous path for ion transport through the membrane. It may be a pore through which ions travel rather freely or a chain of binding sites across which the ions can hop. The significant aspect of the channel is that the transport through it is not closely connected to the state of the membrane, and the channel structure itself does not move to carry the ions across. Carriers, on the other hand, are objects in the membrane which combine with ions to carry them across. The carriers can be saturated if they cannot process all the ions coming at them, and they can be stopped if the membrane is made too viscous.

Certain antibiotics, which have been discovered to act as carriers, function by combining with ions and diffusing across the membrane, but this is not the only possible way for carriers to work. The important requirement of a carrier is that it have a binding site which is alternately exposed to either side of the membrane. Models have been proposed for the specialized proteins which act as carriers—revolving doors, conveyor belts, etc. (Kotyk and Janacek, 1970). Such models are of value insofar as they stimulate experimenters to design tests to distinguish between the various possible transport entities.

Transport Sites within the Membrane

Thus far, we have assumed that ions pass through the membrane at discrete sites rather than through the membrane as a whole. Historically, the basis for this assumption has been indirect. The ease with which small molecules permeate the membrane is proportional to their solubility in oil, a fact known since the 1920s (Dowben, 1971). This was one of the first causes for supposing that the membrane was an oily film. But, at the same time, it was seen that certain small molecules, such as sugars, amino acids, and ions, which are not at all soluble in oil, were also permeable through membranes. Thus, from an early date, membranes were thought to be mosaic structures with special pores or inhomogeneities designed to allow the hydrophilic substances to pass.

That ion conduction occurs only at special sites on the membrane can also be inferred from the record of conductance changes which take place during a nerve impulse. At this time, the ionic conductance of the nerve membrane increases by a factor of 40, without any change in the electrical capacitance of the membrane (Cole, 1968). However, the resting membrane has an electrical capacitance characteristic of a thin oil film. The only way for ions to diffuse through such a layer, without the expenditure of prohibitive amounts of energy, is for the membrane dielectric to change to a value closer to that of water or for conducting paths to be opened in the membrane to allow ions to bypass the insulating barrier. The lack of capacitance change during nerve activity rules out the former possibility and sets the stage for a search for specialized ion-conducting regions.

Such arguments for permeability sites in the membrane are indirect because they are based on assumptions about the membrane structure. One of the exciting developments at present is the emergence of direct experimental evidence for specialized transport sites in membranes. The evidence comes both from studies of membrane transport and from recent work on membrane structure. In one group of experiments, transport processes have been blocked by incredibly small numbers of drug molecules (Kotyk and Janacek, 1970). This means that either a drug molecule can precipitate cooperative processes or that one drug molecule can knock out a discrete transport site. In the latter case, such drug experiments may give numerical estimates for the number of transport sites at the membrane surface. For the axon, one such potent drug is tetrodotoxin which blocks the Na channel reversibly. Experiments have been done in which nerves are soaked in tetrodotoxin (Moore et al., 1967; Keynes et al., 1971); several nerves are soaked in the same solution until the solution loses its potency. Such experiments indicate an upper bound to the number of Na channels, ranging from about 15 to 50 channels per square micron. Estimates from other experiments place the number of K transport sites in the human erythrocyte at only 100 to 200 per cell (Stein, 1968).

Once again we can see a difference between membrane channels and possible carrier mechanisms. From the density of Na channels estimated in the tetrodotoxin experiments and the known maximum Na flux during nerve activity, one finds that each Na channel must have 10^7 ions per second flowing through it. In contrast, blocking experiments with dinitrofluorobenzene place the number of glucose transport sites in the erythrocyte at about 800,000 per cell, and each site must handle 180 glucose molecules per second (Stein, 1968). The glucose turnover is well within the capability of carriers which might diffuse through the membrane, whereas the Na transport rates are just too high for diffusion through the lipid (Ehrenstein and Lecar, 1972).

Such conjectures about the adequacy of a particular mode of transport raise questions about both membrane function and structure. On one hand, if individual sites can pass such intense currents, there may be means for detecting the activation of individual conducting channels. On the other hand, better knowledge of the fluidity or rigidity of the membrane core would tell us whether carrier motions are possible.

One way to "see" conducting channels is to observe indications of discrete bursts of membrane currents when individual channels are activated. The drug experiments indicate that the transport sites are sparsely distributed throughout the membrane. However, the fewer the sites, the greater must be the flux at an individual site. Thus, if a group of sites are activated at random, the resulting random bursts of current may appear as electrical voltage fluctuations. A number of laboratories are studying electrical fluctuations in membranes with the hope of determining the properties of individual conducting channels.

One such experiment is the study of "shot noise" during activation. Shot noise is the electrical voltage jitter which appears because of the random bursts of current caused by the activation of individual molecular conductances in the membrane. Such shot noise has been shown to occur in photoreceptors when they are activated by light (Hagins, 1965) and in the neuromuscular junction when it is activated by an increase in the extracellular concentration of transmitter (Katz and Miledi, 1970). From this phenomenon, one can obtain an estimate of the unit of conductance which is activated within the membrane. The unit measured, 10^{-11} to 10^{-10} mho, is about the same as was determined from the site-counting experiments with blocking drugs. Thus, it is appealing to conjecture that channels of this order of conductance are the conduits for ion transport in excitable membranes. A conductance of about 10^{-10} mho is what one might expect if the channel were a 5 A.U. pore through the membrane—an oversimplified, but perhaps not unreasonable, picture.

The second question which we raised about the physical state of the lipid core of the membrane is one which has finally been resolved by new technology. Experiments using spin labels, nuclear magnetic resonance, and immunofluorescence all show that the lipid core of the membrane is fluid (Singer and Nicolson, 1972). However, much more has come out of the new studies of membrane structure, and we shall digress a bit to describe this field.

Membrane Structure

The recent literature on membrane structure is pervaded by a great sense of optimism (Culliton, 1972). At present, the favored model is a fluid mosaic model which embodies many of the features of the lipid bilayer proposed by Danielli and Davson thirty years ago. Advances in X-ray diffraction have enabled investigators to determine that the membrane possesses large coherent patches of lipid bilayer. Parallel hydro-carbon chains form a moiety about 40 A.U. thick which extends over regions of at least 50 lipid molecules.

The membrane protein has been shown to be distributed throughout the lipid in the form of globules. There is spectroscopic evidence to show that most of the amino acid chains are in the alpha-helix form (Singer and Nicolson, 1972). The major tool for revealing the positions of the proteins in the membranes is the technique of freeze-fracture electron microscopy. In this technique, the membrane is frozen and cleft. The surface thus revealed is the cleavage plane through the middle of the bilayer. The freeze-fracture pictures show a lipid sea in which globules of protein about 75 A.U. in diameter float.

Enzyme digestion and radioactive label experiments show that some proteins penetrate through the membrane and that the membrane proteins can have different chemical groups on the two surfaces of the membrane—results presaged by the drug experiments on transport. Immunofluorescence studies show that the proteins are mobile and can move laterally through the membrane (Frye and Edidin, 1970).

There are many other results and many new techniques, and we refer the reader to several recent articles for a more detailed description of current work in membrane structure (Singer and Nicolson, 1972; Fox, 1972). If we seek the structures which perform the functions we have been discussing, we find many different membrane proteins. No universal proteins have been discovered. Much of the specific experimental work has been done on special proteins found only in particular membranes. This is compatible with the functional picture—sparsely distributed, highly specialized transport units—deduced from membrane physiology.

To summarize both the structural studies and the transport studies, one can say that the focus is upon minority constituents of the membrane. The lipid bilayer membrane is the barrier, and the protein structures floating about are the doors. The next phase of research will concern itself with the properties of the doors. Can they be isolated chemically? Can spectroscopic probes of sufficient sensitivity be developed for the study of the rare doors?

In answer to the first question, at least two transport proteins have already been isolated, and there are reports of others. One such protein is a component of the sodium pump. A sodium-potassium ATPase, with all of the specificities of the Na pump, has been isolated and studied extensively (Kotyk and Janacek, 1970). In time, an assay will be developed for showing its role in transport.

The answer to the second question will be more difficult. It is hard to do spectroscopy on the critical membrane components because they are so rare. A number of experiments have been attempted to detect some physical change occurring when the permeabilities of excitable membranes change. Many of these experiments detect changes in the membrane induced by the transmembrane electric fields, but they do not necessarily have anything to do with the conducting channels (Cohen and Landowne, 1971).

The most promising development for the answer to this second question is the use of synthetic lipid bilayer membranes. These membranes serve two functions. They allow us to make very accurate molecular analogs of the processes we think go on in living membranes. They also serve as matrices for testing the properties of membrane constituents isolated from natural membranes. For a putative channel or carrier which has been isolated, the synthetic bilayer may provide for the study of transport processes the equivalent of *in vitro* biochemistry. It is not yet clear, however, that the transport structures can be exported so easily from their native membrane to a synthetic bilayer. There may be specialized proteins sitting in the membrane like raisins in a pudding, but there may also be more complicated lipoprotein structures composed of subunits which will not take kindly to being dismembered.

At least one synthetic membrane has been produced which exhibits the major physical feature of electrical excitability—the steeply voltage-sensitive conductance. When normally nonconducting lipid bilayers are doped with Excitability Inducing Material (EIM), an uncharacterized protein of bacterial origin, the conductance increases by several orders of magnitude and exhibits the steep voltage dependence characteristic of electrical excitability (Mueller and Rudin, 1969). Just as for the axon, the EIM-induced conductance goes through its full range of variation over approximately 20 millivolts. EIM can be added to the membrane in small amounts, and discrete steps of current can be observed as conducting channels form.

For this model system, the origin of permeability change has been determined (Ehrenstein et al., 1970). The conducting channels each have two or more structural states corresponding to different values of conductance. The applied electric field causes transitions between these states. The quantal fluctuations of current when a conducting channel opens can be observed. The relative frequency of the conductance transitions changes with membrane voltage in such a way that individual channels spend more or less time in the conducting state at different voltages. The variation of the transition frequency of these channels gives rise to the voltage-dependent conductance observed when a membrane possesses many channels.

There are many other interesting additives which have been studied on bilayers; some act as channels, some as carriers (Mueller and Rudin, 1969). Much work has been done with the polyene antibiotics, such as valinomycin. These small peptides act as carriers. They form complexes with ions which can diffuse across a bilayer. The complexes exhibit selectivity, and they allow one to study the kinetics of carrier-mediated transport in precise detail. One recent experiment demonstrated the inhibition of carrier motion when the lipid region is made viscous, the hallmark of this mode of transport (Krasne et al., 1971).

There are reports of the isolation of natural membrane components and of attempts to incorporate them in lipid bilayers. This area of investigation is still very new, and the principles of chemical extraction do not guarantee the reconstitution of a functioning membrane subunit. However, the bilayer provides the tool for observing membrane components in their natural geometric arrangement.

The use of bilayers and bilayer vesicles and lipid liquid crystalline forms allows one to recapture some of the organization of membranes. In addition, the study in synthetic bilayers of reactions taking place at membrane surfaces may be as full of surprises as the chemistry of soluble enzymes.

In summary, the biochemistry, physiology, and biophysics of membrane transport are converging in their emphasis on specialized structures within the membrane.

Although a number of membrane transport proteins have been isolated, nothing is known about the structure of the transporting units within the membrane. The future may show a variety of structures for ion binding or possibly some single universal pattern, such as the dough-nut-shaped polypeptides which function as carriers and channels in synthetic membranes (Urry, 1971). Permeability changes may then emerge as conformational changes which somehow open and close the doughnut holes. Perhaps when some channel structures are known, it will become clear why the structural changes of membrane channels can be induced by such a diversity of stimuli. For example, an electri-cally excitable channel may differ from other channels by being more flexible or having a large charged group which acts as a lever so that it can be deformed by the transmembrane field. Similarly, some link be-tween an enzymatically active site and a particularly flexible doughnut structure might give a pump the ability to pop its ions across the mem-brane in response to a chemical interaction. These are the kinds of spec-ulations which can be raised at present. However, it must be remembered that the permeability structures are still conjectural. The next stage of membrane research must involve reconstituting these specialized struc-tures in working form in a synthetic bilayer structure.

References

Adelman, W. J., Jr. (ed.). 1971. *Biophysics and Physiology of Excitable Membranes.* Van Nostrand Reinhold, New York.

Baker, P. F. 1968. Nervous conduction. *British Med. Bull.,* **24**: 179.

Bennett, M. V. L. 1967. Similarities between chemical and electrical mediated transmission. *In*: F. D. Carlson (ed.). *Physiological and Biophysical Aspects of Nervous Integration.* Prentice-Hall, Englewood Cliffs, N. J.

Case, J. 1966. *Sensory Mechanisms.* Macmillan, New York.

Cohen, L. B. and D. Landowne. 1971. Optical studies of action potentials. *In*: W. J. Adelman (ed.). *Biophysics and Physiology of Excitable Membranes.* Van Nostrand Reinhold, New York.

Cole, K. S. 1968. *Membranes, Ions and Impulses.* University of California Press, Berkeley.

Culliton, B. J. 1972. Cell membranes: A new look at how they work. *Science,* **175**: 1348.

Diamond, J. M. and E. M. Wright. 1969. Biological membranes: The physical basis of ion and nonelectrolyte selectivity. *Ann. Rev. Physiol.,* **31**: 581.

Dowben, R. M. 1971. *Cell Biology.* Harper and Row, New York.

Eccles, J. C. 1964. *The Physiology of Synapses.* Springer-Verlag, Barlin.

Eckert, R. 1972. Bioelectric control of ciliary activity. *Science,* **176**: 473.

Ehrenstein, G. and H. Lecar. 1972. The mechanism of signal transmission in nerve axons. *Ann. Rev. Biophys. Bioengr.* **1.** (In press.)

———, ———, and R. Nossal. 1970. The nature of the negative resistance in bimolecular lipid membranes containing excitability-inducing material. *J. Gen. Physiol.,* **55**: 119.

Eigen, M. and L. De Maeyer. 1971. Carriers and specificity in membranes. *Neurosci. Res. Prog. Bull.,* **9**: 300.

Eisenman, G., J. P. Sandblom, and J. L. Walker, Jr. 1967. Membrane structure and ion permeation. *Science,* **155**: 965.

Fox, C. F. 1972. The structure of cell membranes. *Sci. Am.,* **226**: 30.

Frye, L. D. and M. Edidin. 1970. The rapid intermixing of cell surface antigens after formation of mouse-human heterokaryons. *J. Cell. Sci.,* **7**: 319.

Hagins, W. A. 1965. Electrical signs of information flow in photoreceptors. *Cold Spring Harbor Symp. Quant. Biol.,* **30**: 403.

———. 1972. The visual process. *Ann. Rev. Biophys. Bioengr.,* **1.** (In press.)

Hille, B. 1970. Ionic channels in nerve membranes. *Progr. Biophys. Mol. Biol.,* **21**: 1.

———. 1971a. Voltage clamp studies on myelinated nerve fibers. *In*: W. J. Adelman, Jr. (ed.). *Biophysics and Physiology of Excitable Membranes.* Van Nostrand Reinhold, New York.

———. 1971b. The hydration of sodium ion crossing the nerve membrane. *Proc. Nat. Acad. Sci. USA,* **68**: 280.

Hodgkin, A. L. 1964. *The Conduction of the Nervous Impulse.* Thomas, Springfield, Ill.

Katz, B. 1966. *Nerve, Muscle and Synapse.* McGraw-Hill, New York.

———. 1970. *Synaptic Transmission.* Thomas, Springfield, Ill.

——— and R. Miledi. 1970. Membrane noise produced by acetylcholine. *Nature,* **226**: 962.

Keynes, R. D., J. M. Ritchie, and E. Rojas. 1971. The binding of tetrodotoxin to nerve membranes. *J. Physiol.,* **213**: 235.

Kotyk, A. and K. Janacek. 1970. *Cell Membrane Transport.* Plenum Press, New York.

Krasne, S., G. Eisenman, and G. Szabo. 1971. Freezing and melting of lipid bilayers and the mode of action of monactin, valinomycin, and gramicidin. *Science,* **174**: 412.

Lowenstein, W. R. 1970. Intercellular communication. *Sci. Am.,* **222**: 78.

Miledi, R. and L. T. Potter. 1971. Acetylcholine receptors in muscle fibres. *Nature,* **233**: 599.

Moore, J. W., T. Narahashi, and T. I. Shaw. 1967. An upper limit to the number of sodium channels in nerve membrane. *J. Physiol.,* **188**: 99.

Mueller, P. and D. O. Rudin. 1969. Translocators in bimolecular lipid membranes: Their role in dissipative and conservative bioenergy transductions. *Curr. Top. Bioeng.,* **3**: 157.

Rosenberg, L. E. 1969. Hereditary diseases with membrane defects. *In*: R. M. Dowben (ed.). *Biological Membranes*. Little Brown, Boston.

Singer, S. J. and G. L. Nicolson. 1972. The fluid mosaic model of the structure of cell membranes. *Science,* **175**: 720.

Stein, W. D. 1967. *The Movement of Molecules Across Cell Membranes.* Academic Press, New York.

———. 1968. The transport of sugars. *British Med. Bull.,* **24**: 146.

Urry, D. W. 1971. The gramicidin A transmembrane channel: A proposed $\pi_{L,D}$ helix. *Proc. Nat. Acad. Sci. USA,* **68**: 672.

5 The Impact of Molecular Biology on Study of Cell Differentiation

FRED H. WILT
DEPARTMENT OF ZOOLOGY
University of California, Berkeley

> "It is sufficiently obvious that in a phenomenon as complex as the differentiation of tissues and organs, several profoundly different mechanisms must be at work." (Monod, 1947)

Introduction

In August of 1947, the year of founding of the AIBS, American plant and animal embryologists gathered at Storrs, Connecticut to attend the annual meeting of their society. Among the seven speakers were two developmental biologists (Brachet and Braun) while the others represented disciplines ranging from genetics of bacteria and protozoa (Monod and Sonneborn) to physical biochemistry (Rothen), virology (R. C. Williams), and carcinogenesis (Haddow). It is no accident that developmental biologists were listening to "outsiders," and the practice, happily, has continued. The study of development, while the home of some of the most exciting fundamental problems in biology, is also the most derivative. I can think of no problem properly belonging only to students of development unless it is the subject of close range tissue interactions. The central concern of developmental biology is the mechanisms of origin of relatively stable new properties of cells and cell groups. What sets the field apart is the study of one of the fascinating properties of metazoa—a single stem cell or egg may give rise to mitotic descendants that specialize in different and orderly ways, leading to the normal histological tissue types encountered in adults, and almost always arranged in the correct spatial and temporal relations.

The paradoxical nature of cell specialization during development has been apparent for well over a century and a half. A concise hypothesis of the mechanism of differentiation, stated in modern terms, was available by at least 1934. Thomas Hunt Morgan, a geneticist and embryologist said:

> It is known that the protoplasm of different parts of the egg is somewhat different, and that the differences become more conspicuous as the cleavage proceeds, owing to the movements of materials that then take place. From the protoplasm are derived the materials for the growth of the chromatin and for the substances manufactured by the genes. The initial differences in the protoplasmic regions may be supposed to affect the activity of the genes. The genes will then in turn affect the protoplasm which will start a new series of reciprocal reactions. In this way we can picture to ourselves the gradual elaboration and differentiation of the various regions of the embryo. (Morgan, 1934)

Knowledge of the mechanisms of differentiation involve a detailed understanding of the regulation of gene expression. We do not know in any detail how genes express themselves in higher organisms, nor do we know how this expression is regulated. We do have a whole new language which describes the general levels of regulation of gene expression and an armamentarium of techniques for study of the biochemical basis of gene expression. It is the feeling of many that the analysis of differentiation is just a mopping-up operation following the successful beachhead established by molecular biology.

The principal purpose of this essay is to speculate on what needs to be mopped up and how, and whether there are new surprises, technical and/or conceptual, in store for us that are necessary for a deeper understanding of how developing cells specialize. Is our theoretical framework of the regulation of cell function, largely gained from studies on bacteria, sufficient for the enterprise of the next few decades? If it is, then the experiments and achievements of the coming years can be predicted with some accuracy. However, I will contend in a second section of the essay that, as our knowledge of cell structure and function advances, new and important regulatory mechanisms of gene expression will become apparent. My point of departure is an examination of the impact of molecular biology on studies of differentiation, and this will place boundaries on the discussion. I have largely excluded many approaches to study of cell specialization, such as cell fusion, ionic communication, actions of hormones and persistence of specialized functions in cell cultures, as well as neglected important developmental issues like origins of organ symmetry and how cells in a tissue fabric obtain positional information; e.g., how neighboring cells in an insect wing imaginal disc are determined to produce a precise pattern of veins and bristles. These issues and approaches do not deserve neglect, but the limits of space and my ability to synthesize these different approaches dictate restricting the discussion.

The Mopping Up Operation

In my opinion the principal advance in the study of differentiation during the last 25 years has been the acquisition of a new vocabulary of cellular regulation, and the concepts defined by it, from molecular biology. Neither Morgan in 1934 nor Monod in 1947 could have foreseen the importance of thinking about levels of regulation of gene expression in terms of transcription, translation, post-translational mechanisms, self assembly, and allosterie. But these concepts, together with the new technical developments—the electron microscope, spectrophotometers, ultracentrifuges, isotopes, nuclear transplantation, tissue culture, and cell fusion—are the stock in trade of any modern laboratory studying differentiation. The kinds of experiments probing the differentiation process are dictated by the new language. It is a wonderful achievement to transform the old polemics about the importance of the nucleus and the cytoplasm into experiments describing transcription and translation. We can now ask: Is the genome really constant? Is there extrachromosomal genetic information? How is transcription controlled—by proteinaceous coverings around genes, by specific RNA polymerases, by cofactors or activators or derepressors from the environment, by other genes? What controls the export of messenger RNA from the nucleus, and how does it attach to polyribosomes? What controls the rate of translation and the rate of degradation of proteins? What are the precise conditions leading to self assembly of organelles, and how do other cells influence establishment of these conditions?

TRANSCRIPTION

It is obvious that the details of the synthesis, transport, translation and degradation of messenger RNA are essential for knowledge of how genes "express" themselves in higher organisms. This enterprise is particularly difficult. First, it is very often not possible to obtain rigorous interpretations with experiments using a collection of putative messenger RNA's; the criteria defining messenger RNA as a class in eucaryotic cells are often lacking; there is no uniformity of base ratio or of stability. Furthermore, the nucleus of metazoan cells contains large amounts of metabolically-unstable high molecular weight RNA. The function of this RNA is unknown, but it does represent the vast majority of the transcribed RNA. Unstable nuclear RNA is a particular annoyance when studying messenger RNA for it is often a substantial contaminant of so-called pure cytoplasmic messenger. Large scale efforts are now under way to isolate messengers for specific proteins and, as of this writing, at least two have been isolated and analyzed in some detail, hemoglobin and fibroin (Evans and Lingrel, 1969; Suzuki and Brown, 1972). In both these instances, conventional fractionation methods have been applied to tissues in which a single, or a few predominant, proteins are synthesized in the hope that this would be reflected in a high differential rate of accumulation of a few messengers. The unusual amino acid composition of fibroin offers a convenient route for identification of the messenger by nucleotide sequence analysis. It is likely several other messengers, coding for proteins found in large amounts or with unusual properties (size or amino acid composition), will soon be demonstrated; histone (Kedes and Birnstiel, 1971), ovalbumin (Schimke, 1972), myosin (Heywood, 1968), and collagen are likely candidates in the race for new messengers. Assay methods for particular messengers are becoming available and are of the greatest importance; e.g., translation of the messenger in reticulocyte or ascites cell lysates (Housman et al., 1971) or in living *Xenopus* oocytes (Lane et al., 1971) is now feasible, and these assay systems are being used to identify and titrate specific messenger RNA's.

The utility of having particular messengers is great for problems of developmental interest. The complementary DNA sequence can be synthesized by reverse transcriptase (Ross et al., 1972) or isolated from the genome by appropriate molecular hybridization methods. The DNA thus obtained provides a biochemical route to the study of gene anatomy, and the availability of these genes also allows one, potentially, to follow the course of messenger RNA synthesis, export, translation, and degradation. The length relationships between genes and messengers may be subjected to analysis. The hemoglobin messenger has been found to be about 200 nucleotides longer than is required for the length of the globin subunits (Gaskill and Kabat, 1971). Are the extra nucleotides required for export, for recognition and binding of ribosomes, for interaction with protein synthesis initiation factors?

The isolation and characterization of the ribosomal genes has been one of the great accomplishments of the past decade. Several years ago David Kohne (1968) applied DNA-RNA hybridization procedures to isolate the DNA sequences coding for ribosomal RNA from some bacteria and was able to show that there were repetitive identical sequences (about 5 per genome). Because of the unusual base composition of the genes coding for ribosomal RNA in amphibia (and most higher animals), Brown (Brown and Weber, 1968) and his colleagues have been able to isolate the ribosomal genes and describe some interesting features of this genetic region which may have general significance. The genes are present in many identical copies, are arranged in tandem, and have associated with each coding sequence a rather long stretch of nucleotides, called the spacer region, that is not transcribed. Although the sequence of the spacer region has diverged much more than the ribosomal RNA region in *Xenopus* species, it is homogeneous in any given species. What evolutionary forces select for the inclusion of large segments of non-transcribed DNA? This ribosomal system has also provided an exception to one of the ground rules by which Morgan operated, the constancy of the genome. For it is now known that the genes for ribosomal RNA are synthesized into many thousands of extra copies during oogenesis in *Xenopus,* although these extra copies of ribosomal genes are later lost (Brown and Dawid, 1968).

The availability of pure genes in test tubes allows a biochemical approach to some of the central problems of regulation of transcription, which can be listed here. Is there specificity to the enzymes that transcribe DNA? If so, what is the precise nature of the control of specificity (Roeder and Rutter, 1970; Reeder and Brown, 1970; Roeder et al., 1970)? To what extent is the nucleotide sequence of a gene the determinant in whether transcription occurs and its rate? Do non-transcribed DNA sequences play a role in the specificity of interaction of polymerase with transcriptive enzymes? Are extra copies of the genes synthesized and exported to the cytoplasm as Bell (1971) proposes for I-DNA? Is the specificity of transcription due to non-DNA components of the chromatin? Or is this discussion an instance of "putting the cart before the horse?"

The evidence for specificity of transcription in development, while we all earnestly believe it, is weak. One of the best-studied examples is the synthesis of ribosomal RNA (rRNA) in amphibia, and the experiments in this research area illustrate a number of interesting points. The rate of ribosomal RNA synthesis was measured in *Xenopus* by Brown and Littna (1963), and rRNA synthesis became detectable near the time of gastrulation. They concluded that ribosomal RNA synthesis was regulated, with transcription of these genes occurring from gastrulation onward. Emerson and Humphreys (1970, 1971) have challenged this conclusion by pointing out that ribosomal RNA synthesis could have occurred at the same rate during cleavage but would have been obscured for two reasons: First, the number of cells at early stages, and hence, the number of genomes available for transcription, is very much lower; and second, the rate of heterogeneous nuclear RNA synthesis per genome is so high during early stages that the ribosomal RNA synthesis would have been obscured. Two additional reasons supporting the contention of Humphreys can also be presented: The cell cycle is so rapid during cleavage that G-1 is usually nonexistent, and the time available to chromatin to serve as a template may be limited; and second, the turnover of ribosomal RNA's (turnover of the ribosomal precursor has been demonstrated in some unusual instances, notably in the developing lens [Papaconstantinou and Julku, 1968]) was not ruled out. Emerson and Humphreys have carried out experiments showing that nucleoli (albeit, lacking an obvious granular component) do transiently exist in cleavage-stage sea urchins, and they were able to detect the predicted levels of ribosomal RNA synthesis in blastulae. For technical reasons, the matter is not settled, and the original conclusions of Brown were drawn from experiments on *Xenopus* while the challenge of Humphreys is based on work on sea urchins. But there is now doubt that changing levels of ribosomal RNA synthesis do occur in amphibia and sea urchins. What has been clearly demonstrated is that the absolute rate of synthesis of total RNA, most of it heterogeneous nuclear RNA (HnRNA), proceeds from a high level early in sea urchin development to a much lower level after gastrulation (Kijima and Wilt, 1969; Brandhorst and Humphreys, 1971). This contradicts the widely-held view that genes are quiescent during cleavage and only become active during gastrulation, but the facts seem convincing. Of course, most of the HnRNA is rapidly degraded, and it may not serve as a template for protein synthesis. An understanding of the relationship of total RNA synthesis to differential gene expression will await a better understanding of the biological role of HnRNA.

The proposal that transcription is not extensively regulated during differentiation offends all our prejudices. The heterodox view is worth consideration, and at least, the heresy may force us to more rigorous interpretations of the evidence for specific transcription. Or, perhaps the heresy will serve as a starting point for evaluating what biochemical reactions are in fact regulated; as Paul Gross (1964) put it, we may ask what is "the immediacy of genomic control"? The evidence that specificity of transcription is a principal element in differential genetic expression comes from two recent sources. First, the dramatic phenomenon of localized RNA synthesis in diffuse regions of giant chromosomes of diptera—the chromosome puffing—is usually considered good evidence for selective transcription. The evidence for localized RNA synthesis associated with puffs is fairly good (Berendes, 1971), but there is little evidence to show that these transcription products have anything substantial to do with the functioning or development of the cells that contain the giant chromosomes. There are few reliable biochemical indices of differentiation in this tissue. One phenotypic character associated with a certain puff is the presence of particular cytoplasmic secretion granules. Contrary to the postulate that the "gene activation" involved in puffing is a controlling element, treatment of salivary gland cells with an inhibitor of RNA synthesis, actinomycin D, does not affect the synthesis of these secretion granules, nor for that matter does inhibition of RNA synthesis have much effect on cytoplasmic protein synthesis in these cells (Clever et al., 1969). The tissue specificity of these puffs has been overemphasized (Kroeger and Lezzi, 1966), and the chains of evidence linking tissue-specific puffs to development of particular phenotypes are largely missing.

A second type of evidence for specificity of transcription as an important determinant of cell differentiation relies on the DNA-RNA hybridization reaction to evaluate similarities and differences of the RNA molecules in differentiated tissues. If RNA is extracted, for example, from adult liver and kidney, the population of RNA molecules can be shown by "competition" experiments to be different (Paul, 1971;

Shearer and McCarthy, 1970). If the chromatin from the two tissues is prepared and used as a template for heterologous RNA polymerase, the spectrum of RNA molecules made in the test tube is remarkably similar to that found in the living tissue, as assayed by DNA-RNA hybridization procedures. But these experiments are not rigorous for several reasons: First, the RNA which is used in hybridization experiments represents some sample of molecules which is subject to turnover, and it is not at all clear whether the specific patterns observed are due to specific transcription or specific degradation and export. Second, and more serious, is the limitation of the assay, DNA-RNA hybridization. All the experiments of this type have been carried out with conditions under which only so-called redundant DNA can react. This is DNA in the genome which reacts extraordinarily rapidly in hybridization reactions, and the interpretation offered by Britten and Kohne (1968) for this behavior is that this rapidly reannealing DNA is present in large families of similar but not identical sequences. The relation of such families of DNA sequences to typical Mendelian genes is completely unclear at present, and it is not even known in most instances if redundant DNA contains any information used by the cell for protein synthesis. The RNA-DNA hybrids formed with such DNA contain a very large number of non-complementary hybrid regions; i.e., there is a high degree of nucleotide mis-matching, so that as much as 10 to 25% of the bases are not paired (McCarthy and Church, 1970). Experiments based on hybridization reactions in which the reaction has not approached completion and in which only poorly matched sequences are detected do not provide strong evidence for the importance of specificity of transcription for acquisition of different phenotypes. It is logically impossible to have differential genetic expression without some occurrence of specificity of transcription from the genome. But just when, how, and to what extent differential transcription occurs during a developmental sequence is largely unknown, and precisely how differential transcription is involved in differentiation of phenotype is obscure. I predict good evidence for differential transcription will be demonstrated for some cases of differentiation where large amounts of a few proteins are produced; e.g., the galea of silk moths and developing erythrocytes, but I also anticipate that regulation of m-RNA export and stability will be of general importance.

POST-TRANSCRIPTIONAL MECHANISMS

Mechanism of translation.

The details of polypeptide synthesis by cells are rapidly being worked out. The aminoacyl tRNA species involved in chain initiation in eucaryotes usually have a blocked aminoterminal, just as N-formyl methionine in procaryotes does. The involvement of ribosomal subunits in aminoacyl tRNA and template binding, the role of GTP and the several protein factors in initiation of a new polypeptide chain, and mechanisms of polypeptide chain elongation are under intense study (Lengyel and Söll, 1969). These details are of great importance for the development of suitable assays for m-RNA (as discussed above) but are also of the greatest importance in and of themselves. One of the generalizations of the past decade, illustrated in particular by developing systems, is that messenger transcription is often not rate-limiting in determining translation rate. For example, the unfertilized sea urchin egg increases the rate of synthesis of all the proteins being made by 10 to 20 fold about 5 to 10 minutes after egg activation, and this occurs in enucleated or poisoned eggs in which RNA synthesis is lacking (Gross, 1964). The conclusion is unavoidable, and is now backed up by additional direct evidence (Humphreys, 1971), that some kind of post-transcriptional control is involved here. Is the messenger sequestered somewhere, only to be released by the stimulus of egg activation, or do ribosomes and the associated machinery leading to chain initiation change their locations and properties leading to a more efficient initiation of translation? These are not mutually exclusive mechanisms, and both have their champions. Many other examples exist; during the development of the erythroblast, the synthesis of messenger for hemoglobin seems to precede the onset of hemoglobin synthesis by several hours (Wilt, 1965). Synthesis of several enzymes in polysaccharide synthesis by the developing cellular slime mold occurs from a pre-transcribed template (Sussman, 1967), as does synthesis of proteins in the developing lens (Papaconstantinou, 1967) and the germinating wheat embryo (Weeks and Marcus, 1971).

Furthermore, it is very often true that the terminal stages of differentiation of various organs, characterized by the massive synthesis of characteristic products and organelles (like zymogen granules), sooner or later become insensitive to drugs and analogs which eliminate or derange transcription. For example, the formation of zymogen granules

in the galea of silk moths becomes insensitive to administration of Actinomycin some hours before the granules can be detected cytologically
(Kafatos, 1969). Similarly, the formation of zymogen granules in the
embryonic mouse pancreas shows an acquisition of insensitivity to Actinomycin (Wessels and Wilt, 1965). In these cases, it is assumed that
translation is occurring from stable messages and that there may well be
regulation of the rate of messenger translation. The molecular basis of
the stabilization of the template is completely obscure. To what extent
are the different recognizable events of a differentiative life history due
to the control of messenger degradation? It is now very well known that
degradation of structural proteins and enzymes is as influential in determining the steady state level of the protein in a cell as is the synthesis of
the protein (Schimke and Doyle, 1970). It is not unexpected that control of RNA degradation would be equally important. There is only the
barest beginning of research on this important topic. Since many embryos are completely closed systems and carry out all their metabolic
synthesis by degrading preformed materials, I would be surprised if control of degradation of proteins and RNA were not of great importance
(cf. Kafatos, 1972).

Even if we understood how the steady state level of a particular RNA
template were controlled, a detailed knowledge of translation mechanisms is crucial. How is the attachment of the template to the ribosomal
subunit accomplished? And what is the role of the endoplasmic reticu-
lum and the microenvironment in this process? To what extent do rare-
isoaccepting transfer RNA molecules control initiation and translation
rate? Are there stage-specific and tissue-specific initiation factors? Ilan
(1971) has reported that formation of initiation complexes for protein
synthesis in extracts of larvae of the mealworm do depend on stage-
specific protein factors, and Heywood (1970) has marshalled evidence
for tissue specificity of initiation during a comparison of protein synthesis in muscle and red cells. The translation of rabbit globin m-RNA
in *Xenopus* oocytes (Lane et al., 1971) clearly shows that specific initiation factors are not a complete explanation for translational specificity.

Post-translation mechanisms

Perhaps even more puzzling and of equal importance are the problems of assembly of functional complexes and organelles. For example,
during morphogenesis of the salivary gland, collagen is deposited over

the epithelium, and this collagen is apparently important in the generation and maintenance of specific shape and branching patterns of the
developing rudiment (Grobstein, 1966). The tropocollagen is primarily
synthesized, in this instance, by the mesenchyme and then transferred to
the epithelium for deposition (Bernfield, 1970). What determines the
specific pattern of collagen deposition? Available evidence indicates
that the epithelium, even though it does not synthesize the collagen,
does determine the deposition pattern, as well as stimulate the mesenchyme to synthesize collagen. Is there a relationship between the putative contractile activities of microfilaments, which are also important in
morphogenesis, and the deposition of collagen, as Bernfield and Wessels
have proposed (1970)?

The so-called "self assembly" of structure really means one has to
deal with the control of specific microenvironments favoring the poly-
merization, aggregation, and bonding important to structure formation.
How is local pH, ionic strength, and the ionic spectrum controlled?
Many events of early embryogenesis occur by the rearrangement of already synthesized elements into new structures, such as the reorganization of the egg cortex and formation of the fertilization membrane.
What are the inter-relationships between changes of membrane permeability, cortical granule breakdown, fertilization membrane formation
and hardening, and the initiation of an increased rate of protein synthesis that follow activation of the sea urchin egg? The discovery of the
rapid changes of potassium conductance in activated sea urchin eggs may
provide a breakthrough for this problem (Steinhardt et al., 1971). Likewise, the discovery of localized conductance changes and microcurrents
in eggs of the alga, *Fucus,* provides an opportunity to study the role
of ionic changes in development of cellular asymmetry (Jaffe, 1969).
Sooner or later the mechanisms of regulation of the ionic microenvironment and its impact on structure generation will have to be attacked
frontally. And the regulation of ionic environment is not only important
for formation of new structure, but it is also important in the function
of organelles already in existence. There is an upsurge of interest, a
healthy one if I am any judge, in the effect of the ionic milieu on genome
replication, transcription, and translation (Orr et al., 1972). The elegant
work of Ray (1969), showing that the primary effect of auxin on cole-
optiles is at the post-transcriptional level, indicates the importance of
post-transcriptional regulation.

We might close this section on post-transcriptional mechanisms by drawing attention to a curious aspect of development of the ascidian embryo. Lambert (1971) has shown that an ascidian egg will develop into a tadpole without any RNA synthesis whatsoever; presumably all the developmental mechanisms occur by control of translation and control of the assembly of structures. Arguments concerning the relative importance of transcription and translation are a little reminiscent of the controversy between the proponents of preformation and epigenesis during the last century. But we now know that control of transcription, translation, and organelle assembly are not mutually exclusive possibilities but are all involved in the epigenetic drama.

Some embryological issues

Morphogenesis and tissue interactions—Two decades ago embryologists appreciated that the forces that produced changes of shape and form in embryos and organs were a fascinating part of the developmental history, but there was really hardly a glimmer of how to proceed. In the intervening time, the use of the electron microscope, together with application of some curious drugs, has helped us understand how embryos change shape. The ubiquitous appearance of microtubules and microfilaments in morphogenetically active regions has provided an impressive array of circumstantial evidence that implicates these two classes of cell structures in shape change and movement (Trinkaus, 1969). The chemistry of microtubules is advancing rapidly, and their role in ciliary motion and as a cytoskeleton seems certain. The contractile role of microfilaments in morphogenesis is less securely established, and the relationships of microfilaments to actin are debatable (Forer and Behnke, 1972). The circumstantial evidence based on sensitivity of certain morphogenetic processes to the drug, cytokalaim, and the distribution of microfilaments, makes a proposal involving microfilaments in morphogenesis a promising working hypothesis (Wessels et al., 1971); we should note, though, that the specificity of cytochalasin is now suspect (Sanger and Holtzer, 1972). Certainly a major effort will be forthcoming to isolate microfilaments and characterize them. More difficult to investigate will be the mechanisms that govern the assembly and function of these filamentous structures: The mechanism governing the coordination of movements among large numbers of cells in a tissue fabric seems completely obscure at present, but certainly these mechanisms are of cardinal importance.

We know a great deal more about tissue interactions than we did 25 years ago; yet, the subject seems inordinately complex. What seemed to be a simple stimulus-response situation has turned out to be a whole series of reciprocal interactions between tissues, and the responding tissues may respond in a large variety of ways—by proliferation, determination, overt cytodifferentiation, morphogenetic movement, or combinations of these (Wessels, 1970). Although the range of systems under study has increased, and we know that intimate contact of the plasmalemma of the interacting cells need not exist (Grobstein, 1966), it is probably misleading that the wide range of embryonic cellular communications are all grouped under the single rubric of tissue interactions; for the responses, stimuli, and mechanisms involved may turn out to be quite diverse. If there are unifying regulatory principles, they have yet to be enunciated. I am struck by the fact that, as different examples of tissue interactions are studied more intensively, it seems the specificity of the "inducing" tissue is less and less stringent. The view that the "inducer" simply creates a complex conditioned medium that permits differentiation to proceed, as opposed to the supposition that information-carrying molecules instruct the responding tissue, seems to me likely to be correct.

Nucleo-cytoplasmic interactions—The mechanisms by which the cytoplasm of embryonic blastomeres affect "nuclear activity" seem ripe for a concerted attack (Gurdon and Woodland, 1968). By the use of cell isolation experiments and interspecific hybrids, experimental embryologists clearly established that the egg cytoplasm and cortex was heterogeneous and of crucial importance for determination. It should be possible, with available techniques, to isolate and characterize the relevant components of the cytoplasm and learn whether they are involved in transcriptional or post-transcriptional level controls. A great accomplishment was the elaboration of the nuclear transplantation technique by King and Briggs (1956). Their work, and the elegant nuclear transplantation experiments of John Gurdon (1962) resolved a really important question. Nuclei from determined, and even highly differentiated, cells may serve as the vehicle for a completely new round of embryogenesis; i.e., nuclei are not irreversibly differentiated. Translated into the language of molecular biology, this means that even if genomic constancy is not observed, changes in nuclear DNA content must either be trivial or reversible and do not involve irreparable losses of information. Similar experiments involving culture of cells from mature plants showed that these differentiated somatic cells could give rise to a complete new plant (Steward et al., 1964; Vasil and Hildebrandt, 1965). The nuclear transplantation technique has been exploited, especially by Gurdon, to show that the cytoplasm of the maturing oocyte acquires at the time of germinal vesicle breakdown the machinery to replicate DNA of somatic nuclei from mature tissues that do not normally undergo DNA synthesis (1967). The oocyte can serve as a virtual test tube to analyze in detail what the cytoplasm contains that forces intense DNA synthesis to occur. Whether there is regional localization of the DNA synthetic machinery in the cytoplasm and how egg activation sets the machinery in motion for autologous nuclear replication are research goals for the near future.

The vegetal pole of amphibian egg contains a cytoplasmic region necessary for the development of germ cells, and L. D. Smith (1966) has shown that injection of this "polar plasm" will confer upon eggs rendered incompetent (by UV irradiation) for germ cell differentiation the ability to make germ cells during development. Hence, an assay now exists for one cytoplasmic determinant(s), and the tedious, but important, business of identifying the relevant substances and learning something about the mechanisms of the action can proceed. Briggs and Cassen (1966) also discovered that the failure of a mutant axolotl to undergo gastrulation is due to a cytoplasmic component of the oocyte, and they also developed an egg microinjection assay for the component. Malacinski (1972) has characterized the cytoplasmic determinant as a large protein. The continued use of nuclear transplantation and microinjection assays should provide powerful tools for a partial unraveling of the nature of "organstoffe."

Even though use of large eggs which can sustain the injury of microinjection are desirable, the reinvestigation of interspecific hybrids in small marine invertebrate eggs may prove to be extremely rewarding. For instance, interordinal hybrids between sand dollars and sea urchins fail to gastrulate normally although they undergo early development. Some enzymes which show electrophoretic species differences have been used to monitor "gene expression," and it has been shown that only the enzymes of the maternal member of the cross appear in extracts of developing embryos (Whitely and Whitely, 1972). Does this mean that the paternal genome cannot be replicated, or that its DNA cannot be transcribed, or is it a failure in translation? Since some of the nucleic acids of the two genera can be distinguished by RNA-DNA hybridization procedures, these questions can be posed. The experiments are extremely difficult to control, but there is no conceptual barrier to getting clear answers to the general modus operandi of the cytoplasm on the foreign genome. Similar types of experiments are being carried out on interspecific hybrids of sea urchin (Denis and Brachet, 1969). Why is replication of paternal chromosomes in many such crosses slow and imperfect? Are some, or many, of the chromosomal proteins synthesized on pre-existent and stable maternal messengers, and are some of the complement of chromosome proteins unable to construct proper chromosomes with paternal DNA? This very old tool of experimental embryology should quickly give us new and interesting leads to the nature of nucleo-cytoplasmic interactions.

New Principles of Cellular Regulation

In the preceding section, I have tried to indicate some areas where questions have been posed, and the techniques required to execute the experiments either exist or are now being developed. What is vague in all this are approaches to two central problems of development: 1) How is transcription of the genome regulated; and 2) how does the microenvironment make its impact on cell function? The principal reason for conceptual vagueness is because the operon model for procaryotic genomic regulation, while it probably does operate in metazoa, has been helpful only in that it has provided a new way of thinking and talking about regulatory problems. The model does not really clearly define how regulation is accomplished in cells with chromosomes and nuclear membranes. It is my belief that new and important devices, lacking in procaryotes, exist in metazoa that are superimposed upon the regulatory devices of *E. coli*. After all, the impact of selection pressures on eucaryotes and procaryotes are rather different. The procaryote adapts rapidly and reversibly to changing environmental conditions. But the metazoan, while sometimes retaining an organismal capacity for rapid adaptation, has dispensed with some flexibility at the cellular level in favor of maintaining a more or less constant interior milieu; the cells are insulated from the external environment. A comparison of growth media for bacteria and vertebrate tissue culture cells supports this assertion. Is there any connection between the developmental strategies of metazoa and the appearance during evolution of elaborate membrane systems and complex structures in which the DNA is embedded? I suspect we have not even posed the key questions in this area. We are still ignorant of many details of cell structure, especially the chromosomes and membrane system of the cell; perhaps this is because of an apparent unwillingness of developmental biologists to use the tools of modern genetics.

MEMBRANE STRUCTURE

There has been a revolution in the last few years in our grasp of the essential structural features of cell membranes. The models recently proposed by Singer and Nicolson (1972) and Branton and Deamer (1972) visualize a very dynamic structure of a viscous fluid lipid bilayer in which are embedded a mosaic of proteins, some of which traverse the entire bilayer, some of which may have their non-polar portions buried in the lipid fluid and their polar groups exposed to the external or internal ionic environments. In this view, the membrane is an extremely dynamic structure, and this is consistent with a rapidly accumulating and impressive body of evidence for movement of membrane proteins within the plane of the membrane, and for the possible pinocytotic engulfment of membrane areas in which aggregation of a particular constellation of membrane proteins has taken place. These continuing structural studies, both of the cell membrane and internal membrane system, may have an incredible impact on developmental biology. What factors in the environment induce rearrangement of the mosaic of protein molecules in the membrane? What influence does this have on the molecules in the microenvironment that the cell encounters? Perhaps we have been too impressed with the constancy of composition of sea water or blastocyst fluids; even though the overall ionic milieu in which an embryo develops may seem uniform, a heterogeneous distribution of cell surface sites provides a lovely amplification system for developing and perpetuating cellular heterogeneity. How do the different molecules, admitted entry by the cell membrane system, manifest effects on translation and transcription, on cell movement, and on the interaction of cells with the physical substrate on which they are arrayed? The practical importance and conceptual challenge are superbly illustrated by the problems of specificity of neuronal connections. The regenerating optic nerves of an amphibian larva re-establish a point for point connection with cells in the optic tectum, almost regardless of the trick the experimenter plays to confuse the ingrowing optic nerve fibers (Jacobson, 1967). How do the microenvironment and the neuronal membranes interact to produce this exquisite specificity? While it may be presumptuous to predict that important new principles of structures and function will be discovered as a consequence of a better understanding of the molecular anatomy of the membrane, our knowledge of the structure of lipid fluids and their modes of interactions with proteins and ions is so fundamental that important surprises may be the order of the day.

CHROMOSOME STRUCTURE AND FUNCTION

Interesting models of chromosome structure and function are being proposed (Georgiev, 1969; Crick, 1971; Britten and Davidson, 1969). The models are interesting because they are essentially models of regulation. Watson and Crick had the structural information of X-ray diffraction and knowledge of the chemical composition of DNA to apply to their speculations on DNA structure. We still have nothing comparable as regards chromatin, although progress is becoming rapid. The protein, RNA, and lipid components of chromatin are still largely undescribed although the histone components are now being studied intensively (Stellwagen and Cole, 1969). The non-histone proteins may account for 10 to 30% of the mass of the chromatin, yet we know little about them. Attempts are now being made to specifically dissociate and reassociate various protein components and to monitor transcription specificity during such procedures in order to learn what factors are responsible for specificity (Huang and Kleiman, 1971). As far as they go, these results suggest that the non-histone components are largely responsible for specificity although, as pointed out previously, the assays for transcription specificity suffer from serious deficiencies (Spelsberg et al., 1971). There probably could be no chromatin without basic proteins, and histones may be an essential structural component of chromosomes without imputing to them a specific regulatory role. A chemically defined "chromatin" preparation is not yet available. Exhaustive extraction at low ionic strength, the usual method, leads to adventitious association of proteins and nucleic acids; high ionic strength leads to dissociation of proteins from nucleic acids (Baltimore and Huang, 1970). The RNA content of chromatin is widely variable (Artman and Roth, 1971), and the degradation of RNA during the extractions at low ionic strength is extensive. For example, during the preparation of chromatin from sea urchin blastulae nuclei by the method of Shaw and Huang (1970), over 90% of the pulse-labeled RNA is degraded to acid-soluble material (Wilt, unpublished). Chromatin is notoriously insoluble, and the use of traditional physical-chemical and biochemical techniques is usually not possible without preparations that involve formation of artifacts that are not fully understood. What is the importance of the association between portions of chromosomes and the nuclear envelope? Is the imaginative and rigorous task of a biochemical and physical description of chromatin likely to lead to anything more than pedestrian results? I have a hunch it will, especially if the biochemical approach is coupled with use of genetic operations to be discussed shortly.

The amount and sequence complexity of the DNA found in metazoa is strikingly different from that found in bacteria. Is the correlation between the amount of DNA in the genome, the presence of reiterated DNA, the synthesis of heterogeneous nuclear RNA, and the evolution of cell differentiation spurious? It is a circumstantial correlation, but almost without exception, recent speculations on the regulation of differentiation try to accommodate these curious features. The amount of DNA in higher organisms is incredibly large. We still do not know how much of the DNA is transcribed, but some sequences, such as mouse satellite DNA, cytologically sequestered in the centromere region of the chromosome (Pardue and Gall, 1970), are not transcribed. The molecular hybridization methods are available for a reasonable minimal estimate of the amount of DNA that serves as a template for RNA synthesis; these types of experiments are just beginning, and the amount of DNA transcribed may turn out to be extremely large (Davidson and Hough, 1971). One class of fascinating hypotheses proposes that some of the DNA in the genome is present for the kind of three-dimensional structure it generates rather than the precise sequences of nucleotide bases it contains (Crick, 1971). For example, extensive lengths of redundant DNA, in combination with histones, may form three-dimensional globular chromatin, vital for regulation of the transcription of the adjacent linear chromatin-containing unique DNA. If it is true that DNA is a structural element as well as a purely informational element, this would constitute a completely new principle of molecular biology not foreseen by the founding fathers. Of course, in procaryotes the sequence of certain regions is crucial for the expression of the structural gene, but the three-dimensional structure of long regions of double helical DNA combined with protein is not required.

Some curious phenomena, of which I will mention only one, almost cry out for some kind of "structural" DNA. In a wide variety of cell types from higher organisms, incorporation of large amounts of 5-bromodeoxyuridine (BrdU) in place of thymidine into the DNA results in loss of the ability for certain kinds of specialized synthesis. For instance, chondroblasts fail to synthesize matrix (Abbott and Holtzer, 1968); proerythroblasts fail to undertake hemoglobin synthesis (Miura and Wilt, 1971); myoblasts fail to fuse and synthesize myosin (Bischoff and Holtzer, 1970), and retinal pigment cells fail to synthesize melanin (Coleman and Coleman, 1970). The effects of BrdU are reversible. The drug is not very toxic, and many other, probably most, genes are properly expressed in BrdU treated cells (Stellwagen and Tomkins, 1971). Holtzer (Holtzer and Abbott, 1968) has speculated that the effects show a fundamental regulatory distinction between genes responsible for luxury proteins, proteins characteristic of the terminal differentiated state responsible for specialized function, and "housekeeping" genes responsible for proteins necessary for cellular living. It is possible that the presence of large amounts of BrdU in the genome interferes with transcription, and only proteins from long-lived messengers can persist (Stellwagen and Tomkins, 1971). Another possibility, not a mutually-exclusive one, is that BrdU interferes with the interaction of regulatory molecules in the modes of genetic expression of higher cells. The structural alterations of the globular DNA of Crick or of the battery of regulatory elements in the model of Britten and Davidson would be seriously altered in all probability by the presence of large amounts of BrdU in place of thymidine.

As much as 50% of the DNA of higher organisms may be of the so-called redundant class; i.e., under arbitrary conditions, single-stranded molecules of this class reassociate more rapidly than is predicted by kinetic theory (Britten and Kohne, 1968). The interpretation of this behavior is that much of the DNA is composed of families of closely-related, but not identical, sequences. Unfortunately, the relationship between reiteration and conventional genes, defined by genetic analysis, is not at all clear. Measurements are only now being carried out with various RNA types to learn something about the transcription of DNA's of varying sequence complexities and relationships. For certain defined RNA's, like putative histone message (Kedes and Birnstiel, 1971), hemoglobin message (Bishop et al., 1971), and ribosomal DNA (Brown and Weber, 1968), there is little or no evidence for transcription from DNA of similar-but-*non-identical* families although there is good evidence for multiple copies of identical sequences. Hybridization of nuclear and cytoplasmic RNA is seriously hampered by cross-contamination of the two RNA types, and the interpretations from various laboratories are presently different (Darnell and Balint, 1970; Greenberg and Perry, 1971; Shearer and McCarthy, 1970). The distinction between unique and moderately-redundant DNA may not be as fundamental as once believed, however, as Southern (1971) and others have recently pointed out. There are serious discrepancies between the chemical sequence analysis and the renaturation rates for guinea pig satellite DNA which may be due to effects of mismatching on renaturation kinetics, a factor not considered previously. The point here is that the "uniqueness" of a particular DNA sequence, as defined by renaturation kinetics, depends on the conditions, and on one's ability to understand the reaction mechanisms of renaturation. The methods are available for really rapid and prodigious progress on studies of sequence complexity and arrangement, but the answers are just not in yet.

Another puzzling attribute of metazoa is the presence of an incredibly large amount of transcribed RNA that is rapidly degraded and is never exported to the cytoplasm to subserve some kind of messenger function. This is the so-called heterogeneous nuclear RNA (HnRNA) whose importance was first underlined by Henry Harris (Harris and Watts, 1962). Where quantitative measurements have been made (Soeiro et al., 1969; Aronson and Wilt, 1969), HnRNA may represent over 90% of the amount of RNA synthesized. The steady state amount of the RNA is quite low, however, because of its high metabolic instability. Is this HnRNA largely "junk"? Are larger regions of the genome transcribed than are necessary for the structural gene information and the messenger portion then excised and the remainder discarded? Synthesis of ribosomal RNA in vertebrates proceeds by such a mechanism, for the transcribed ribosomal precursor may be twice as large as the 28s + 18s ribosomal RNA portion (Darnell, 1968). Is the extra RNA important for regulation, for processing of the RNA molecules destined for the cytoplasm? Is a polyadenylate sequence tacked on to HnRNA to serve as a handle (Darnell et al., 1971) for the degradative enzymes to properly degrade the unutilized portions of the HnRNA? These are the kinds of experimental questions currently being posed; only one proposed function of HnRNA has been satisfactorily ruled out. Recent experiments in my laboratory by W. R. Allen (unpublished) have shown that nuclear protein synthesis in sea urchin blastulae is less than 0.1% of the total protein-synthesizing capacity of the whole cell, and this would demand use of less than 1% of the steady state level of HnRNA as an intranuclear template for protein synthesis. With the stricture that we assume any nuclear protein synthesis proceeds by conventional polyribosome-associated mechanisms, it is unlikely that HnRNA is a kind of short-lived intranuclear messenger.

Decisive experiments have not been carried out to distinguish other types of hypotheses: HnRNA may be the non-conserved portion of a messenger precursor; it may be an intranuclear regulatory molecule; it may be messenger precursor that is not processed and/or exported because of the negative decision of some post-transcriptional regulatory step governing export of messenger, or it may be simply excess baggage (Scherrer and Marcaud, 1968), synthesized because it costs the cell less energy to make it and degrade it than to spend energy regulating against its synthesis.

Many of the basic facts about HnRNA are not even known; e.g., its true molecular weight and heterogeneity of molecular weight (Bramwell and Harris, 1967), an accurate knowledge of its half life, and heterogeneity of half life, and a comparison of RNA synthesis time with its stability. This is not the proper occasion to review all the speculations and soft facts about HnRNA, but simply to indicate how important an issue it is and to guess that the outcome may be full of surprises.

GENETIC ANALYSIS OF DIFFERENTIATION

Perhaps an even more important aspect of the problem of regulation of genetic expression is based on our limited knowledge of the biochemical genetics of higher organisms. During the symposium held at Storrs in 1947, Monod said:

> The widest gap, still to be filled, between two fields of research in biology, is probably the one between genetics and embryology (Monod, 1947).

I believe that is still true. Practically every one of the problems mentioned above would benefit by the use of appropriate mutants, mutants that have to a large extent never been isolated from higher organisms. It would be really exciting to have at one's disposal a series of mutants affecting cell membrane synthesis, assembly, and behavior—or to have mutations affecting microfilament assembly and function, or collagen synthesis, ovalbumin synthesis and secretion, etc. The technical difficulties to surmount are considerable—diploidy, selection techniques, long generation times—and need not be discussed here, except to mention the brilliant work of Barbara McClintock (1961) which demonstrates that the impediments can be surmounted. I think it fair to say that developmental biologists have done little to exploit possibilities of genetic manipulation, and the exceptions have often led to very important and substantial pieces of work; e.g., the nucleolar deletion in *Xenopus* and the limb mutants of chickens (Zwilling, 1961). There is another more fundamental reason underlying this plea for genetic analysis. What are the genetic regulatory elements underlying differential genetic expression? We do not yet have the kind of fine structural genetic analysis to know if there are regulatory genes comparable to operator and repressor regions of procaryotes in higher organisms. There is a homily that embryology may eventually have to be done on embryos; I have my doubts about that. But I would propose another homily that genetic regulation in metazoa will eventually have to be studied using "real" genes defined by genetic methods.

The genetic crusade will hopefully be launched sometime during the coming quarter of a century. There is probably no one ideal organism or system. The criteria for satisfactory systems will have to include short generation time, and growth on defined media so that auxotrophs can be obtained. Regulatory mutants affecting the expression of structural genes and modifying the stability and timing of expression of characters will have to be sought. Many of the mutations of interest will be lethal, and conditional lethal conditions for selection will be required. I would venture a guess that those fungi amenable to genetic manipulation and biochemical analysis and that show simple kinds of "differentiation" will prove to be the most suitable systems for this enterprise (cf. Katz and Sussman, 1972).

Summary

The purpose of this article is to point out the considerable impact of molecular biology on studies of the mechanisms of differentiation. New ways of thinking and talking about developmental problems, and some new facts, show clearly that there are a variety of regulatory levels involved in cell specialization. I have tried to discuss a sample of the variety of research now underway that is attempting to find out how these several regulatory levels work in differentiating cells; I have termed this the "mopping up operation." Further, I have expressed the bias that we are largely ignorant of the structural and functional basis for specific transcription and translation, and it is my belief that the problems faced by metazoa and procaryotes are sufficiently different to promise the discovery of new and interesting regulatory phenomena during the next 25 years. A rigorous analysis of the mechanisms of cell differentiation not only requires a very creative and carefully controlled application of the best that molecular biology and experimental embryology has to offer, but an intensive effort to use the tools of modern genetics.

ACKNOWLEDGEMENTS

I could not in so short a space mention all the achievements that deserve it. While all the prejudices expressed here are mine, I want to thank the students and colleagues with whom I've had the pleasure to work for stimulating me to think about the issues discussed here, and criticizing the manuscript. I appreciate Dr. Daniel Mazia's criticisms of a draft version. And especially, I want to thank Dr. James Ebert, an inspiring teacher, who first introduced me to the problem of differentiation. Work discussed that was carried out in the author's laboratory has been supported by research grants from NSF and NIH.

References

Abbott, J. and H. Holtzer. 1968. The loss of phenotypic traits by differentiated cells. *Proc. Nat. Acad. Sci.,* **59**: 1144-1151.

Aronson, A. I. and F. H. Wilt. 1969. Properties of nuclear RNA in sea urchin embryos. *Proc. Nat. Acad. Sci.,* **62**: 186-193.

Artman, M. and J. S. Roth. 1971. Chromosomal RNA: An artifact of preparation? *J. Mol. Biol.,* **60**: 291-302.

Baltimore, D. and A. S. Huang. 1970. Interaction of HeLa cell proteins with RNA. *J. Mol. Biol.,* **47**: 263-274.

Bell, E. 1971. Information transfer between nucleus and cytoplasm during differentiation. *Symp. Soc. Exp. Biol.,* **25**: 127-143.

Berendes, H. D. 1971. Gene activation in dipteran polytene chromosomes. *Symp. Soc. Exp. Biol.,* **25**: 145-161.

Bernfield, M. R. and N. K. Wessells. 1970. Intra- and extracellular control of epithelial morphogenesis. *Dev. Biol.* (Suppl.), **4**: 195-249.

———. 1970. Collagen synthesis during epitheliomesenchymal interactions. *Develop. Biol.,* **22**: 213-231.

Bischoff, R. and H. Holtzer. 1970. Inhibition of myoblast fusion after one round of DNA synthesis in 5-bromodeoxyuridine. *J. Cell. Biol.,* **44**: 134-150.

Bishop, J. O., R. E. Pemberton, and C. Baglioni. 1971. Are the genes for hemoglobin reiterated? *Develop. Biol.,* **26**: 357-358.

Bramwell, M. and H. Harris. 1967. The origins of the polydispersity in sedimentation patterns of rapidly labelled nuclear RNA. *Biochem. J.,* **103**: 816-830.

Brandhorst, B. P. and T. Humphreys. 1971. Synthesis and decay rates of major classes of deoxyribonucleic acid like ribonucleic acid in sea urchin embryos. *Biochem.,* **10**: 877-881.

Branton, D. and D. W. Deamer. 1972. *Membrane Structure. Protoplasmalogia.* Springer-Verlag, New York.

Briggs, R. and G. Cassens. 1966. Accumulation in the oocyte nucleus of a gene product essential for embryonic development beyond gastrulation. *Proc. Nat. Acad. Sci.,* **55**: 1103-1109.

Britten, R. J. and D. E. Kohne. 1968. Repeated sequences in DNA. *Science,* **161**: 529-540.

——— and E. H. Davidson. 1969. Gene regulation for higher cells: A theory. *Science,* **165**: 349-357.

Brown, D. D. and E. Littna. 1963. RNA synthesis during the development of *Xenopus laevis,* the South African clawed toad. *J. Mol. Biol.,* **8**: 669-687.

——— and I. B. Dawid. 1968. Specific gene amplification in oocytes. *Science,* **160**: 272-280.

——— and C. S. Weber. 1968. Gene linkage by RNA-DNA hybridization. *J. Mol. Biol.,* **34**: 681-697.

Clever, U., H. Bultmann, and J. M. Darrow. 1969. The immediacy of genomic control in polytenic cells. *In*: E. W. Hanly (ed.). *Problems in Biology*: RNA *in Development.* p. 403-423. University of Utah Press, Salt Lake City.

Coleman, J. and A. W. Coleman. 1970. The reversible control of animal cell differentiation by the thymidine analog, 5-bromodeoxyuridine. *Exp. Cell. Res.,* **59**: 319-328.

Crick, F. H. C. 1971. General model for the chromosomes of higher organisms. *Nature,* **234**: 25-27.

Darnell, J. E. 1968. Ribonucleic acids from animal cells. *Bacteriol. Rev.,* **32**: 262-290.

———— and R. Balint. 1970. The distribution of rapidly hybridizing RNA sequences in heterogeneous nuclear RNA and m-RNA from HeLa cells. *J. Cell. Physiol.,* **76**: 349-356.

————, L. Philipson, R. Wall, and M. Adesnik. 1971. Polyadenylic acid sequences: Role in conversion of nuclear RNA into messenger RNA. *Science,* **174**: 507-510.

Davidson, E. H. and B. R. Hough. 1971. Genetic information in oocyte RNA. *J. Mol. Biol.,* **56**: 491-506.

Denis, H. and J. Brachet. 1969. Expression du génome chez les hybrides interspécifiques. *Eur. J. Biochem.,* **13**: 86-93.

Emerson, C. P. and T. Humphreys. 1970. Regulation of DNA-like RNA and the apparent activation of ribosomal RNA synthesis in sea urchin embryos: Quantitative measurements of newly synthesized RNA. *Develop. Biol.,* **23**: 86-112.

———— and ———— 1971. Ribosomal RNA synthesis and the multiple, atypical nucleoli in cleaving embryos. *Science,* **171**: 898-901.

Evans, M. J. and J. B. Lingrel. 1969. Hemoglobin messenger RNA. Distribution of the 9S RNA in polysomes of different sizes. *Biochem.,* **8**: 829-831.

Forer, A. and O. Behnke. 1972. Cytochalasin B: Does it affect actin-like filaments? *Science,* **175**: 774-776.

Gaskill, P. and D. Kabat. 1971. Unexpectedly large size of globin messenger ribonucleic acid. *Proc. Nat. Acad. Sci.,* **68**: 72-75.

Georgiev, G. P. 1969. On the structural organization of operon and the regulation of RNA synthesis in animal cells. *J. Theoret. Biol.,* **25**: 473-490.

Greenberg, J. R. and R. P. Perry. 1971. Hybridization properties of DNA sequences directing the synthesis of messenger RNA and heterogeneous nuclear RNA. *J. Cell. Biol.,* **50**: 774-786.

Grobstein, C. 1966. *Mechanisms of Organogenetic Tissue Interaction.* Nat'l Cancer Inst. Monograph No. 26: 279-299.

Gross, P. R. 1964. The immediacy of genomic control during early development. *J. Exp. Zool.,* **157**: 21-38.

Gurden, J. B. 1962. The developmental capacity of nuclei taken from intestinal epithelium cells of feeding tadpoles. *J. Embryol. and Exp. Morphol.,* **10**: 622-640.

————. 1967. On the origin and persistence of a cytoplasmic state inducing nuclear DNA synthesis in frogs' eggs. *Proc. Nat. Acad. Sci.,* **58**: 545-552.

———— and H. R. Woodland. 1968. The cytoplasmic control of nuclear activity in animal development. *Biol. Rev.,* **43**: 233-267.

Harris, H. and J. W. Watts. 1962. The relationship between nuclear and cytoplasmic ribonucleic acid. *Proc. Royal. Soc. B.*, **156**: 109-121.

Heywood, S. M. 1970. Specificity of m-RNA binding factor in eukaryotes.
Proc. Nat. Acad. Sci., **67**: 1782-1788.

—————— and M. Nwagwu. 1968. De novo synthesis of myosin in a cell-free
system. *Proc. Nat. Acad. Sci.*, **60**: 229-234.

Holtzer, H. and J. Abbott. 1968. Oscillations of the chondrogeneic phenotype
in vitro. *In*: H. Ursprung (ed.). *Stability of the Differentiated State.*
p. 1-16. Springer-Verlag, New York.

Housman, D., R. Pemberton, and R. Taber. 1971. Synthesis of γ and β chains
of rabbit hemoglobins in a cell-free extract from Krebs II ascites
cells. *Proc. Nat. Acad. Sci.*, **68**: 2716-2719.

Huang, R. C. C. and L. Kleiman. 1971. Specificities in the structure and
function of interphase chromosomes. *Symp. Soc. Exp. Biol.*, **25**: 93-
115.

Humphreys, T. 1971. Measurements of messenger RNA entering polysomes
upon fertilization of sea urchin embryos. *Develop. Biol.*, **26**: 201-208.

Ilan, J. and J. Ilan. 1971. Stage specific initiation factors for protein synthesis during insect development. *Develop. Biol.*, **25**: 280-292.

Jacobson, M. 1967. Retinal ganglion cells: Specification of central connections in larval *Xenopus laevis*. *Science*, **155**: 1106-1108.

Jaffe, L. 1969. On the centripetal course of development, the Fucus eggs, and
self-electrophoresis. *Dev. Biol. Suppl.*, **3**: 83-111.

Kafatos, F. C. 1969. Cocoonase Synthesis: Cellular differentiation in developing silk moths. *In*: E. W. Hanly (ed.). *Problems in Biology*: RNA *in
Development*. p. 111-140. University of Utah Press, Salt Lake City.

—————. 1972. The cocoonase zymogen cells of silk moths. *Current Topics in
Develop. Biol.* (In press.)

Katz, E. R. and M. Sussman. 1972. Parasexual recombination in *Dictyostel-
ium discoideum*: Selection of stable heterozygotes and stable haploid
segregants. *Proc. Nat. Acad. Sci.*, **69**: 495-498.

Kedes, L. H. and M. L. Birnstiel. 1971. Reiteration and clustering of DNA
sequences complementary to histone messenger RNA. *Nature New
Biol.*, **230**: 165-169.

Kijima, S. and F. H. Wilt. 1969. Rate of nuclear ribonucleic acid turnover
in sea urchin embryos. *J. Mol. Biol.*, **40**: 235-246.

King, T. J. and R. Briggs. 1956. Serial transplantation of embryonic nuclei.
Cold Spring Harbor Symposia on Quantitative Biology, **21**: 271-290.

Kohne, D. E. 1968. Isolation and characterization of bacterial ribosomal
RNA cistrons. *Biophys. J.*, **8**: 1104-1118.

Kroeger, H. and M. Lezzi. 1966. Regulation of gene action in insect development. *Ann. Rev. Entomol.*, **11**: 1-22.

Lambert, C. C. 1971. Genetic transcription during the development and metamorphosis of the tunicate *Ascidia callosa*. *Exp. Cell Res.*, **66**: 401-409.

Lane, C. D., G. Marbaix, and J. B. Gurdon. 1971. Rabbit haemoglobin synthesis in frog cells: The translation of reticulocyte 9s RNA in frog oocytes. *J. Mol. Biol.,* **61**: 73-91.

Lengyel, P. and D. Söll. 1969. Mechanisms of protein biosynthesis. *Bact. Rev.,* **33**: 264-301.

McCarthy, B. J. and R. B. Church. 1970. The specificity of molecular hybridization reactions. *Ann. Rev. Biochem.,* **39**: 131-150.

McClintock, B. 1961. Some parallels between gene control systems in maize and in bacteria. *Am. Nat.,* **95**: 265-277.

Miura, Y. and F. H. Wilt. 1971. The effects of 5-bromodeoxyuridine on yolk sac erythropoiesis in the chick embryo. *J. Cell. Biol.,* **48**: 523-532.

Monod, J. 1947. The phenomenon of enzymatic adaptation. *Growth,* **11**: 223-289.

Morgan, T. H. 1934. *Embryology and Genetics.* Columbia University Press, New York. p. 10.

Orr, C. W., M. Yoshikawa-Fukuda, and J. D. Ebert. 1972. Potassium: Effect on DNA synthesis and multiplication of baby-hamster kidney cells. *Proc. Nat. Acad. Sci.,* **69**: 243-247.

Papaconstantinou, J. 1967. Molecular aspects of lens cell differentiation. *Science,* **156**: 338-346.

———— and E. M. Julku. 1968. The regulation of ribosomal RNA synthesis and ribosomal assembly in the vertebrate lens. *J. Cell. Physiol.,* **72** (Suppl. 1): 161-180.

Pardue, M. L. and J. G. Gall. 1970. Chromosomal localization of mouse satellite DNA. *Science,* **168**: 1356-1358.

Paul, J. 1971. Transcriptional regulation in mammalian chromosomes. *Symp. Soc. Exp. Biol.,* **25**: 117-126.

Ray, P. H. 1969. The action of auxin on cell enlargement in plants. *Dev. Biol.,* Suppl. 3: 172-205.

Reeder, R. H. and D. D. Brown. 1970. Transcription of the ribosomal RNA genes of an amphibian by the RNA polymerase of a bacterium. *J. Mol. Biol.,* **51**: 361-377.

Roeder, R. G. and W. J. Rutter. 1970. Multiple ribonucleic acid polymerases and ribonucleic acid synthesis during sea urchin development. *Biochem.,* **9**: 2543-2553.

————, R. H. Reeder, and D. D. Brown. 1970. Multiple forms of RNA polymerase in *Xenopus laevis*: Their relationship to RNA synthesis *in vivo* and their fidelity of transcription *in vitro*. Cold Spring Harbor Symp. Quant. Biol., **35**: 727-735.

Ross, J., H. Aviv, E. Scolnick, and P. Leder. 1972. *In vitro* synthesis of DNA complementary to purified rabbit globin in RNA. *Proc. Nat. Acad. Sci.,* **69**: 264-268.

Sanger, J. W. and H. Holtzer. 1972. Cytochalasin B: Effects on cell morphology, cell adhesion and mucopolysaccharide synthesis. *Proc. Nat. Acad. Sci.,* **69**: 253-257.

Scherrer, K. and C. Marcaud. 1968. Messenger RNA in avian erythroblasts at the transcriptional and translational levels and the problems of regulation in animal cells. *J. Cell. Physiol.,* **72** (Suppl. 1): 181-212.

Schimke, R. T. and D. Doyle. 1970. Control of enzyme levels in animal tissue. *Ann. Rev. Biochem.,* **39**: 929-976.

————. 1972. *J. Biol. Chem.* (In press.)

Shaw, L. M. J. and R. C. C. Huang. 1970. A description of two procedures which avoid the use of extreme pH conditions for the resolution of components isolated from chromatins prepared from pig cerebellar and pituitary nuclei. *Biochem.,* **9**: 4530-4542.

Shearer, R. W. and B. J. McCarthy. 1970. Characterization of RNA molecules restricted to the nucleus in mouse L-cells. *J. Cell. Phys.,* **75**: 97-106.

Singer, S. J. and G. L. Nicolson. 1972. The fluid mosaic model of the structure of cell membranes. *Science,* **175**: 720-731.

Smith, L. D. 1966. The role of a "Germinal Plasm" in the formation of primordial germ cells in *Rana pipiens. Develop. Biol.,* **14**: 330-347.

Soeiro, R., M. H. Vaughan, J. R. Warner, and J. E. Darnell, Jr. 1969. The turnover of nuclear DNA-like RNA in HeLa cells. *J. Cell. Biol.,* **39**: 112-118.

Southern, E. M. 1971. Effects of sequence divergence on the reassociation properties repetitive DNA's. *Nature New Biology,* **232**: 82-85.

Spelsberg, T. C., L. S. Hnilca, and A. T. Ansevin. 1971. Proteins of chromatin in template restriction. *Biochim. Biophys. Acta.,* **228**: 550-562.

Steinhardt, R. A., L. Lundin, and D. Mazia. 1971. Bioelectric responses of the echinoderm egg to fertilization. *Proc. Nat. Acad. Sci.,* **68**: 2426-2430.

Stellwagen, R. H. and R. D. Cole. 1969. Chromosomal proteins. *Ann. Rev. Biochem.,* **38**: 951-990.

——— and G. M. Tomkins. 1971. Preferential inhibition by 5-bromodeoxyuridine of the synthesis of tyrosine aminotransferase in hepatoma cell cultures. *J. Mol. Biol.,* **56**: 167-182.

Steward, F. C., M. O. Mapes, A. E. Kent, and R. O. Holsten. 1964. Growth and development of cultured plant cells. *Science,* **143**: 1.

Sussman, M. 1967. Evidence for temporal and quantitative control of genetic transcription and translation during slime mold development. *Fed. Proc.,* **26**: 77-83.

Suzuki, Y. and D. D. Brown. 1972. Isolation and identification of the messenger RNA for silk fibroin from Bombyx mori. *J. Mol. Biol.,* **63**: 409-430.

Trinkaus, J. P. 1969. *Cells into Organs.* Prentice-Hall, Englewood Cliffs, N.J.

Vasil, V. and A. C. Hildebrandt. 1965. Differentiation of tobacco plants from single isolated cells in microcultures. *Science,* **150**: 889.

Weeks, D. P. and A. Marcus. 1971. Preformed messenger of quiescent wheat embryos. *Biochim. Biophys. Acta,* **232**: 671-684.

Wessells, N. K. and F. H. Wilt. 1965. Action of Actinomycin D on exocrine pancreas cell differentiation. *J. Mol. Biol.,* **13**: 767-779.

―――. 1970. Some thoughts on embryonic inductions in relation to determination. Herman Beerman Lecture. *J. Investigative Dermatology,* **55**: 221-225.

―――, B. S. Spooner, J. F. Ash, M. O. Bradley, M. A. Luduena, E. L. Taylor, J. T. Wrenn, and K. M. Yamada. 1971. Microfilaments in cellular and developmental processes. *Science,* **171**: 135-143.

Whitely, A. H. and H. R. Whitely. 1972. (In press.)

Wilt, F. H. 1965. Regulation of the initiation of chick embryo hemoglobin synthesis. *J. Mol. Biol.,* **12**: 331-341.

Zwilling, E. 1961. Limb morphogenesis. *Adv. Morph.,* **1**: 301-330.

6 Integration of the Whole Organism—A Foundation for a Theoretical Biology

F. EUGENE YATES
DONALD J. MARSH
BIOMEDICAL ENGINEERING
University of Southern California

ARTHUR S. IBERALL
GENERAL TECHNICAL SERVICES, INC.
Upper Darby, Pennsylvania

Prelude

In science, it is often true that "believing is seeing." Therefore, as we contemplate the future of biology and wonder how the enormous complexity of integrated structures and functions will be understood 25 years from now, we must decide what it is that we "integrative" biologists should be seeking. A scientific conservative would probably point to further development of principles and concepts already present in modern physiology and integrative biology. He would extend what T. S. Kuhn, in his provocative book "The Structure of Scientific Revolutions", calls "normal science" (Kuhn, 1962).* However, as Kuhn points out, great advances in science may occur when the context of explanation supplied by "normal science" is replaced by a new framework of explanation—by a new paradigm.

In this essay, we suggest that the great advances in molecular biology which have provided us with new facts concerning ontogenesis and evolution (Monod, 1971) have failed so far to include an explanation of the dynamics of complex organisms. Our purpose is to set forth a general

This work was supported in part by Grant AM 15145-02 to Dr. F. E. Yates and by Grant AM 15968-01 to Dr. D. J. Marsh; the biophysical research at General Technical Services has been supported by the Army Research Office.

* A new and revised edition of this book has appeared, but we prefer the initial version of the ideas, which, though more susceptible to attack, is also more definite.

principle of design, based upon physical considerations, that we believe applies to living systems and explains their thermodynamic characteristics. This principle, which we present as a set of five propositions, provides a paradigm new for biology that we expect may ultimately replace the biochemical paradigm now dominating the life sciences. It seems to us that this revolution in paradigms will be necessary if we are to find concepts broad enough to encompass the new facts of modern biology.

The new facts of modern biology have revealed the intricate and complicated machinery of whole organisms, integrating both structure and function, and manifesting adaptation, invention, and goals of self-preservation and reproduction. They challenge our comprehension and embarrass our current explanations. We do not go far in trying to explain human goals in terms of molecules before we feel frustration and impotence. The synthesis of molecular biology into an integrative physiology of whole organisms eludes us. We lack a philosophy of hierarchical systems adequate to our task of understanding the behavior and the organization of whole organisms, and we are left with a persistent dichotomy between reductionism and holism. Fortunately, this dichotomy generates a valuable intellectual tension.

The recent triumphs in the life sciences have come in the world of the small. Some outstanding molecular biologists convey a confidence that the fundamental problem of life has been solved in the discovery of the cooperation between nucleic acids and proteins, and that what remains is to explain how these two classes of macromolecules formed an alliance in the first place, and how the human nervous system subsequently emerged from their association. Yet, among many who study the integrative aspects of biological systems, a vague dissatisfaction stirs because no guideline exists to tell them how to reconstruct function at higher levels of organization in biological systems from the knowledge we have of their macromolecular processes.

In his very thoughtful book, Monod (1971) claims that the molecular theory of the genetic code "does today constitute a general theory of living systems." He admits, of course, that it doubtless will never be able to predict and resolve the whole biosphere and points out that complex structures and functions of organisms cannot be deduced from this theory, nor are they always directly analyzable on the molecular level. He then proceeds to consider properties at higher levels of organization in the light of properties at lower levels in an appealing fashion—but without providing formal rules of procedure. What is missing from his treatment is the exhibition of common properties of dynamical systems operating at various scales between molecules and man. Monod's thesis for evolutionary development assumes the invariant reproduction of DNA. However, this invariance involves arrangements of components including repair enzymes and polymerases. Beyond the invariance of DNA lies—another system with invariances! We believe that the molecular biologist confronts a crevasse between his world and that of the mammalian neurophysiologists as philosophically treacherous as is the world of atomic physics and that of the molecular biologist. We shall try to indicate how a new paradigm can help to close these gaps.

In contrast to the optimistic view that macrophenomena in the life sciences will find adequate explanation in knowledge of microphenomena, stands the bias of the holists who argue that complex systems always have emergent properties—properties not found in their separated components and not analytically or intuitively extractable from their arrangements. Holists believe that there must be something beyond (as Arthur Koestler [1967] put it; there must be a "ghost in the machine") and, therefore, that analysis must ultimately fail to provide sufficient explanation of phenomena occurring at high levels of organization. Holists give most emphasis to one level—that of the complete system.

We believe that both those who see the whole as greater than the sum of its parts and those who believe that the essential principles of organization are discoverable at the level of small parts and their connections, overlook the design of life. Both the reductionist and the holist views fail to recognize a common principle behind all hierarchical systems—that the basis for explanation is the same at all levels within the system. In the description of the new paradigm we hope to specify that basis for explanation and to show how it applies at any level of organization ranging in scale from atom to solar system.

This essay, dealing as it does with revolutions and the future, takes us far beyond the edge of certainty. We travel there because we agree with Colodny (1965) that "a rather common feature of the history of science is the preparation by one age of the mathematical and technological instruments to be exploited fully by later generations of scientists who will work in a philosophical climate that may be completely different." It is to today's student who may wonder what that climate may be like that we address this essay.

To begin, we first consider the questions to be answered.

The Questions

To formulate our questions clearly, we must identify some universal properties of systems and processes. In physical systems of objects ranging in size from the atom to the solar system, all observed processes involve some degradation of free energy. These systems also involve some random statistical elements at any level out of which the organized processes of the next succeeding levels emerge.

All living systems are "objects endowed with a purpose or project" which they "exhibit in their structure and carry out through their performances"; they are self-constructing and show reproductive invariance (Monod, 1971). They also persist, are hereditary, and evolve. The basic persistent living system is the species—the ensemble of individuals capable of providing a succession of generations that progresses down the corridor of time. DNA, RNA, proteins, cells (or in multicellular organisms, the individuals) are subsystems, albeit complex in themselves. These subsystems, though less persistent, also resist degradation and dissolution, as does the species.

RELATION BETWEEN LIVING SYSTEMS AND PHYSICAL SYSTEMS

Living systems conform to the known laws of physics but are not derivable from them. Molecular biology is no more derivable from statistical or quantum mechanics, or nuclear physics, than is the function of the human brain provable from the principles of molecular biology. Both cases might not have happened. The most that can now be said is that the human brain, when it is understood in detail, will be consistent with the principles of molecular biology and with those of physics. These views, though sound, are not satisfying. What is missing is a viewpoint that explains the above characteristics of physical and biological systems, that relates the two types of systems, and that gives us some basis for judging whether life was improbable or inevitable, given the physical conditions that preceded it on earth. We wonder if there is a general principle of design applicable in our corner of the universe that embraces all phenomena—living as well as non-living.

We believe that a general principle of design does exist and that it will be found adequate to answer the basic question underlying the issue we have raised above. That question may be stated in various ways, several of which are given below:

1) What physical principles account for that most intriguing of all processes—organization? (To be definite, we define organization in space as structure and organization in time as function.)

2) On what physical basis are we to explain the observation that out of randomness, uncertainty, and dissipative processes inter-actions can lead spontaneously to stable forms and behavior?

3) What is it that underlies the tendency for local accumulation of "order" and "design" instead of progression to homogeneous chaos and macroscopic uniformity?

4) How does chance breed necessity, all in a universe running down?

Until the underlying basic question is answered, we are likely to have only deceptive philosophies concerning the remarkable integration of whole organisms. We have not discovered in present day biology, dominated by the biochemical paradigm, the clue to the answer, and so, we propose a revolution in paradigms to find it. Our approach has been to examine critically four prominent classes of paradigms, all lying outside "normal" biology, from which future understanding of integration of whole organisms might come. These paradigms are not mutually exclusive, and we do not claim to have found a basis for "proving" that one is absolutely superior to the others. However, the purpose of this essay is to call special attention to the attractions of one of the four.

Possible Directions Towards the Answers

We wish to consider briefly three directions from which an explanation of the phenomenon of organization might arise: 1) further development of an abstract, general mathematical theory of systems; 2) further applications of control theory, including techniques of systems identification and of criteria for maximization, minimization, or optimization; and 3) further exploration of the nonintuitive behavior of complex, nonlinear, hierarchical systems by means of computer simulation. We will consider each of these possible directions separately and give our reasons for offering a fourth—the new paradigm.

ABSTRACT MATHEMATICAL THEORY OF SYSTEMS

Mathematics is rich in concept but is only loosely tied to physical reality. Its abstract theories often consist of tautologies about conceivable relationships, built on the idea that some correspondence with a real system may be possible (Kalman, 1968). It is true that these tautologies sometimes contain surprises that the originator did not foresee. They may guide attention back to "realities" of the physical system. Some mathematicians approach physical systems from sets of data, often in input-output form, to indicate the space-time transformations within the capacity of a given system, and then attempt to put bounds on what logical relations might connect inputs and outputs. But this endeavor usually results only in conclusions about internal mathematical relationships. Contributors to an algebraic approach of this kind have been McCulloch and Pitts in their modelling of neural nets, as well as von Neumann, Ashby, Arbib, Grossberg, Bellman and Kalman.

The abstract mathematical approach to systems has no obligation to acknowledge realities of any kind, and indeed, realities are often ignored in an attempt by the mathematician to extract a smooth description of a single level of the world whose real graininess defies his methods. But for those who view mathematical physics, not as a branch of mathematics but as a branch of physics, there is no longer much warmth to be had from those dim fires of the abstract provided by mathematical formalisms devoted to elucidation of principles of optimization (e.g., principles of least time, least action, minimum energy, etc.). Vitiated by its lack of physical content, however fertile it may seem, a mathematical-abstract systems theory tends to spawn only sterile offspring. These offspring, the new logical equivalences, may help in the manipulation of data, but they lack the substance to lead toward a theoretical biology capable of explaining integration at the level of whole organisms. The emptiness of formal mathematics as employed by the algebraicist is especially noticable when he is asked to cope with hereditary or evolutionary systems. The features of such systems and the perplexities they provoke have been well described by Pattee (1968) and by Monod (1971).

A different and, we think, striking mathematical approach to systems can be found in the work of René Thom (1968, 1971). His approach, in contradistinction to an algebraic approach, has been to apply a geometric construct to the design of life. Although algebraic structures and geometric structures, under proper conditions, can be made mathematically isomorphic, the assumption of geometrical structure adds content missing from the algebraic approach. Other attempts to link the mathematical approach more closely to biophysical reality also seem promising. Examples can be found in the three volumes of "Towards a Theoretical Biology" (Waddington, 1968, 1969, 1970), and also in an article by Wolpert (1969).

CONTROL THEORY

Modern control theory, like the abstract mathematical theories of systems, derives much of its inspiration from notions of optimization. It begins by assuming some criteria defining the "desired" performance of a system. It then specifies how that performance might be achieved. However, in so doing, it overemphasizes the communication (small signal) aspects of systems and underestimates the equally important contribution made by the higher power, energy-converting machinery (the "plant processes"). Connections between power fluxes and communicational processes are fundamentally important. Among the few contributors to control theory who have attended to this issue are S. Lees (Lees, 1956; Lees and Blaschke, 1957; Lees, 1966) and C. R. Kelley (Kelley, 1968). Designers of real control systems must deal with this problem, but the available theory is inadequate to do so.

Control theory fails in two respects: First, it does not respect the test of matching which says, in effect, that although you can imagine many possible ways to couple controllers and systems being controlled, only those involving some matching between scales of energy or mass—or some trick to avoid the necessity of close matching—will operate effectively. In other words, an ant cannot control the behavior of a horse unless you make very particular arrangements for him to do so. Second, control theory cannot assure the biologist that the way an "ideal" controller might work is in fact the way a biological controller does work. The problem for theoretical biology is to discover how the attributes of power and control arise together rather than to determine what one of these aspects should be like when the other is already given. In biological systems, these two attributes are inherent in the genetic code. However, the capability to join them resides in the system itself during its unfolding; this capability is not in the genetic code.

COMPUTER SIMULATION

Although computer simulation is merely a technique and not a theory, we consider it here in order to provide a perspective for judging the likelihood that computer simulations may capture the general principle of design that we seek. The great advantages of computer simulation over verbal language in the explanation of complicated systems are that the computer can deal with many variables at the same time, and it can "solve" sets of nonlinear equations. Modern computers have a high capacity for information, and so simulations may have great complexity. But simulations cannot account for the origin or the actual design of the model system. No general theory of systems can arise from simulation because a simulation extracts specific case solutions where general solutions are not available. Therein lies the merit and the limitations of simulation as an approach to the understanding of systems.

Physical systems work "on line and in real time." For such systems, computer simulation of special cases becomes an extremely valuable expository art, especially so since the most interesting properties of a system arise out of nonlinearities. Complicated systems can behave in ways that defy human intuition (Forrester, 1969), and we have no other means than simulation to explore most of them. Simulations force the user to codify his facts and beliefs about relationships, and they can take his assumptions to their logical conclusions.

Simulations can, of course, be based upon some physical insights. They usually begin by recognizing within each unknown system the existence of thermodynamic "plant" processes, of controlling processes, and of information flows that convey decisions to control points. No doubt much of the future progress toward explanation of the phenomenon of integration at the level of the whole organism will require the use of simulations, based upon physical and chemical unit processes, and we, too, have encouraged such activities (Yates, 1971). But such efforts will be insufficient, even at their best, for the elucidation of the design principles underlying life.

A STATISTICAL-MECHANICAL THEORY OF SYSTEMS

Having considered, and found wanting or incomplete, abstract mathematical systems theory, modern control theory, and computer simulation as the appropriate general direction to be followed in creating an understanding of organization and the integration of structure and function in the whole organism, we now turn to a more promising route, along which we believe the future lies. We propose the development of a general theory of systems based upon a mixture of concepts from quantum mechanics, statistical mechanics, and non-linear mechanics. In this brief article, the mixture can be held together only by literary devices. For a defense of the declarations and for justification of the physical claims, we direct the reader to "Toward a General Science of Viable Systems" (Iberall, 1972) where an extensive bibliography and more rigorous discussion can be found. Present-day physics, as we shall show, cannot provide all the theoretical structure we require, but we see in the above three branches of physical knowledge elements out of which a comprehensive, and content-rich theoretical biology can emerge. We call our synthesis a statistical-mechanical view of systems, but it should be understood that the principles we develop here include some not ordinarily encompassed by the classical science of statistical mechanics.

A Statistical-Mechanical View of Systems

If, as biologists believe, living systems obey the laws of physics, we might profitably look for explanation of these systems in the forms of explanation that comprise physics itself. In what follows, we briefly review prominent characteristics of mechanical and hydrodynamic systems that have served as the basis for the development of powerful explanations in physics. We believe these features of physical systems offer a useful starting point for the development of a theoretical biology. Therefore, we hope that the reader will follow us through a discussion of those topics in physics out of which we suggest biologists can assemble the answer to the basic question before them: What is the design of life? In the course of this discussion, we shall introduce five postulates or propositions, and a corollary, to provide a physical basis for explanation of organization and integration in living systems. These five propositions comprise the physical paradigm we think will gain ascendancy over the biochemical paradigm in biology over the next 25 years.

COMPONENTS OF EXPLANATION IN PHYSICS

The physicist explains organization by considering four forces (electrical, gravitational, nuclear binding, and weak), plus a few constants or coefficients (e.g., velocity of light, Planck's constant, Boltzmann's constant, Avogadro's number, electronic charge and mass, the acceleration of gravity), and by using arithmetic. From such primitive building blocks and processes, the physicist exercises his scientific art to build patterns to represent the world around us. His explanations are not totally abstract, even though the primitive construction materials themselves defy explanation.

STABILITY AND CYCLICITY IN ACTIVE SYSTEMS

Systems can be regarded as being either active or passive. A passive system is completely dependent for its behavior upon the relatively immediate application of external forces or agencies, and it cannot defend itself against wear and tear or dissolution, and it does not renew stores of energy through its behavior. Active systems, in contrast, manifest energy transformations and storage for an appreciable period of time. They contain or are themselves sources of potentials. The most interesting class of active systems is that of autonomous systems. These systems sustain themselves by their own activities and can resist dissolution. All living systems are open, active, autonomous thermodynamic systems. (A few autonomous systems have been built by man—for example, the latest generation of Perceptron-like devices that seek out an electrical socket for recharging their batteries whenever their internal energy stores run low.) To provide an explanation of the design of living forms, it is, therefore, necessary to identify the requirements for persistence of autonomous systems generally.

The notion of persistence implies some notion of stability. If we place a marble in a bowl and shake the system once, not too hard, the marble will eventually return to a point at the bottom of the bowl. This passive system shows a simple, statically stable performance. However, if we put a rat in the bowl, or a man in a swimming pool, we observe instead dynamic behavior; yet, both the rat and the man are stable in some sense, since "ratness" and "humanness" are preserved in the individuals from day to day and are only slowly altered by aging. How, then, shall we describe the dynamic stability of living forms? Bacteria in a bowl filled with a paradisical medium provide a clue, for they show a remarkable dynamic behavior. Their observed behavior is an autonomous, cyclic process: grow, divide; grow, divide; grow, divide. . . .

In the above cyclic process, the bacteria preserve their essential nature, and the system persists as long as the environment provides a rich source of chemical potential to support the processes of growth and replication. More generally, open thermodynamic systems may exhibit either of two relationships with their local environments. Either their local environment exists as a boundary condition providing a constant potential that supports the activity of the system (as in the case of a device driven by a solar battery), or the system operates by providing its own variable interactions and couplings to its immediate environment which need not be available as a pure source of constant potential (as in the case of a man). In the former case, behavior is limited, and persistence is unlikely because of the limited repertoire of behavior. If the environment changes (e.g., if clouds come by), the system may be doomed. Only in the latter case is persistence to be expected. Of course, the bacteria in the bowl superficially seem to resemble the first case more than the second, because eventually they would die out as the medium became exhausted. But actually, bacteria in the world at large, with its vicissitudinous environment, have not died out! Therefore, they must comprise in the wild a system of the second kind.

These considerations hint that there is a general principle relating the phenomenon of persistence in an open-autonomous thermodynamic system and the cyclicity of processes within it. The bacteria in the bowl still show the cyclicity that preserves them in the wild, but they do not persist; so, we see that cyclic energy transformations are not alone sufficient to guarantee persistence—in addition, there must be a somewhat hospitable environment. The important point is that autonomous systems are able to persist because they can maintain their activity in a wider range of environments than can those systems that fail sooner, and this maintenance of activity always seems to be associated with cyclic energy transformations. The principle is general, and applies to autonoma made by man, as well as to the self-constructing autonoma we call living forms.

NONLINEARITIES, CYCLICITY, AND DYNAMIC STABILITY

Behind the general principle that associates persistence of an autonomous system with cyclicity lies a fundamental relationship between nonlinearities and periodic behavior. The grandfather's clock periodically taps the potential stored continuously in its hanging weights by means of a nonlinear device called an escapement. Similarly, with all other continuous engines built by man, or by nature, nonlinear processes dominate and these nonlinearities account for the dynamic stability manifested by these machines. The only known stability regime for a nonlinear system whose processes degrade free energy (as all real processes must) is a dynamic stability consisting of periodicities, cycles, or repeated motions.

We can now state the first of several propositions that constitute the new paradigm we propose to account for integration of whole organisms.

Proposition I. All real, active, thermodynamic machines (including all living forms), capable of sustained performance, manifest a dynamic stability characterized by nonlinear, cyclic processes. The primitive function is periodic; the basic element of temporal organization is the cycle.

EMERGENCE OF STRUCTURE

The first proposition, described above, provides a fundamental element of function (temporal organization), but it does not account for the emergence of structure (spatial organization) in a universe, presumably, moving overall toward a state of homogeneity and uniformity that has been called "thermal death." To account for the emergence of structure, we first note that the basic form of matter in the universe is atomic (particulate or granular). Second, we note that the particles attract each other from long distances (e.g., by gravitational attraction) and repel each other at close range (e.g., by nuclear repulsion). Interactions are universal, and electrical interactions are especially important at the scale of distances found within living systems. These interactions may either attract or repel.

Systems of interacting particles have an astonishing and important characteristic: As the scale of the system is changed, the system may change from continuous to discontinuous at any one level of observation. For example, water vapor has the smooth and uniform character of a gas at the macroscopic level of observation (in spite of its underlying, microscopic atomicity). However, if we contain the water vapor in a stout vessel, and then introduce additional water molecules one after another, we eventually obtain a new atomicity: A phase change occurs, and macroscopic water droplets appear. The change in scale (in this example, an increase in number density) has led to the appearance of a new structure, the droplet.

A more interesting example of the principle that a system of interacting particles will change between atomistic and continuous forms as a function of scale effects has been provided by an experiment performed by G. I. Taylor (*see* Goldstein, 1965). He placed water between two concentric cylinders that could be rotated in opposite directions, and varied the relative velocity of the cylinders. (One could also vary the size of the chamber, or the density of the water by adding solute and creating a solution, or the viscosity of the water by changing the temperature.) In hydrodynamic systems, scale effects are related in the well-known Reynolds number, R, which gives the dimensionless ratio between inertial and viscous forces:

$$R = \frac{\rho vl}{\eta}$$

$$\text{where: } \rho = \text{density}$$
$$v = \text{velocity}$$
$$l = \text{length}$$
$$\eta = \text{viscosity}$$

As is well known, at values of R below a critical value, fluid flow is smooth (laminar), but above that value, it may become turbulent. Taylor showed that as a result of scale effects only (increased velocity) laminar flow would become turbulent, and the turbulence would progress into stable, organized patterns or vortices, often with complicated geometrical structure.

The phenomena described above lead us to the second general proposition:

Proposition II. Although matter is fundamentally atomistic in character, it has continuous properties if the scale of observation is large compared to the mean free path of the particles, and if the time of observation is long compared to the relaxations after collisions of the particles. New (atomistic or quantized) structures will emerge from the apparent continuum as a result of interactions among particles, scale changes, and constraints (such as initial and boundary conditions, etc.) on the system. These three agencies (interactions, scale, and constraints) account for a universal tendency for structure to appear out of chaotic, random, atomistic backgrounds. As a result of this tendency, all systems may be viewed as consisting of a hierarchy of atomistic (A) and continuum (C) levels: ACACAC. . . .

As an example of the applicability of proposition II to living systems, consider the properties of lipid/water systems. If the lipids are amphipathic, the interactions within the mixture lead to spontaneous organization into membranous structures or micelles if the scale of the system is favorable. Similarly, separated components of phage particles can reassemble spontaneously from a more homogeneous solution of smaller component particles. Thus, we see the principle operating in the transition of water gas to water liquid, of water liquid to geometrically complicated vortices, of lipid/water emulsions into membranes, of proteins and nucleic acids into the phage virus . . . of man into families, families into neighborhoods, neighborhoods into cities. . . .

THE FUSION OF STRUCTURE AND FUNCTION

Proposition I offers a basis for temporal organization, and proposition II offers a basis for spatial organization. But an autonomous system must fuse the two characteristics so that its function can maintain its structure. It is in this fusion that autonomy can be created, and it is here that living systems are commonly thought to be too rich in behavior to be described by known physical principles. We take a contrary view. We postulate that the nonlinear mechanics, accounting for the emergence of temporal organization, and the statistical thermodynamics, accounting for the emergence of spatial organization, merely describe different aspects of a more general physical tendency we have embodied as a third proposition.

> *Proposition III.* The combination of the effects of scale, constraints, and interactions in a system of interacting entities always produces a tendency for the local emergence of structures capable of persistent, cyclic energy transformations and self-preservation.

At this point, the reader may wonder if we are not deducing physics from biology instead of providing a physical basis for understanding life. Unfortunately, the physical issues we address have not been popular in physics itself where most of the conceptualization has dealt with idealized situations. Our hypotheses address exactly those aspects of physical reality that arise out of the interactions and constraints that cause systems to be "nonideal."

The notion of nonideality is closely tied to the analytical intractability of the equations describing a system. Nonlinearities, inhomogeneities, nonintegrable constraints and interactions lead often to equation sets for which no closed form solution has been shown to exist. Therefore, physicists have had no clear way to proceed with attack on those problems we are emphasizing here. Since this article addresses the future, it seems unnecessary and unwise to confine ourselves, in prophesy, to the established physics or to the established biology. We believe that a general systems science built along the lines indicated here, and more completely in the book "Toward a General Science of Viable Systems" (Iberall, 1972), will contain the explanatory powers sufficient to encompass living systems. In the next 25 years, we see physics being inspired by the problems of the life sciences. The resulting solutions will be in terms of the evolving physics. That evolution seems to us to require a synthesis of some of the themes of quantum mechanics, statistical thermodynamics, and nonlinear mechanics.

Scientists differ in their tolerance of mystical extensions of their fields into new domains. Some prefer rigor at all points and accept the narrow range of problem solving that results from their choice. Others, like us, rely on an informed intuition to press the boundaries of their science and extend its range. When such efforts are successful and useful, rigor follows. In the interim, the appeal is to intuition, and the value of the theoretical effort is unclear. But if the future were clear, why bother to predict it?

INVARIANTS

A chief aim of science is to identify the invariants in any phenomenon of interest. In mechanical systems, following collisions, the invariants are the individual, total sums of energy, momentum, and mass. In a crude sense, we can say that the "goal" of a mechanical system is to conserve these quantities (called summational invariants). The properties that Monod has found especially descriptive of living systems are heredity and evolution, self-construction, invariant reproduction, and goal-directed behavior (Monod, 1971). These properties are richer than those seen in mechanical systems, and their richness suggests that living systems have at least one additional invariant whose conservation or satisfaction may be said to be a goal. We propose that the additional summational invariant is preservation of population density (i.e., number of functioning organisms).

In every meeting or coupling between person and person, cell and cell, the goal is to preserve each organismic mechanism, each cell, and, at the end, to replace one mechanism with another, its offspring. Biological ensembles surely behave as if they mean to persist *in numbers* and, thus, attempt to preserve number at all levels, from macromolecules to whole organisms and individuals. Both number and function will persist. If you remove one kidney, the other will hypertrophy; if you remove all but one bacterium from a container of enriched medium, you will soon find several billion.

Since populations may grow or dwindle, the invariant described above has a slightly different character from those of simpler, mechanical systems. It is not the absolute number of individuals that is defended but, rather, the tendency for interactions to be carried out so as to assure that there will always be some functioning individuals left is invariant. This tendency is seen directly in the invariant replication of DNA and, less directly, in the vigor with which threatened social groups attempt to ensure their persistence (and dominance) by encouragement of profuse breeding of their kind. (That this invariant tendency has led to the difficulties of overpopulation for some human societies hardly denies the existence of the tendency—it merely attests to its strength.)

The additional invariant constitutes proposition IV:

> *Proposition IV.* Systems that arise spontaneously and preserve themselves as individuals act also to preserve their kind, often through interactions with others of their kind. In the simplest case, periodic crystals seed the growth of additional crystalline structure. In a more complex case, the aperiodic fibrillar crystalline structure of DNA tends to duplicate itself (even without the aid of catalysts). In the most elaborate case, men and women have children.

SELECTION FOR COMPATABILITY AND FAST PROCESSING— MATCHING OF INFORMATION AND POWER

As a system emerges according to the propositions we have set forth, the form that persists is the one that is selected by the system itself to assure compatibility and fast processing. It is not only competition among organisms that exerts the immediate selection pressure but competition within an organism among alternative forms. Monod has aptly remarked in this vein: ". . . any 'novelty,' in the shape of an alteration of protein structure, will be tested before all else for its compatability with the whole of the system already bound by innumerable controls commanding the execution of the organism's projective purpose." (Monod, 1971, page 119).

Eigen has developed an impressive account of the physical issues involved in the evolution of biological macromolecules (Eigen, 1971). From his themes, we conclude that fast processing can lead to dominance. If several system elements compete for the same materials, the faster elements will be better assured of persistence in numbers. The same principle of selection operates as effectively between organisms or species as it does within organisms. We consider it as our final proposition.

> *Proposition V*. A persistent, autonomous system, by its physical nature, is ultimately forced to select, from among alternative internal processes, those that are most compatible with its persistence, and these usually are the faster processes. Among autonomous systems, those capable of faster processing (faster transfers or transformations of energy, matter, and information) tend to exclude or dominate their rivals for the available sources of power, whether or not these are limiting.

Fast and effective transfers or transformations of energy, matter, and information always require efficient coupling between information fluxes and power fluxes, and it is the above selection principle that accounts for the impressive operation of biological controllers. Their principles of optimization appear to be those of proposition V.

RELIABILITY AND INTEGRATION

A theme common to all five propositions is that persistence and, therefore, reliability of processes is likely to occur in systems of interacting entities. As a corollary, we conclude that, under geophysical constraints, life is probable. Integration of structure and function, of parts with other subsystems, of information flow with larger scale thermodynamic processes will tend to arise spontaneously. The deep issues raised by the reliability of biological operations have been well discussed elsewhere by Pattee (1968).

We conclude that a comprehensive and meaningful explanation of integration of the whole organism must take into account the fundamental properties of all autonomous systems. Any theory that does not do so will be incomplete. The combination of partial insights from statistical mechanics, quantum mechanics, and nonlinear mechanics, embodied in our five propositions, we believe provides a physical basis for the expectation that order will always tend to arise out of chaos, and that cyclic thermodynamic engines will always tend to appear and sustain themselves. If this is so, then the mathematics of dynamic processes may permit us to gain insight into the interactions and constraints and, thus, into the directions which evolutionary unfolding may take, through chemistry and into life.

From our view that biosystems are ensembles of nonlinear oscillators, coupled and mutually entrained in various clusters at each hierarchical level, new descriptions can be derived for their stability, their remarkable timekeeping properties, and their metabolic and behavioral states, all of which now lack precise designations. But, most important, we can expect to be able to rationalize, with the new theory, the behavioral goals of biosystems, including man, by encompassing them within the general requirements for stability and persistence shared by all autonomous, open systems in our region of the physical universe. That, we believe, is what it will mean to say at last that we comprehend the design principles underlying the integration of whole organisms.

Experimental Tests—Biospectroscopy

We have attempted in the foregoing to pose a question central in biological science today, viz., what is the physical basis of organization? We then proposed a direction in which the answer may be found. In describing the direction, we have dealt with theoretical considerations. We now turn to some possibilities we see for experimental validation that will be required along the way if any systems theory is to have acceptance in the life sciences.

Scattered through the biological literature are various unrelated accounts of periodicities, with periods ranging from the domain of milliseconds to years. Cycles of one day (the circadian rhythms) have gained most attention because they are conspicuous and often easily entrained by daily geophysical rhythms of temperature and light. There is little doubt that daily cycles of solar radiation were influential on the course of evolution at a stage when photochemical reactions were incorporated into life processes. However, only a tone-deaf biologist would insist on hearing merely the circadian pitch in the symphony of processes that characterize life.

We predict that an important aspect of experimental work in the next 25 years will be the development of a disciplined field that one might call "biospectroscopy." Experiments will be conducted with proper sampling technique and precautions to minimize errors, such as those caused by sampling too infrequently, in order to discover, both in the power flux domain and in the information flux domain, at all levels of organization, those many particular frequencies at which business is conducted. We predict the discovery of numerous oscillators and evidence of their mutual entrainments. Hints of causality in biochemical chains will emerge from correlations of frequency, instead of from correlations of magnitudes or levels only, as is now the case. (Correlations do not prove causality, but they raise questions of causality, and the human mind finds a strong temporal correlation highly provocative in the formulation of hypotheses. As experience shows, it is rightly so. Unfortunately, mathematical techniques for correlations of frequencies in nonlinear systems ars so far poorly developed.) The experimental description of integration of structure and function at the level of the whole organism will in the future give new emphasis to fluctuating processes and less to constancies and static morphological structure. We expect to find this new emphasis applied to biochemical processes within cells, to metabolic and endocrine phenomena among organs, and even, in the most difficult case of all—that of animal and human behavior.

Although much data in the field of experimental psychology are in the form of frequencies (of pecking or lever pressing, etc.), little data on behavior provide a spectral description. That is, the data do not show the distribution of frequencies within the system in a particular state. Thus, the new emphasis might even contribute to a fresh view of human "personality" and behavior. For example, the past two decades have made much of the content of human sexuality. The content of the sexual mode may be autoerotic, homosexual, or heterosexual. We do not dispute the pertinence of such data. However, we point out that simultaneous considerations of frequencies of hormone, metabolic and behavioral events also provide a basis for classifying sexuality. The endocrine system discharges independently of the love object. A person who is sexual (toward whatever object) twice each day differs from one who is sexual (whatever the object) only twice each month. The goal measures of the two systems cannot be the same, nor can the requirements for internal system stability.

To illustrate the spectroscopic approach, we show in Table I the various discrete behavioral modes of humans. We believe that there are twenty such modes, though the exact number can be settled, if at all, only by experimental observation. The table also specifies our estimates, based on a variety of reading and personal observations, of which modes are periodic and which are not. We have further specified a mean (ensemble or population average) period or frequency for the periodic modes. Matters of interest in this approach are the transitional probabilities from one mode to another (i.e., if you are in mode 9, what is the likelihood that you will enter any one of the other modes next?), and the historicity of the path through the modes (i.e., how do the modes entered in the recent past affect these transitional probabilities into the future?). For a fuller discussion of the underlying principles, the reader may consult Bloch, et al. (1971). Here we merely point out that experiments designed to fill out the matrix in Table I are likely to lead to fresh descriptions of both normal and abnormal behavior, and the effects of therapy. A full account of a behavioral state would also provide spectral analysis of the endocrine and metabolic processes associated with each of the periodic modes. When such data are available, we predict that we will at last glimpse the design of man in the light of physics.

Postlude

We have sought the foundations for a suitable, general theory of systems that can account for integration of structure and function at the level of the whole organism, as well as for evolution and adaptation. Others also have already begun the work. Foreshadows of the edifice to be built are present in the work of Monod (1971) and Eigen (1971). In Eigen's brilliant discussion of the evolution of macromolecules and in the notion that selection for fast processing may itself lead to organization in the forms of closed cycles of catalytic activity, we find a basis for the expectation that such catalytic loops will preserve all their members, and that thermodynamic engines will appear. Our general views and those

TABLE I. *Behavior Modes of Man**

Mode	Periodic?	Estimated free-running period or frequency
1. Resting	yes	10 min, 2-3 hrs, 5 days, 3 months
2. Eating	yes	2-4/day
3. Drinking	yes	4 hours
4. Sleeping REM non-REM	yes	1-2/day
5. Voiding	yes	4/day urine 1/day feces
6. Grooming	yes	10 mins
7. Changing posture	yes	1-2 mins
8. Using body (exercise, play, gross motion)	yes	90 mins
9. Working	yes	2-3/day
10. Being sexual	yes	3 days
11. Relating to others Loving Caring Cooperating Stroking, touching Conversing Sheltering	yes	4/day
12. Fantasizing	yes	100/day
13. Withdrawing escaping	no	—
14. Attending Arranging Planning Problem-solving Learning Studying Creating Being introspective Reading Thinking	yes	—
15. Being aggressive Competing Striving	yes	—
16. Contending Fighting Hating Being hostile Being angry	no	—
17. Being acquisitive Being greedy Stealing Cheating	yes	—
18. Envying Being jealous	no	—
19. Feeling loss Grieving	no	—
20. Fearing	no	—

* Reprinted from Bloch et al., 1971.

of Eigen appear to be close, although a sense of the specific details are developed more extensively by Eigen. A different example of a biologist's view of dynamic organization may be found in the review by Kushner (1969).

We have published elsewhere a first attempt to develop in detail a biological systems science based upon the principles discussed in this article (Iberall, 1972; Bloch et al., 1971). We have begun there to review the increasingly rich literature documenting the existence of periodicities in biological processes. We know that biologists, however imaginative and given to theorizing, are ultimately respectful of experimental results. Therefore, we believe that it is the accumulation of hard evidence that nonlinear cycles are ubiquitous in the biosphere (and, as we have indicated, in the physical universe generally) that will force the development of a biological systems science based on the principles of nonlinear mechanics and statistical mechanics in the direction we have described above. No one disputes that the heart beats, mammals breathe, brain rhythms persist. However, whether or not periodic behavior is part of a general strategic design is the question at issue.

The choice of experiments to be performed in the future requires the making of a decision according to a policy. The policy to adopt a spectroscopic approach to biological systems will either be formed slowly out of the pressures arising from accumulated evidence, or it can be adopted more rapidly on the basis of theoretical considerations such as those presented in this chapter. Our hope is that this paper will catalyze the development of that systems science necessary for explanation of integration at the level of the whole organism. If so, it is ironic to note that the authors will have performed the function of—an enzyme. But perhaps that is, after all, the true nature of life processes, for among the bees it is not workers that beget workers, nor drones that beget drones. Instead, catalysts beget catalysts!

References

Bloch, E., S. Cardon, A. Iberall, D. Jacobowitz, K. Kornacker, L. Lipetz, W. McCulloch, J. Urquhart, M. Weinberg, and F. E. Yates. 1971. Introduction to a Biological Systems Science. NASA Contractors Report, CR-1720, Washington.

Colodny, R. G. (ed.). 1965. *Beyond the Edge of Certainty.* Prentice-Hall, Inc., Englewood Cliffs, New Jersey. p. 3.

Eigen, M. 1971. Self organization of matter and the evolution of biological macromolecules. Die Naturwissenschaften, **58**: 465-523.

Forrester, J. W. 1969. *Principles of Systems*. Wright-Allen Press, Cambridge, Massachusetts.

Goldstein, S. 1965. *Modern Developments in Fluid Mechanics*. Dover Publications, Inc., New York.

Iberall, A. S. 1972. *Toward a General Science of Viable Systems*. McGraw-Hill Book Co., New York.

Kalman, R. E. 1968. New developments in system theory relevant to biology. *In*: M. D. Mesarovic (ed.). *Systems Theory and Biology*. Springer-Verlag, New York. p. 222-232.

Kelley, C. R. 1968. *Manual and Automatic Control*. John Wiley and Sons, New York.

Koestler, A. 1967. *The Ghost in the Machine*. Macmillan Co., New York.

Kuhn, T. S. 1962. *The Structure of Scientific Revolutions*. University of Chicago Press, Chicago.

Kushner, D. 1969. Self assembly of biological structures. *Bact. Revs.,* **33**: 303-345.

Lees, S. 1956. Design basis for multiloop positional servomechanisms. *Trans. ASME* (August 1956), 1339-1366.

———— and T. C. Blaschke. 1957. Design basis for cascade-type positional servomechanisms. *Trans. ASME* (November 1957), 1873-1896.

————. 1966. Uncertainty and imprecision. *J. Basic Engineering,* **88**: 369-378.

Monod, J. 1971. *Chance and Necessity*. Alfred A. Knopf, New York.

Pattee, H. H. 1968. The physical basis of coding and reliability in biological evolution. *In*: C. H. Waddington (ed.). *Towards a Theoretical Biology*. Vol. 1. Aldine Publishing Co., Chicago. p. 67-93.

Thom, R. 1968, 1971. "Une theorie dynamique de la morphogenese". *In*: C. H. Waddington (ed.). *Towards a Theoretical Biology*. Vol. 1. Aldine Publishing Co., Chicago. p. 152-179.

————. Proceedings of the 1971 Meeting of the American Association for the Advancement of Science. (In press.)

Waddington, C. H. (ed.). 1968, 1969, 1970. *Towards a Theoretical Biology*. Vols. 1, 2, 3. Aldine Publishing Co., Chicago.

Wolpert, L. 1969. Positional information and the spatial pattern of cellular differentiation. *J. Theor. Biol.,* **25**: 1-47.

Yates, F. E. 1971. Systems analysis in biology. *In*: J. H. U. Brown, J. E. Jacobs, and L. Stark (eds.). *Biomedical Engineering*. F. A. Davis Co., Philadelphia. p. 3-20.

7 The Understanding and Control of the Aging Process

BERNARD L. STREHLER
DIVISION OF BIOLOGICAL SCIENCES
University of Southern California

Introduction

Man and nearly all of his relatives among the plants and animals are not evolved along such lines that they live indefinitely. The enigma and challenge of this fact of biology has fascinated religious and secular philosophers, and more recently natural scientists, ever since the concept of causality in natural processes was developed. But it was not until the last decade that the possibility that men might substantially modify, or even reverse, this "natural" process has seemed other than wishful thinking.

This early reluctance to take seriously the possibility of a greatly or indefinitely extended youthfulness was based partly on the fact that early research in this area was, by and large, uncritical and inconclusive—promising spectacular changes in longevity and delivering little or nothing; the skepticism also appears to be founded on a deep-seated and natural aversion among otherwise rational persons to even thinking about death and its precedent—aging. This denial that death is real and inevitable (by not thinking about it), coupled with the conviction that it is biologically necessary—since nobody has exceeded 120 years in the past —has effectively blocked an early attack on this problem in favor of apparently more attainable goals. But with the increasing awareness that the changes that lead to aging also supply a more hospitable medium in which specific disease processes can take root and develop, a new level of attention to the underlying causes of aging has begun to emerge.

Despite a severe shortage of research funds in this area during the last decade, a considerable measure of progress has been made. A substantial early impetus to this effort was provided by the AIBS, whose "Committee for Basic Biological Research in Aging" in the middle fifties focused attention on the emerging opportunities in the field and encouraged an increase in NIH commitment in the succeeding five years. Unfortunately, this momentum was not maintained during the 60s, although other agencies, notably the AEC and the Veterans Administration did increase their funding of basic research related to biological aging during the same period. There are now quite hopeful signs that the Administration and the Congress are responding to the unanimous recommendation at the White House Conference in 1971 that a central administrative research organization—a National Institute of Gerontology —be established within NIH. Enactment and implementation of this legislation will do much to fund and stimulate the additional high quality research needed to identify the key details of the process and to determine the extent to which substantial intervention is feasible and/or desirable.

As will be discussed in the remainder of this chapter, there are persuasive reasons to believe that not only the principles, but also the details, of the process will be understood before the last decade of this century. By the year 2000, it seems almost certain that methods will be at hand to modify (retard or reverse) this process. The extent to which healthy human lifespan can be lengthened cannot be estimated accurately until the details of the process are unraveled. The basis of the prediction that some modification is within reach is summarized in the remainder of this essay.

Origins of Aging

EVOLUTIONARY FACTORS

The evolutionary origins of aging are not so clouded in mystery and conjecture as they once were. Human lifespan, like the other evolved features of living things, is a result of the kinds of selective forces that operated during our evolution. Since we are among the most long-lived of animals (only the Galápagos turtle—175-250 years—is believed to exceed our longevity), the evolution of humans must have involved selection for a sufficient longevity to permit the brain we possess to be a useful evolutionary investment. In many ways, we seem to age due to intrinsic processes at a substantially lower rate than do other vertebrates. For example, the cross-linkage of collagen approaches an asymptote in man at about 40 years, in the rat at about 2 years or less; similarly, lipofuscin age pigment occupies about 25% of the intracellular volume of rat neurons at two years of age, a figure not attained in human neurons until 70 years or so of age. It, therefore, appears that the clocking of various age changes is on a longer time scale in humans than in short-lived mammals, probably both because of intrinsic differences in the stability of certain molecules and because the addition of new or replacement parts continues to be effective for a much longer time in the human.

The long term stability of any machine, including a living entity, depends on two factors: First, the intrinsic stability of the various parts that make it up; and second, whether damaged parts are repaired, supplemented, or replaced at a rate which approaches the rate of deterioration and loss of parts. From this it follows that we and other aging systems do not replenish parts as rapidly as they become non-functional—otherwise, obviously, we should be immortal.

The ubiquity of this disbalance between damage and repair strongly implies that some evolutionary force is responsible. Although, from time to time, it has been suggested that aging, per se, is evolutionarily valuable (because it provides for turnover and, thereby, furthers evolutionary plasticity), these arguments ignore several facts: The first of these is that our ancestors, as well as other animals in the wild, almost never died of old age. Rather, they were the victims of accidents, starvation and predation. Thus, the postulated "evolutionary advantages" of aging could not be selected for. The second fact, as succinctly pointed out by Williams (1957), is that genes leading to the deadaptations of aging will ordinarily be selected against, because they, causing progressive deadaptive processes, will reduce vigor below the maximum even during prereproductive life.

Williams (and Medawar, 1951 as well) has pointed out that aging must, for the above reasons, be a pleiotropic side effect of genes which provide clear advantages early in life. Although they did not specify them, the class of regulator genes whose actions lead to the programmed suppression of other genes are pleiotropically ideally suited to these authors' predictions, for if there are advantages to "switching-off" certain genes during ontogeny (after they have served to produce a reproductively-competent adult), it follows also that this repression will inevitably lead to failure of the system as the previously synthesized parts decay due to the operation of the law of entropy increase.

At least two factors seem important in determining the activation of "off-switches." The first, as pointed out by Bidder (1925), is the fact that each kind of land vertebrate, unlike fish, generally functions best within a narrow size range. This means that genes which inhibit growth will become active as a system approaches its species-size norm. The second, and probably more dominant factor, is that it is disadvantageous for an animal with access to a limited food supply to produce structures which do not serve to perpetuate the line. Since most of our ancestors subsisted on limited or fluctuating food supplies, efficiency of food utilization must have been an important factor in survival, particularly to the time of reproduction. More to the point, limited or fluctuating food supplies will cause the selective perpetuation of genes which limit energy and material use to those synthetic activities which promote survival of the line. Any product which continues to be manufactured after enough has been produced to optimize survival up to and through the reproductive period is a luxury without compensating benefit. Thus, selection for metabolic-economic efficiency prior to reproduction will lead to the expression of senescence as materials whose production is suppressed gradually deteriorate.

From the above, it may be concluded that senescence is a late and indirect result of the programmed repression of a considerable ensemble of structural genes and that a key to its understanding and control lies in the nature of the off-switches and the genetic program that activates them.

LOCUS OF AGE CHANGES

The genetically programmed non-replenishing components of the body include both extracellular substances, such as collagen, and a specific class of cells, called "fixed post-mitotics." There is little evidence that the structural changes during the "aging" of collagen are detrimental to function, except perhaps for solar elastosis which is responsible for facial wrinkles and involves the conversion of collagen into an elastin-like material as a result of the absorption of actinic light (U.V.). It seems unlikely that cross-linkage of collagen, per se, would appreciably retard the diffusion of nutrients from the circulation to parenchymal cells (although an analogous cross-linkage of ground substance might well do so). Rather, the decreases in function which are part of aging seem largely to be ascribable to decreases in the numbers of nonreplacable cell types and/or to qualitative changes in the functional capacities of those cells that survive.

Such loss of functional capacity can, in principle, be due to 3 kinds of causes: 1) loss of genetic information; 2) displacement of functional parts by non-functional residues; 3) loss of ability to use genetic information still present (Strehler, 1962).

Damage to DNA

Much evidence is now available that genetic damage of the kind produced by chemical and physical mutagens is not sufficient in amount to cause the loss of function observed during aging (Welch, 1967; Clark, 1964; Strehler, 1959). Key experiments that have led to this conclusion are: 1) one can induce in a young animal many times the lifetime load of mutation with mutagens without shortening life (Curtis, 1963). If damage to the DNA of this type were the key in aging, doubling or quadrupling its dose should shorten life proportionally; 2) although haploid organisms are more sensitive to radiation than diploid ones of the same species, the lifespans of the two ploidy classes are indistinguishable (Clark and Rubin, 1961).

Nevertheless, the possibility remains that aging is due to some kind of damage to DNA—a kind of damage which occurs at a high rate compared to point mutations and chromosomal aberrations but which is increased by mutagens in a lower proportion than is the spontaneous rate of the above mutational events. Among the possible mechanisms that might produce such an effect is "faulty repair" of damage to tandemly duplicated genes (Strehler, 1971). Should consecutive copies of the same gene "melt" and subsequently anneal in misregister, two single-stranded loops would occur which, if excised as part of a normal repair process, will not be able to be reinserted during repair (no template is accessible). The result may be the gradual deletion of tandemly duplicated genes (a process which should not be accelerated by mutagens in proportion to other kinds of known damage). Only one piece of evidence is available that bears on this question. Recently (Johnson and Strehler, 1972) it has been found that the dosage of DNA that codes for rRNA is reduced by 20% in DNA isolated from the brains (but not livers or spleens) of old dogs—as compared to DNA from young dogs. Further studies are required to determine whether these initial findings apply generally or not.

Displacement of Functional Parts by Non-functional Residues

There is good evidence that non-functioning components accumulate both within and without cells during aging. The accumulation of collagen, intimal thickening and calcium deposition in arterial walls, is an important example that results in a specific loss of function (Lansing, 1959); the accumulation, extracellularly, of amyloid is another feature of aging or response to disease in many older individuals and experimental animals; but the most striking change that occurs intracellularly is the accumulation of lipofuscin age pigments (Björkerud, 1964; Reichel et al., 1968). The entire cell body is occupied by this substance in neurons of very aged persons. Lipofuscin begins to accumulate even in young persons, increases at a more or less constant rate with age, and may occur in greatly increased amounts in the brains of individuals suffering from Batten's disease, a recessive hereditary disease, with characteristic lipo-pigment accumulation, that results in blindness and loss of mental function at an early age (Zeman, 1971). The degree to which lipofuscin residues reduce cell function has not yet been established. It seems unlikely, however, that the occupation of a major fraction of cell space by non-functional residues would be without harmful effect. The symptoms that accompany Batten's disease are consistent with this interpretation.

Other altered inclusions that occur in aging brains are the neurofibrillar tangles of Alzheimer's disease (Robert Terry, personal communication). These neurofibrils have a spiral, rather than smooth, appearance and are associated with foci of neural degeneration in the cerebral cortex of many, perhaps all, older persons. Severe afflictions of this type are classified as Alzheimer's disease and are associated with "senile dementia."

Orgel has suggested that non-functional residues may accumulate during aging as a result of self-amplifying transcriptional or translational errors. He pointed out that such errors in the proteins involved in transcription and translation would lead, autocatalytically, to further errors, including those of a similar nature, and eventually result in an "error catastrophe," unless the turnover rate were such as to limit this accumulation. No conclusive evidence in higher forms of life for the occurrence of such errors in measurable numbers has been presented, although certain fungal mutants seem to behave according to the theory.

In summary of this displacement hypothesis of aging, there seems to be little doubt that such processes are important in some aspects of aging. The localization of such displacement residues in fixed postmitotic cells implies that the repression of cell division ultimately leads to such degenerative changes, changes which cannot be diluted out to a low steady state level through cell division.

Programmed Gene Repression

The evolutionary advantages of a programmed restriction of synthesis (including the synthesis of new cells through mitosis) to those manufacturing operations that contribute to the survival of a line, rather than the individual, implies that specific substances, the direct repressive agents, are produced at specific and appropriate times in the life cycle.

This clocked switching-off of genes could, in principle, occur either: 1) through deletion of specific DNA segments; 2) through accumulation of transcription inhibitors (or loss of transcription promoters); or 3) through repression of specific steps in the translational mechanism. No clear evidence for transcriptional inhibitors of the operon-repressor type has been produced in studies of mammals, although age-related changes in message profiles, consistent with this concept, have been reported.

There is, however, abundant evidence that changes in the translational apparatus do accompany development and aging. This evidence has been summarized elsewhere recently (Strehler et al., 1971). Particularly suggestive is a finding by Bick and Strehler (1971) that the aging of soybean cotyledons is accompanied by the loss of ability to charge specific isoaccepting tRNA molecules to normal levels. Recent evidence indicates that this repression involves a triple complex between aminoacylated tRNA, synthetase, and a synthetase inhibitor, the last essentially absent in extracts of young cotyledons. The mechanism for gene repression suggested by these studies is that certain genes code for synthetase inhibitors and that these repressors are synthesized at specific times in the life cycle, thereby switching off the translation of other messages whose encoding involves a repressed genetic code word.

The auto-production of repressors of gene action is also suggested by studies on "chalones,"[1] in many respects similar to the inhibitory substances that Carrel described in the serum of aging animals (Carrel and Ebeling, 1923). It has been suggested that chalones may be repressors of synthetases necessary for the translation of messages involved in the mitotic process. Such inhibitors, acting at the cell surface as integral parts of the plasma membrane, may also be responsible for contact inhibition, and should they accumulate in irreversibly bound forms in membranes—through cross-linkage reactions like those that lead to age-pigment formation intracellularly—they may also be responsible for the phenomenon of clonal aging. (*See* Strehler et al., 1971.)

Clonal aging, quantitatively described by Hayflick (1965), results in the gradual loss of mitotic potential in diploid cells maintained *in vitro* for extended periods of time. A limit of about 50 "doublings" applies to human fibroblasts; somewhat lower numbers of doublings characterize cells from several more short-lived lines of animals (e.g., dogs—about 25 doublings; chickens—about 18 doublings). Some reduction in doubling potential of fibroblasts from adult humans (as compared to embryonically derived fibroblasts) has been reported. No strong correlation has been observed, however, between the age of the adult donor and doubling potential.

The above lines of evidence strongly implicate auto-produced repressors of mitosis as agents in the program of development and aging. The extent to which they operate largely or exclusively at translational sites has yet to be established. For reasons given elsewhere (Stent, 1964; Strehler, 1966), such sites would appear to be particularly suited as specific control points, could readily be programmed genetically and be highly versatile in their selectivity.

Effects of Aging

The most universal effect of aging processes is that they double, in humans, the chances of dying every 7 or 8 years—more frequently in

---

1. The term chalone was applied by Bullough (1965) to substances he was able to extract from tissues which acted specifically to reduce the mitotic rate of the tissue of origin, when these substances were injected into other animals.

lower forms. This fact, first described by B. Gompertz in 1825, is expressed by the equation: $R = R_o e \gamma^t$ (where R = death rate at age t; R_o is the death rate extrapolated to zero age; and γ defines the time required for the death rate to increase by a factor of 2.71 ($= e$).

This continual increase in the "force of mortality" obviously reflects decreases in key functional abilities during aging. Many of these physiological changes have been documented by Shock and co-workers. Generally it appears in a variety of different organ systems, that, on the average, slightly less than 1% of the reserve function is lost per year of age beyond age 30. These functional changes include: nerve conduction velocity; muscular strength; cardiac index; maximum kidney function; maximum breathing rate; capacity to produce antibodies to new antigens; glucose tolerance; BMR; and responses to, and levels of, a variety of hormones.

Many mental functions, particularly tasks that are unrelated to prior learning and experience, also decline in accuracy and speed during aging (Birren, 1959). This decline is accompanied by a 15 to 20% slowing of the alpha rhythm of the brain. To some extent, this decrease in mental speed is due to loss of sensory acuteness, but part also seems to be due to the fact that the greater store of experience an older person has means that a longer time is required to sort through it than through the more limited memory store of a less-experienced person. In many persons, however, some creative functions, particularly those which depend on richness of experience and memory, are undiminished, even at great ages.

Some Projections of Possible Modifications in Aging Rate by 2000 A.D.

It is still too early to be able to predict with confidence the degree to which advances in the understanding of aging will permit a drastic modification of the process itself. If it should turn out that specific losses of tandemly-duplicated genes is an important part of the aging clock, the retardation of the process would require the development of means to restore or amplify these discrete segments selectively. Such a repair or gene-amplification process may well occur during zygote maturation, for there is no a priori reason to believe that germinal cells would be completely immune to such damage while other body cell types are selective targets. This implies, then, that zygote maturation involves repair of, or selection against, such kinds of damage as well as more classical kinds of genetic abnormalities.

If the key reactions leading to senescence are a clocked sequence of gene repressions, as described above, the extent to which senescence will become modifiable depends on the degree to which such "off-switches" can be modified by specific pharmacological, humoral, or immunogenic agents. An understanding of the controls permitting regeneration of lost parts in those species of animals that are able to do so will probably furnish some of the needed insights.

Even if the re-institution of switched-off genes turns out to be prohibitively cumbersome, certain techniques already available should permit a 10- to 30-year extension of average healthy life span by the turn of the century. Restriction of dietary intake and weight to healthful levels, systematic programs of exercise, and enhancement of immunological defense mechanisms against specific pathogens, including oncogenic viruses, should reduce the incidence of circulatory and neoplastic diseases in the middle-late years.

Dietary supplementation with anti-oxidants, such as vitamin E and selenium, may reduce the rate at which lipofuscin and other oxidatively cross-linked materials accumulate. Drugs which stimulate mental function and supplementation with hormones which become deficient should provide additional years of productive health.

An as yet unexplored and probably modifiable factor that may influence longevity is body temperature. Experience with both vertebrates and invertebrates indicates that the rate of aging of all systems yet studied is a direct function of body temperature. The "activation energy" calculated for the aging process is about 18 kcal. Thus, a 2°C decrease in body temperature reduces the rate of aging by about 25%. If this rule applies to humans, as it does to all other systems studied thus far, reduction of body temperature to 35°C would add about 15 to 20 years to healthful life. Side effects of such a modest decrement in body temperature would probably not be particularly unpleasant, for some persons function normally at about 36°C; neural function has a much lower activation energy (about 6 kcal) than aging; and studies on experimental hypothermia in animals indicate no gross behavioral impairment even down to 33°C in certain dogs. Drugs which modify body temperature are already at hand (e.g., tranquilizers and novocaine).

Some Challenging and Specific Research Frontiers in Aging Research

An article of this length cannot deal in extenso with all of the areas of basic research on which the understanding of the phenomenon of aging depend. However, among the central questions that are ripe for attack are the following 10:

1) Is damage to DNA, such as the gradual loss of tandemly duplicated DNA a major factor in the genesis of aging? Measurement of the dosage of such genes in dividing and non-dividing cell types may be achieved through DNA-RNA hybridization studies.

2) Is clonal aging due to nuclear or extra-nuclear changes in cells *in vitro*? This question should be resolvable by transplanting nuclei from late to early passage cells.

3) Is the decrease in immune competence that accompanies aging and which parallels the increased susceptibility to tumors due to decreased population of responsive cells or to a decreased responsiveness of individual cells? A possible answer may be derived from examination of the competence of transplanted reticuloendothelial cells to support immune responses in transplants between Young and Old donors and recipients as compared to Young to Young and Old to Old. Unfortunately, the system in which this concept has been tested is highly tumor-prone.

4) Does the accumulation of lipofuscin reduce the maximum work rate of a particular cell type? This may be tested by measuring the fatigability of individual neurons (as measured by their responses and by their excitation of other neurons), followed by sacrifice of the animal and measurement of the lipofuscin content of that cell (previously labelled *in vivo* with fluorescent dyes). A sufficiently large sample of cells studied in this fashion may lead to an answer.

5) Do cells accumulate auto-inhibitory substances active at the plasma membrane (e.g., chalones) in irreversibly bound form? Isolation of plasma membrane fractions from cells of various ages and measurement of their effects on mitotic potential or specific syntheses *in vitro* may furnish an answer.

6) Do important sites for gene off-switches exist at the sites of tRNA aminoacylation? Possible test: Older tissues should contain larger amounts of specific inhibitors of tRNA aminoacylases.

7) Is the accumulation of neuro-fibrillar tangles in Alzheimer's disease a reflection of an altered intracellular milieu or of altered protein syntheses? Isolation and characterization of the subunit structure sequence should answer this question.

8) To what extent is the decreased speed of response of the elderly due to a reduced neural informational processing rate (e.g., a slower γ rhythm) or to a greater time requirement to "sort through" a larger store of memories? Possibly this could be answered by increasing the γ rhythm frequency by conditioning and then observing response time or by determining whether novel (e.g., nonsense words) stimuli are less rapidly recognized by the elderly—after compensating for sensory changes.

9) To what extent is male sexual potency reduced during aging as a result of conditioning or self-fulfilling prophecy, and to what extent does it result from systemic changes (e.g., vascular, endocrine, nutritional factors)? Possible tests involve comparison of performance (longitudinal studies) of men who have recently acquired young partners with their previous performance and effects of hormone administration or aphrodisiacs on the performance of men of various ages with a constant partner. A quadruple blind study would be of interest.

10) Is aging accompanied by the activation of many different kinds of latent viruses as surveillance mechanisms deteriorate? Possible tests involve the identification of new species of RNA in aged individuals and a demonstration that these are viral products rather than those of late acting genes.

Relationships of Life Span Modification to other Human Biological Problems

Nearly every means man has devised to control nature is pleiotropic—has brought with it a mixture of benefits and potential harms: Civilization permitted culture and human populations to flourish but made war more potentially devastating; modern medicine has accentuated the population explosion; science, technology, and the agricultural revolution have produced pollution and urban dislocations of mammoth proportions; humane concern for our fellow humans appears to favor the selective perpetuation of less-than-optimum genotypes; conquest of cancer or circulatory disease will increase the proportion of the post-retirement population in nonproductive years; mechanization of industry has led to technological unemployment and perhaps decreased the sense of satisfaction in creative work.

The modification of the rate of aging, or even its elimination, will, like these other changes man has introduced to improve specific aspects of his life, present new opportunities but also introduce new problems.

The opportunities include:

1) An increased level of health. (One cannot extend life by retarding aging without improving health.);
2) the opportunity to undertake multiple careers consecutively;
3) the stabilizing influence of 4 or 5 generational families;
4) a decrease in the trauma of untimely death and its prospects;
5) an opportunity to acquire a greater range of experience and the wisdom that can derive from it;
6) an improved ratio between the goods and services an individual consumes and contributes during his lifetime.[2]

The challenges posed include:

1) A greater proportion of persons at advanced chronological (but not physiological) ages and the reduced social plasticity this *may* involve;
2) a need to restructure social security and to re-adjust the retirement age upwards if the increased healthy life span is to be socially useful;
3) a slight effect (assuming that complete elimination of aging is unlikely before the end of this century) on the rate of population growth or steady state size at any given stable level of population replacement.

The last problem is usually high in the concerns of persons aware of the "population bomb," but the challenge is perhaps more illusory than real (Strehler, 1970). In the first place, extension of life by 20 years would result in an increase of about 25% in population density *90 years after the inception of such a program*. This means that 90 years would

---

2. At present about 30 years of dependency are required before a professional person begins to contribute his acquired skills at a maximum level; retirement at 65 means a ratio of about 1.2 of productive to dependent years. Extension of life by 20 years would increase this ratio to about 2.0, thereby increasing the return on the social investment a human being is by almost 70%.

be required to produce the same effect as about 7 years of population growth as it presently occurs (assuming a doubling time of about 30 years as at present on the world scene). Stated another way, long before the challenge begins to materialize, man will either have reached the improbably high level of 24 billion persons or have developed humane or inhumane means to keep population within reasonable bounds.

It seems significant, and possibly a basis for optimism, that man has solved most of the problems that have previously challenged him without compounding chaos. It seems not unlikely that our species will both modify the clocked chaos that grows within the individual as he ages and find means both to deal rationally with the population explosion and with the slight effect the probable conquest of aging will have on the present trends of population growth.

References

Bick, M. D. and B. L. Strehler. 1971. Leucyl transfer RNA synthetase changes during soybean catyledon senescence. *PNAS,* **68**: 224-228.

Bidder, G. P. 1925. The mortality of plaice. *Nature,* **115**: 495-496.

Birren, J. E. (ed.). 1959. *Handbook of Aging and the Individual.* University of Chicago Press, Chicago.

Björkerud, S. 1964. Isolated lipofuscin granules—A survey of a new field. p. 257-288. *In:* B. L. Strehler (ed.). *Advances in Gerontological Research,* Vol. I. Academic Press, New York.

Bullough, W. S. 1965. Mitotic and functional homeostasis: A speculative review. *Cancer Res.,* **25**: 1683-1727.

Carrel, A. and A. H. Ebeling. 1923. Antagonistic growth-activating and growth-inhibiting principles in serum. *J. Expertl. Med.,* **37**(5): 653-658.

Clark, A. M. 1964. Genetic factors associated with aging. p. 207-255. *In:* B. L. Strehler (ed.). *Advances in Gerontological Research,* Vol. I. Academic Press, New York.

———— and M. A. Rubin. 1961. The modification by X-rays of the life span of haploids and diploids of the wasp. Habrobracon species. *Radiat. Res.,* **15**: 244.

Curtis, H. J. 1963. Biological mechanisms underlying the aging process. *Science,* **141**: 68-76.

Gompertz, B. 1825. On the nature of the function expressive of the law of human mortality and on a new mode of determining life contingencies. *Phil. Trans. Roy. Soc.* (London), Ser. A., **115**: 513-585.

Hayflick, L. 1965. The limited *in vitro* lifetime of human diploid cell strains. *Exp. Cell. Res.,* **37**: 614-630.

Johnson, R. and B. L. Strehler. 1972. Loss of genes coding for ribosomal RNA in aging brain cells. *Nature.* (In Press.)

Lansing, A. I. 1959. *The Arterial Wall.* Williams and Wilkins Co., Baltimore.

Medawar, P. B. 1951. *An Unsolved Problem of Biology.* An inaugural lecture delivered at University College, London. Lewis, London.

Reichel, W., J. Hollander, J. H. Clark, and B. L. Strehler. 1968. Lipofuscin accumulation as a function of age and distribution in rodent brain. *J. Geront.,* **23**: 71-77.

Stent, G. S. 1964. The operon on its third anniversary. *Science,* **144**: 816-822.

Strehler, B. L. 1959. Origin and comparison of the effects of time and high-energy radiations on living systems. *Quart. Rev. Biol.,* **34**: 117-142.

———. 1962. *Time, Cells, and Aging.* Academic Press, New York.

———. 1966. Code degeneracy and the aging process: A molecular genetic theory of aging. 7th Int. Congress of Geront., Vienna. p. 177-185.

———. 1970. Ten myths about aging. *Center Mag.,* III (4): 41-48.

———. 1971. Aging at the cellular level. p. 49-84. *In:* I. Rossman (ed.). *Clinical Geriatrics.* J. B. Lippincott Co., Philadelphia.

———, G. Hirsch, D. Gusseck, R. Johnson, and M. Bick. 1971. Codon restriction theory of aging and development. *J. Theor. Biol.,* **33**: 429-474.

Welch, J. P. 1967. Somatic mutations and the aging process. p. 1-36. *In:* B. L. Strehler (ed.). *Advances in Gerontological Research,* Vol. II. Academic Press, New York.

Williams, G. C. 1957. Pleiotropy, natural selection and the evolution of senescence. *Evolution,* **11**: 398-411.

Zeman, W. 1971. The neuronal ceroid-lipofuscinoses—Batten-Vogt syndrome: A model for human aging? p. 147-169. *In:* B. L. Strehler (ed.). *Advances in Gerontological Research,* Vol. III. Academic Press, New York.

8 Timing Mechanisms

J. W. HASTINGS
THE BIOLOGICAL LABORATORIES
Harvard University

The past 25 years have witnessed spectacular advances in knowledge of, and important new insights concerning, biological timing mechanisms. From observations which years ago might have been considered curious and interesting, but trivial, there has emerged a generalization of prime importance concerning the regulation of time of physiological and biochemical processes. The generalization states that organisms possess an endogenous timing mechanism which can persist under constant conditions and which serves to regulate a multiplicity of physiological and behavioral phenomena (Chovnick, 1961; Aschoff, 1965a; Menaker, 1971).

The mechanism involved in biological clocks should be clearly distinguished from other systems which have sometimes, but imprecisely, been referred to as "clocks," where timing involves a series of catenary sequential events. Biological clock mechanisms involve regulation with *time* as a parameter; a distinctive feature is that the cellular mechanism regulates in time reasonably accurately under a variety of different environmental conditions—including at different temperatures.

For the future, we look to the elucidation of this mechanism, to the analysis of the biochemistry and biophysics of the oscillatory phenomena which underlie the biological clock, and to the understanding of a mul-

Dedicated to Professor Jurgen Aschoff on the occasion of his 60th birthday.

tiplicity of physiological, behavioral, and ecological aspects of timing functions. The importance of using both genetic techniques and biochemical analysis should be emphasized. For some problems, there is also value in using relatively simple systems, such as the unicells (*Gonyaulax, Euglena, Paramecium, Tetrahymena, Acetabularia*). Before considering some of these future directions, we will review, in very brief outline, the properties and knowledge of circadian systems as exemplified by one of these unicellular forms.

Circadian Rhythms in Gonyaulax

The marine dinoflagellate, *Gonyaulax polyedra,* is a unicellular form which is found ubiquitously and sometimes abundantly (e.g., in red

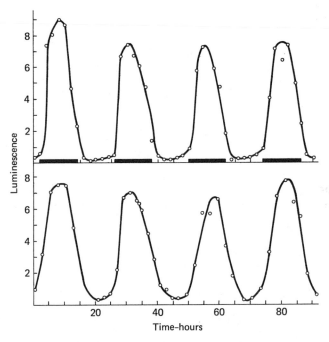

FIGURE 1. These curves illustrate the nature of the rhythm of flashing luminescence in *Gonyaulax*. Top curve shows the rhythmicity in cultures exposed to alternating light and dark periods of 12 hours each (LD 12:12). Transferred to conditions of constant light (120 foot candles) and constant temperature (21° C) the rhythm persists with a period of about, but not exactly, 24 hours (bottom).

tides) in the oceans (Sweeney, 1969). It grows photosynthetically and rather slowly, even under optimal conditions. Like many dinoflagellates, it possesses a thick external "armor," a polysaccharide (probably cellulose) test. It is motile, possessing two flagella. The organism displays several circadian rhythms which we have studied, and it seems likely that there may be more that could be followed if needed. This multiplicity of overt rhythms is in itself of considerable usefulness in studying mechanism: One can study how the several rhythms relate to one another and to the controlling mechanism.

THE LUMINESCENT FLASHING RHYTHM

The organism is brilliantly bioluminescent, emitting flashes of light when stimulated at night. When stimulated in the daytime, however, relatively little light is emitted. This may be quantitatively measured by integrating the light output during a brief (1-2 min) stimulation. When cells are removed from the light-dark cycle and placed in an environment of constant light and temperature, this rhythm continues (Fig. 1) (Hastings and Sweeney, 1958).

THE LUMINESCENT GLOW RHYTHM

In undisturbed cultures, a relatively dim, but measurable, glow occurs toward the end of the dark period. This lasts for only a few hours each day and may be accompanied by occasional spontaneous flashing which can be noted on a recording as a much brighter spike of light. In this case, one measures the intensity of the light output in order to monitor the rhythm (Fig. 2). In cultures kept in constant conditions (except for brief times in the dark to make the measurements), the rhythm persists (Hastings, 1961).

THE CELL DIVISION RHYTHM

In both the laboratory and in the ocean in natural populations, mitoses in many species of dinoflagellates are restricted to a particular time of day; in *Gonyaulax* this falls toward the end of the dark period. This rhythm illustrates a significant and interesting feature of circadian control: Physiological processes may be gated. Not all cells divide each day,

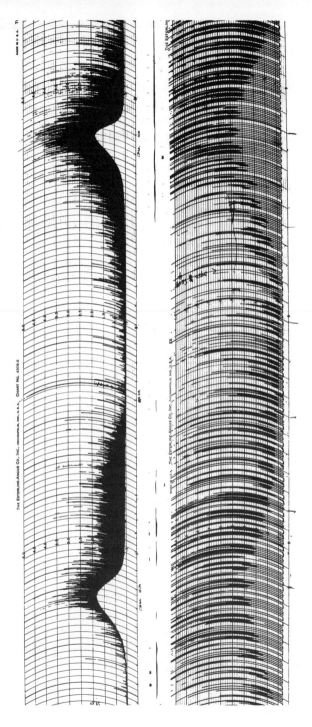

FIGURE 2. The luminescent glow rhythms, measured from one vial of cells kept in constant darkness (top); and (bottom) from 6 vials kept in constant dim light, except for brief periods every hour when the vial was placed in the dark in a phototube chamber to measure luminescence. The change in the baseline level is the steady glow; the vertical lines are from spontaneous flashing of individual cells. Temperature 23°C.

for the growth rate may be relatively slow. Those which do divide during a given day do so at a certain restricted time—when the gate is open. The result is a rhythmic but not synchronous population which, thereby, exhibits a staircase-shaped growth curve. This phenomenon also continues with cells kept under constant conditions (Sweeney and Hastings, 1958).

THE PHOTOSYNTHETIC CAPACITY RHYTHM

Although cells in the dark are obviously unable to carry out photosynthesis, one can test their capacity to photosynthesize by putting them in the light and assaying them under optimal conditions. When this was done, it was found that the cell's ability to photosynthesize varies considerably as a function of time of day. As might be expected, the capacity

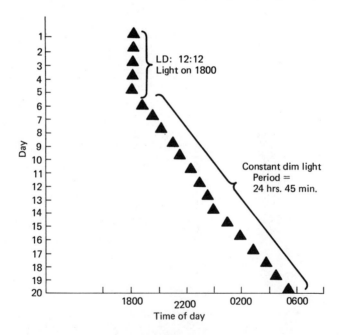

FIGURE 3. The time of day at which the maximum in the luminescent glow occurred on each of 20 successive days. For the first few days, the culture was kept on a daily light-dark cycle. Subsequently, the light remained on continuously, and whereas the rhythm continued, its maximum occurred about 45 minutes later each day, indicating that the period in this case was 24 hours, 45 minutes. Temperature 24° C.

is greatest during the day. Under constant conditions, the rhythmic changes in capacity persist for many days (Hastings et al., 1961).

Properties of These Rhythms

These several rhythms persist under constant conditions with a circadian period. The fact that their periods are circadian (e.g., about 1 day), and not exactly 24 hours, is critical, for it indicates that the timing relies on an internal mechanism rather than on external physical periodicity (Fig. 3). This circadian period is a function of environmental conditions, but the effects are relatively small. The effect of temperature, for example (Fig. 4), is especially instructive. At temperatures 10° apart, the clock mechanism runs at frequencies which are not greatly different (26.5 hr at 27°; 22.8 hr at 17°). This phenomenon—referred to as temperature independence—is a hallmark of circadian rhythms and

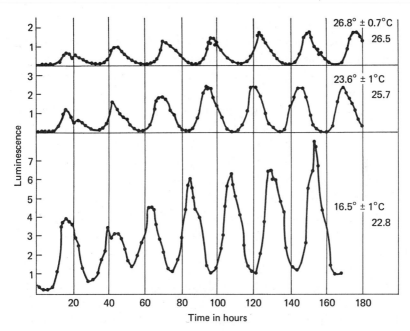

FIGURE 4. Characteristics of the persistent rhythm of luminescence in *Gonyaulax* at the three different temperatures noted in dim light. The luminescence capacity was measured approximately every two hours. The average period in hours, measured for each, is noted on the graph below the temperature.

is a crucially important property for a true timing device. Actually, the system is not completely temperature-independent. The period is only relatively temperature-independent, and in *Gonyaulax* it is, in fact, somewhat longer at a higher temperature—just the opposite of what might be expected if temperature were increasing the rate of underlying metabolic ractions. This result prompted our postulate (Hastings and Sweeney, 1957) that the biological clock mechanism involves temperature compensation reactions—and that it should not be simply viewed as temperature-independent.

Circadian systems are phase labile to light. The rhythm of an organism maintained on a 24 hour light-dark cycle always shows a 24 hour period rather than its circadian period (Fig. 3). A displacement in longitude results in an appropriate phase shift, and this may be simulated in the laboratory by scheduling artificial lights. But phase shifting does not actually require exposure to a new light-dark cycle. With an organism kept under constant conditions, single light flashes (simulating, as it were, dawn or dusk) can reset a clock with full effectiveness, if administered at the correct time (Hastings, 1964). Relatively little is known about the critical (biochemical) part of the receptor system. The action spectrum in *Gonyaulax* reflects the general pigment content of the cell (Hastings and Sweeney, 1960).

This property of phase lability has been, and in my opinion continues to be, a truly crucially important feature to focus upon, both theoretically and experimentally. The biological oscillator, as it appears, can be effectively perturbed (phase shifted) without damping its action, like a pendulum in motion held for an extra moment at one end of its swing. Phase shifting by light must surely be viewed as the result of a photochemical reaction; yet, the fact is, it has never been possible to either truly mimic the effect of this photochemical reaction by externally added substances or to chemically interfere with or inhibit the light-initiated phase shfting. Positive results in experiments of this type would be truly exciting, for the expected specificity should reveal a great deal about the biochemical nature of the mechanism and bring us close to the elements of the clock itself. In the same paragraph, we should note that action spectra are available for only a few cases; no careful effort has been made to utilize this route to gain access to the timing mechanism.

This phase-shifting phenomenon, resetting the clock, should be clearly distinguished from effects which result in frequency changes which stretch or contract the oscillation without altering its essential features. We have noted that, at different (but constant) temperatures, the period in *Gonyaulax* may differ by almost four hours. Different (constant) light intensities have a similar effect. Several chemical substances have been reported which have effects of this sort. For example, Bruce and Pittendrigh (1960) found that the period of the *Euglena* rhythm was several hours greater when maintained in a medium containing D_2O. Similar effects were observed by Suter and Rawson (1968) with mammals (administering D_2O in the drinking water), including the observation that effect was concentration-dependent. Feldman (1967) first showed, and has since elaborated on, an effect of this sort caused by certain inhibitors of protein synthesis. Valuable as they are, these observations are difficult to exploit; they do not seem to lead to the mechanism in a very direct way, and the result should not be mistaken for one which truly perturbs the mechanism.

CONTROL OF SEVERAL RHYTHMS: ARRHYTHMICITY

The concept that there exists a clock mechanism carries with it the implication that more than one process might thereby be controlled or "plugged in." In fact, there is very little experimental evidence relating to this point. Considering unicellular systems, we do not know whether many or only a few processes are clock-controlled. Observations indicating no rhythmicity are, by the nature of the inquiry, usually discarded or not closely scrutinized. It is thus difficult to evaluate the status of this question.

The impact of many of these considerations may depend very much on how you pose the question or how you formulate the experiment. For example, in terms of mechanism, do we postulate that the cell is a clock, or that the cell has a clock? If the latter, can we say whether the cell has only a single clock, or might there be several quasi-independent oscillators (McMurry and Hastings, 1972a)?

In the experimental sense, there is a distinction between the "mechanism" and the controlled process. It has been shown that there are rhythmic phenomena that can be blocked by using inhibitors without any substantial effect on the operation or phase of the clock (Hastings, 1961). For example, photosynthesis in *Gonyaulax* can be blocked using the highly specific drug, dichlorophenyl dimethyl urea (DCMU); yet, the glow rhythm of bioluminescence continues all the while. Furthermore, the rhythm of photosynthetic capacity will resume in phase following the removal of the inhibitor. We also know from experiments like this that there is no feedback from the controlled process to the mechanism. A change in the biochemical status of the process does not alter the timing.

These and other experiments lead us to ask quite explicitly whether or not the cell can or does exist in an arrhythmic state and, indeed, what is meant by an arrhythmic cell. It may be a Talmudic discussion, for one can argue that the clock is always present and capable of functioning, but its output cannot be observed under certain conditions. Failure to observe rhythmicity in an organism can thus be put down to a breakdown of this sort, not to the absence of the feature.

Rhythms in Isolated Cells

It has been stated frequently and sweepingly that circadian rhythms do not occur among prokaryotes, that it is a property associated only with the eukaryotic level of organization. Although this may be true, it is not clear that the question has been investigated extensively or carefully enough to be certain of the conclusion. Experiments with *Escherichia coli,* which divides every 30 minutes or so, are not critical. It would be desirable to have studies with slow-growing organisms, such as certain marine bacteria, or with blue greens.

In the eukaryotes rhythms, different levels of biological organization may be involved; it is appropriate to inquire concerning the degree of the organization involved in rhythmicity and the nature of its contribution to the phenomenon. There are population cycles; rhythms are also expressed at the level of the organism, organs, tissues, and cells. The fact that cultures of single cells exhibit circadian rhythms in culture fails to deal with the question of the single cell. With *Gonyaulax* it has been possible to isolate and observe single cells and to demonstrate circadian properties. For example, by isolating daughter cells in a capillary microdrop and making regular observations thereafter, it was possible to determine the time interval until the subsequent divisions. Division times clustered around 24, 48, 72, and 96 hours; e.g., $n \times 24$: The "gating" restricts divisions to a single time of day (Hastings and Sweeney, 1964).

Similarly, the rhythm of photosynthetic capacity has been demonstrated in isolated single cells (Sweeney, 1961).

To demonstrate the persistence of circadian rhythms under constant conditions, it is always necessary with *Gonyaulax* to use dim light or darkness, and with isolated cells, the rhythms do, in fact, persist under these conditions. By contrast, rhythmic activity essentially disappears under conditions of constant bright light. To distinguish whether the loss of rhythmicity arises from the lack of rhythmicity in every cell or from a loss of synchrony between cells, isolated *Gonyaulax* cells were observed. It was possible to show that the first of these possibilities holds; i.e., each cell loses rhythmicity. This has been demonstrated both with the rhythm of cell division and with the rhythm of photosynthetic capacity (Sweeney, 1961).

In fact, much discussion has been centered on the question as to whether or not circadian rhythmicity is ubiquitous and indispensable to eukaryotes. It has been argued that it is, but I believe that the basis for making this assertion is weak, often relying on arguments such as those described above. Future research is unlikely to shed much light on this question until the nature of the mechanism is clearly defined at the molecular level. Speculating, I would take the contrary position; namely, that circadian systems are dispensable, analogous to nonessential operons in bacteria which may have a positive function under certain conditions but which are not essential, or even functional, under many conditions. There could be, I believe, conditions where, or a species in which, this property was lacking or not expressed.

Biochemical Mechanisms and Future Prospects

One must, then, look to an elucidation of the biochemical mechanisms in order to provide insight into many fundamental questions, and one must try to formulate the questions in molecular terms. Following the arguments outlined above, one could, for purposes of experimental design, distinguish two aspects of a hypothetical molecular mechanism— the clock mechanism and clock-controlled processes. This does not necessarily mean that it will be a useful or even meaningful distinction.

What is known? Where can we start? In the first place, what is it that oscillates at the molecular level? Is it the quantity of proteins (enzymes) or substrates; is it the activity (via some molecular switch), the localization, or compartmentalization—or some other feature? It is probably fair to say that many workers in the field have assumed that enzyme activities or concentrations are involved, but there are only a few cases in which significant circadian biochemical changes have been observed from *in vitro* analysis and even fewer in which there has been any detailed analysis of these changes.

In *Gonyaulax* we have found a biochemical correlate with the *in vivo* rhythm of light emission (McMurry and Hastings, 1972b). In cell-free extracts of *Gonyaulax*, a soluble enzyme and substrate can be isolated which, when appropriately recombined *in vitro*, results in bioluminescence. In a rhythmic *Gonyaulax* system, it was found that the extractable enzyme activity also varied with time of day correlated with the *in vivo* rhythm (Fig. 5) (Hastings and Bode, 1962). The substrate gave an unexpected result: The maximum in extractable substrate occurred

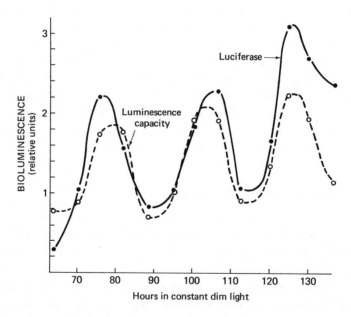

FIGURE 5. The circadian rhythm of *in vivo* bioluminescence capacity (flashing) rhythm compared with the *in vitro* activity of extractable luciferase, measured in cultures of *Gonyaulax* which had been maintained on constant dim light for the time given on the abscissa.

during the day. This apparent paradox was resolved following the observation that the process of filtering the cells resulted in violent bioluminescence flashing during the night, but only a dull glow by day. It was, therefore, hypothesized that differential substrate utilization was occurring. This idea was supported by experiments in which flashing was inhibited prior to harvesting, whereupon greater quantities of substrate could be isolated from cells at night (Hastings and Bode, 1962; Bode et al., 1963).

The nature of the activity difference in luciferase was not discovered; i.e., whether it was by virtue of amounts (i.e., synthesis and destruction), due to activity (i.e., activation and inhibition), or to a differential extraction efficiency (different quantities liberated during extraction at different times of day). Present results support the second (activation and inhibition) hypothesis (McMurry and Hastings, 1972b). But the luminescent system in *Gonyaulax* has now been shown to derive not only from an enzyme-substrate system but also from a particle, apparently a cell organelle. This has been termed the scintillon, and the active particle has been successfully isolated from cells and purified (Fogel and Hastings, 1972). The matter of concern reduces—though the difficulty is not reduced—to the question of circadian control of the activity of this organelle. Such a situation also implicates physiological control mechanisms rather than simple enzyme synthesis and destruction. Membrane systems and changes in their transport and/or permeability properties are very likely of central importance. This underscores the view that biological control systems are in many instances concerned with a complicated target system. Studies concerned with this aspect of the problem are continuing.

A far more extensive and more sophisticated biochemical analysis of rhythmic systems will be needed. We need to pinpoint more biochemical correlates of rhythms, and of equal importance, to know which systems are not involved. We need to know how a biochemical change is correlated with and converted into physiological changes; we need to distinguish, if possible, the driving oscillations from those which are driven.

As is evident from the foregoing comments, the mechanism itself has escaped explicit description at the molecular level. It has not yet been possible to define either the biochemical systems or the cellular components which are critically involved. There are two general types of models which I would like to discuss. One involves a loop of some sort—a series of catenary reactions in the form of a loop, with appropriate feedback and circadian properties.

The second, less explicit and up to now poorly explored, would not involve obligatory steps such as one finds in a loop but perhaps something more like a network of interconnecting reactions which may (or may not; i.e., damped systems) involve oscillations between the elements. We know that there are a great number and variety of organelle and biochemical compartments in the cell; we know that biochemical pathways are replete with shunts, redundancies, and feedback. Biochemical oscillations may very well involve all of these in such a way that blocking any given pathway will have little or no effect on the observed cellular oscillation. In fact, one might think of this as a biochemical hologram. The very interesting short-period oscillations, both from intact cells and *in vitro* yeast extracts, reported by Chance and his colleagues (1967) are instructive in this regard. Their analysis indicates that, even in a relatively simple system, a complexity of shunt and feedback steps are involved. The oscillations of different components in the network possess different relative phase angles such that the control of specific cell functions at specific times of the cycle could readily be envisioned. Models which involve principles of this type should be given more attention, both experimentally and theoretically. The possibility that membrane systems might participate in phenomena of this sort seems evident.

Most models, however, have envisaged a loop of some sort. One of the earliest specific ideas concerning the chemical mechanism was based on the notion that RNA transcription might be programmed on a circadian basis, thereby resulting in time-of-day specific cellular syntheses. This hypothesis received strong support from our observation that a rhythm in *Gonyaulax* was blocked both by Actinomycin D—a drug highly specific for blocking DNA-dependent RNA synthesis—and puromycin, which inhibits protein synthesis (Karakashian and Hastings, 1962).

Although supporting observations were obtained by some workers, several others failed to support the hypothesis. It seemed very attractive and appropriate to hypothesize that the circadian system should be compared to a special type of developmental system in which a daily differentiation was occurring. In fact, several authors were led to develop the hypothesis in greater detail, especially Goodwin (1963) in his broad-ranging monograph on temporal control in biological systems more generally, and Ehret and Trucco (1967) in their highly picturesque "chronon" hypothesis. The latter authors developed a model in which they proposed that the DNA complement of a eukaryotic cell is comprised of functional subunits termed chronons, each of which is composed of a segment of DNA. The chronon is substantial in size; namely, polycistronic, and is functionally distinct because it corresponds to a daily scanning cycle: The chronon is regulated so as to get transcribed in a linear and temperature-independent fashion once a day. The message encoded at the termination of a chronon provides for reinitiation; whether all or only part of the DNA is organized into chronons was left vague, but a considerable number of chronons per eukaryotic cell were apparently envisioned.

The evident consequence of the chronon theory is that the synthesis of much, if not all, new cellular material will be programed on a circadian basis. This is an acceptable, but surely insufficient, hypothesis to account for the very spectacular differences which occur in circadian systems. The activities of specific circadian systems commonly vary by a factor of between 10 and 100 over a time period when cell components increase by a factor of less than two—usually far less than that. One would have to propose, presumably, that a complete (or substantial) turnover of some specific and critical components would occur on a daily basis, while others would be stable and receive only a daily increment. The chronon theory fails to address itself to this critical aspect of the problem.

We believe that "activation," followed by "inhibition," are key features of circadian control; while the effects may be mediated via RNA synthesis, it is difficult to account for the phenomenon on the basis of circadian timing of new synthesis of gross cellular components as such. In fact, it is not clear that this is a necessary part of any comprehensive theory.

The search for true inhibitors of the hypothetical "mechanism loop" has not met with any success. The clock and its approximate frequency is relatively immune to alteration by inhibition, just as it is to different temperatures or light intensities. In principle, an inhibitor of the mechanism should not simply stop the rhythmicity; if it is reversible, there should be a phase shift in the rhythm equal to the number of hours of effective inhibition. An inhibitor of a "controlled process," by contrast, should have no such phase shifting capability. Although the clock mechanism is resistant to chemical perturbation, it is surely not entirely immune, as pointed out in connection with phase shifting by light. Continued study can confidently be expected to be fruitful. But in dealing with the design and interpretation of such experiments, we must not restrict ourselves to models so simple as the single loop, for our results will be restricted by our questions.

Genetic Studies

Genetic analysis of biological systems can reveal more than hereditary mechanisms; it can provide an elegant tool for the dissection of the system controlled by the product(s) of the gene(s) in question. Over the past ten years, there have been several studies concerned with genetic aspects of circadian systems (Sussman et al., 1964; Sargent et al., 1966; Barnett, 1966; Karakashian, 1968). Recent efforts to produce mutants possessing lesions in the timing mechanism have met with success, both in *Drosophila* (Konopka and Benzer, 1971) and in *Chlamydomonas* (Bruce, personal communication). Both period mutants (long and short) and arrhythmic mutants have been reported.

It is not easy to imagine what other specific mutant classes could be screened for easily. One might find mutants which fail to "reset" upon exposure to light, but these might be truly unrelated to the clock mechanism. One might try to find a mutant which has escaped temperature compensation, but this seems a long shot. Nevertheless, it would seem useful to obtain, analyze, and map a considerable number of mutants in the classes now available. The identification of specific cellular systems with which clock lesions are associated would provide a truly valuable insight.

Behavior and Ecological Aspects

Students in behavior and ecology are becoming increasingly aware of the relevance of circadian timing mechanisms to an understanding of many systems. The *Drosophila* clock gates eclosion so that it occurs near dawn, at a time presumed to be favorable in terms of humidity and temperature. The clock of the bee allows scheduling of visitations to specific flowers in concert with the daily rhythm of nectar exudation by each plant. Pheromone release and mating patterns may be elegantly timed in a species specific manner, assisting as an isolation mechanism as well. The clock of birds and many other animals has been found to be involved in orientation and may be functional in direction-finding and migration, although proof of this latter point is still lacking. These and many other aspects are discussed by Hoffman (1971).

In fact, one must insist that we are only at the threshold of an understanding of the kinds of different ways in which timing mechanisms are functionally important. Photoperiodism clearly involves the use of a biological timing mechanism, but the details of this are still far from clear. The chronon hypothesis, irrespective of its specific postulates, is based on the notion that transcription and translation of specific genes can be restricted to specific times of day, thereby varying the capacities of various physiological and biochemical processes with respect to time of day. Whether by this specific mechanism or by another, the importance of timing mechanisms in behavior and ecology of organisms is a real, but still largely unexplored, facet of their biology.

Clocks in Man

We turn, finally, to some comments on the nature of the clock in man and some implications for human biology and medicine. The fact that man has daily rhythms of body temperature, excretion, and many other functions had been known for a very long time, but only recently has it been widely appreciated that these rhythms are driven from within by the ubiquitous circadian clock mechanism.

Aschoff (1965b) tabulated some 50 functions in man that exhibit circadian features, and a recent publication of the U.S. Public Health Service (1970) has set forth in excellent detail many aspects of human biology in health and disease which involve clock-like rhythms. Among the many interesting findings are those which show that animals (and man) may be far more susceptible to drugs at one time of day than at another; a similar finding with sensitivity to X-rays is equally interesting.

Aschoff and his associates at the Max-Plank Institute in Erling-Andechs, Germany have built special underground bunkers for the study of human rhythms under completely controlled conditions. In these sophisticated facilities, human subjects can live in isolation for long periods; various types of experimental manipulations and recordings are possible, and full records of their activities are obtained. Under such conditions, humans live a true circadian day. Most have periods longer than 24 hours so that after, say, 20 days, a subject with a 26 hour period would have "lost" almost two days. The subjects are not aware of this. Thus humans clearly possess the endogenous circadian clock.

Using light-dark cycles, entrainment and phase shifting have been demonstrated. As known to those who have traveled by jet across several time zones, such a phase shift is sometimes an uncomfortable experience that may be felt over a period of several days. In the experiments, a lag is demonstrable physiologically in various rhythmic functions. In several contemporary situations, we are able, indeed required, to establish the activity-rest cycle or schedule to which we subject an individual. In doing so, it would certainly seem wise to evaluate the effects of the period of the cycle upon the circadian system. This is true for shift workers in industry; for efficiency, as well as accident and error rate of workers, varies with time of day. It would be important to understand and define the best conditions and schedule for someone working during the dead of the night. Up to now, there seems to be no clear knowledge or agreement on this matter.

In the military, similar problems are encountered. For example, the enlisted men on some submarines are apparently subjected to an 18-hour cycle (six on; 12 off)—an incredible 6-hour phase shift each day. No basic studies on this situation have been reported so far as I know. Since the officers on the same vessel reputedly live a 24-hour day, it would be difficult to obtain meaningful observations about possible entrainment and phase shifting of biologic rhythms. Space flight, especially when carried out for extended periods, is yet another situation in which it will be very important to make careful evaluation and correct decisions on work-rest schedules for the astronauts.

Some rather unusual new observations concerned with the dissociation of different rhythms have been obtained by Aschoff. It was discovered that rhythms may dissociate in the bunker. For example, the activity rhythm may have a period different from the body-temperature cycle. This is of immense basic and practical importance; within a few cycles, the temperature cycle may fall just $180°$ out of phase with the activity cycle. This is quite different from having the light-dark cycle out of phase with the rhythmic functions. It has been reported that such subjects are "physiologically upset."

A second, quite different type of "desynchronization," has been reported. A few subjects in the bunker exhibit a natural period close to 48, rather than 24, hours—a circa-48-hour rhythm. They live a 48-hour day without being aware of it. Emerging from the bunker after 20 days, they are convinced that only 10 days have elapsed. All activities are accordingly distributed within the 48-hour day: sleep for 16 to 20 hours followed by about 30 hours of activity; three meals a "day" and so forth.

Dedication

From the laboratory of Professor Jurgen Aschoff, and from his inspiration and teaching, has come many of the fundamental contributions to our knowledge of biological timing mechanisms, circadian clocks (Aschoff, 1965). His research, perhaps more than that from any other single laboratory, has dealt both with human rhythmicity and the basic mechanisms and biology. In dedicating this contribution to him, it is a pleasure to acknowledge the profit and enjoyment from our association with him and his associates, both personally and professionally.

References

Aschoff, J. (ed.). 1965a. *Circadian Clocks*. Proceedings of the Feldafing Summer School. North-Holland Publishing Co., Amsterdam.

————. 1965b. Circadian rhythms in man. *Science,* **148**: 1427-1432.

Barnett, A. 1966. A circadian rhythm of mating type reversals in *Paramecium* and its genetic control. *J. Cell Physiol.,* **67**: 239-270.

Bode, V. C., R. J. DeSa, and J. W. Hastings. 1963. Daily rhythm in luciferin activity in *Gonyaulax polyedra. Science,* **141**: 913-915.

Bruce, V. G. 1972. Mutants of the biological clock in *Chlamydomonas reinhardi. Genetics.* (In press.)

———— and C. S. Pittendrigh. 1960. An effect of heavy water on the phase and period of the circadian rhythm in *Euglena. J. Cell Comp. Physiol.,* **56**: 25-31.

Chance, B., W. Pye, and I. Higgins. 1967. Waveform generation by enzymatic oscillators. IEEE *Spectrum,* **4**: 79-86.

Chovnick, A. (ed.). 1961. *Biological Clocks.* Cold Spring Harbor Symposium on Quantitative Biology, **25**. Long Island Biological Assoc., Cold Spring Harbor, New York.

Ehret, C. F. and E. Trucco. 1967. Molecular models for the circadian clock. I. The chronon concept. *J. Theor. Biol.,* **15**: 240-262.

Feldman, J. F. 1967. Lengthening the period of a biological clock in *Euglena* by cycloheximide, an inhibitor of protein synthesis. *Proc. Nat. Acad. Sci.,* **57**: 1080-1087.

Fogel, M. and J. W. Hastings. 1972. Bioluminescence: Mechanism and mode of control of scintillon activity. *Proc. Nat. Acad. Sci.,* **69**: 690-693.

Goodwin, B. C. 1963. *Temporal Organization in Cells.* Academic Press, New York.

Hastings, J. W. 1961. Biochemical aspects of rhythms: Phase shifting by chemicals. *In*: A. Chovnick (ed.). *Biological Clocks.* Cold Spring Harbor Symposium on Quantitative Biology, **25**: 131-144.

————— 1964. The role of light in persistent daily rhythms. p. 333-361. *In*: A. C. Giese (ed.). *Photophysiology: Action of Light on Living Materials.* Vol. I. Academic Press, New York.

—————, L. Astrachan, and B. M. Sweeney. 1961. A persistent daily rhythm in photosynthesis. *J. Gen. Physiol.,* **45**: 69-76.

————— and V. C. Bode. 1962. Biochemistry of rhythmic systems. *Ann. New York Acad. Sci.,* **98**: 876-889.

————— and B. M. Sweeney. 1957. On the mechanism of temperature independence in a biological clock. *Proc. Nat. Acad. Sci.,* **43**: 804-811.

————— and —————. 1958. A persistent diurnal rhythm of luminescence in *Gonyaulax polyedra. Biol. Bull.,* **115**: 440-458.

————— and —————. 1960. The action spectrum for shifting the phase of the rhythm of luminescence in *Gonyaulax polyedra. J. Gen. Physiol.,* **43**: 697-706.

————— and —————. 1964. Phased cell division in the marine dinoflagellates. p. 579-587. *In*: E. Zeuthen (ed.). *Synchrony in Cell Division and Growth.* Interscience, New York.

Hoffman, K. 1971. Biological clocks in animal orientation and in other functions. Proc. Int. Symp. Circadian Rhythmicity (Wageningen). p. 175-205.

Karakashian, M. 1968. The rhythm of mating in *Paramecium. J. Cell. Physiol.,* **71**: 197-210.

————— and J. W. Hastings. 1962. The inhibition of a biological clock by actinomycin D. *Proc. Nat. Acad. Sci.,* **48**: 2130-2137.

Konopka, R. and S. Benzer. 1971. Clock mutants of *Drosophila melanogaster. Proc. Nat. Acad. Sci.,* **68**: 2112-2116.

McMurry, L. and J. W. Hastings. 1972a. No desynchronization among four circadian rhythms in the unicellular alga, *Gonyaulax polyedra. Science,* **175**: 1137-1139.

————— and —————. 1972b. Circadian rhythms: Mechanism of luciferase activity changes in *Gonyaulax. Biol. Bull.,* **143**: August. (In press.)

Menaker, M. (ed.). 1971. *Biochronometry.* Proceedings of a Symposium, Friday Harbor, National Academy of Sciences, Washington.

Sargent, M. L., W. R. Briggs, and D. D. Woodward. 1966. Circadian nature of a rhythm expressed by an invertaseless strain of *Neurospora crassa. Plant Physiol.,* **41**: 1343-1349.

Sussman, A. S., R. J. Lowry, and T. Durkee. 1964. Morphology and genetics of a periodic colonial mutant of *Neurospora crassa. Am. J. Botany,* **51**: 243-252.

Suter, R. B. and K. S. Rawson. 1968. Circadian activity rhythm in the Deer Mouse, *Peromyscus:* Effect of deuterium oxide. *Science,* **160**: 1011-1014.

Sweeney, B. M. 1961. The photosynthetic rhythm in single cells of *Gonyaulax polyedra. In*: A. Chovnick (ed.). *Biological Clocks.* Cold Spring Harbor Symposium on Quantitative Biology, **25**: 145-148.

———. 1969. *Rhythmic Phenomena in Plants.* Academic Press, New York.

——— and J. W. Hastings. 1958. Rhythmic cell division in populations of *Gonyaulax polyedra. J. Protozoology,* **5**: 217-224.

U.S. Department of Health, Education and Welfare. 1970. Biological rhythms in psychiatry and medicine. Public Health Service Publication No. 2088.

9 The Biology of Aggression: Evolution and Physiology

D. D. THIESSEN
DEPARTMENT OF PSYCHOLOGY
University of Texas

Introduction

There is a great breadth of scientific information on aggression. It is a topic of utmost importance and one which is receiving a great deal of attention. Despite its deserved emphasis, the fact is that relatively few species have been studied in any detail, and few secure generalizations have surfaced. Scott (1971) has suggested that agonistic behavior is of recent origin because it has been detected only in some species of arthropods and vertebrates. This may be true, but on the other hand, if aggression is considered as only one form of competition (a highly personalized one), then aggression can be traced to the earliest interaction of molecules and their competition for survival.

Even considering the most personalized aggression, where teeth and claws meet in battle, there are many forms, each with different functions. There are inter-male confrontations, pain- and fear-induced aggression, predatory aggression, territorial defense, maternal aggression, and learned attacks (Moyer, 1971). Obviously, selection pressures are different on each form of aggression. Moreover, physiological mechanisms are likely

The writing of this chapter was supported by NIMH Research Grant MH 14076-05, Career Development Award MH 111-74, NSF-USDP Research Grant GU-1598, and MH 19750 Isozyme Techniques.

to be different. For example, Flynn and his colleagues (Wasman and Flynn, 1962; Egger and Flynn, 1963) demonstrated that the predatory attack of a cat on a rat is elicited by stimulation of the lateral hypothalamus, and that irritable aggression, but not predatory behavior, is evoked by stimulation of the medial hypothalamus. As a matter of fact, there is some doubt that "pure" aggression in primates can be stimulated at all without associated pain (Plotnik et al., 1971), although there are isolated reports that seem to disassociate the two (Delgado, 1968, 1969; Mark and Ervin, 1970). In any case, it is imperative to define clearly the types of aggression being considered, its physiological bases, and possible involvement in Darwinian fitness.

This chapter focuses on recent evolutionary and physiological studies of aggression which are apt to set the tenor of research for years to come. It is not meant to be an exhaustive review but only a background against which developments in these areas can be outlined. Hence, a great deal of interesting work is omitted. Ethological approaches are not highlighted, because in some sense they form a part of all species investigations and will continue to do so. Discussions of cultural influences in man are also omitted. They are assumed to be important, and it is the opinion of the author that the most rapid understanding of aggression will follow increased knowledge in the genetic and physiological areas. For similar reasons, there is no discussion of studies which attempt to modify aggression by the use of reinforcement procedures. It is hoped that eventually the discoveries unearthed in genetic and physiological investigations will have applicability for the greater understanding of these related concerns. Readers interested in more details can find further reading in the references.

As I view the area, there are three major themes of research that can be projected into the future: 1) competition and gene flow; 2) development of aggression and gene expression; and 3) physiological control of aggression in man and other species. In total, they represent some of what we know or need to know about aggression and suggest the trends of tomorrow. Unfortunately, each of these categorical research areas has developed somewhat independently, and is, therefore, most easily discussed separately. One of the greatest challenges for the future will be to merge these investigations and place them all within the context of evolution. Then, and only then, will the biology of aggression be completely understood.

Competition and Gene Flow

Populations are rarely static and almost never homogeneous. Instead, they shift widely in genetic character, display large amounts of polymorphism, and respond rapidly to ecological demands. It is becoming clear that the theory of gene frequency equilibria, which was devised to characterize stable populations, is hopelessly inadequate in explaining population dynamics, and has absolutely nothing to say about behavioral mechanisms that control gene frequency and the vagabondage of genes from place to place.

It is only recently that concepts of gene architecture and gene flow within and between populations have taken on significance for the understanding of social groups and behavior. Or, to put it more properly in the inverse: Recent studies of behavior are offering the keys to the understanding of gene structure and flow. Animals are mobile and adjust their behavior to existing contingencies; hence, behavior will specify which genes are subjected to natural selection and which genes are screened for representation in the next generation.

This observation can be reduced to two related projections: 1) The study of behavior will be one of the most eminent disciplines of the future, and 2) behavioral principles will finally emerge to integrate most of the existing and subsequently discovered biological facts, including those of genetics, biochemistry, and sociology. In particular, an understanding of competitive behavior (be it a matter of differential adaptation to available commodities or overt aggression) will provide the focus for marshalling concepts ranging from macromolecules to urban living.

Already, there are definite signs of these trends with strong implications for future research. Notions are unfolding to the effect that gene dispersal depends almost entirely on successful competition and, further, that the propensity for migration is determined by the character of social organization and individual class status. Man is apparently no exception to this generalization, although, of course, the precipitating factors are more complex and obscure.

What follows is an attempt to specify thrusts in research that appear to touch on issues of consequence for the greater understanding of competitive behavior as a prime determinant of population structure and function. For the most part, the studies represent new approaches that are incomplete in their development but which seem to make surface contact with the problems that must be solved before aggression can be understood or judiciously controlled.

Competitive Success and Gene Dispersal

All species have at least one dispersal phase in their lifetime (Wynne-Edwards, 1962). With insects and wingless larvae, dispersal usually occurs in the adult stage. Sessile marine organisms almost always disperse in the larval condition, usually by the action of current drift. Many mammalian species scatter in adolescence, and even highly territorial species, such as some species of mammals and birds, usually have a juvenile period of distribution before territories are assumed.

In almost no case is dispersal entirely passive, and for almost all species examined, behavior either initiates movement or carries migration through to completion.

> Small species with poor power of locomotion may rely on wind or other agencies. With them, adaptation may take the form of behavior patterns which enable them to become airborne and an enormous fecundity that offsets the great destruction of life inevitable with this method of dispersal. With larger species, better equipped with organs of locomotion, special instincts may be involved, conferring on the individual a high capacity for searching. This makes for less wastage, but even so, the urge for dispersal may be stronger than the instincts for the preservation of the individual. (Andrewartha and Birch, 1954)

Usually, but not always, dispersion has been linked to competition for limited resources. The notion that two species cannot indefinitely inhabit the same area if they require the same resources goes back to Grinnell in 1904 and Gause in 1934 (Ayala, 1970). The most inclusive formulation states that two species, with identical needs, cannot inhabit the same niche. One or the other species will generally prevail. There is, thus, considerable selection for successful competition, and if that fails, there is selection for the use of different resources, and possibly migratory mechanisms.

Qualification is needed here as there are several instances on record for long-term coexistence of species (Ayala, 1970). Generally in these cases, however, competitive advantage will oscillate between species with one showing short-term advantage followed by the other. One explanation proposed for competitive oscillation is this: As one species gains ascendency in competition, there is reduced selection for interspecies competition and an increased selection for intraspecies competition. Similarly, as the opposing species declines in numbers, there is within it a reduced selection for intraspecies competition and an increased selection for interspecies competition. In other words, selection is toward whichever element poses the greater threat. Any competitive advantage of one species over another which is gained through numerical increases is gradually lost as a result of opposing selection pressures to compete successfully with local members. Thus, frequency-dependent shifts in population size occur and species remain in coexistence.[1] The last possibility is that long-term coexistence depends upon oscillating shifts in niche advantage, at one time favoring one species and then the other.

It still remains evident, however, that competition is generally stimulated by basic needs.

> Whatever the competitive technique used . . . whether direct aggression, territoriality, nonaggressive "scrambling," or something else . . . the ultimate limiting resource is usually food. Although the documentation for this statement is still thin enough to be authoritatively disputed, there still seem to be enough well-established cases to justify its provisional acceptance as a statistical inference. It is also true, however, that a minority of examples involve other limiting resources: growing space in barnacles and other sessile marine invertebrates; nesting sites in the pied fly catcher and Scottish ants; resting places of high moisture in salamanders and of shade in the mourning chat in African deserts; nest materials in rocks and herons. (Wilson, 1971)

In some cases, however, populations seem to scatter in anticipation of needs, rather than as a direct result of needs. Social behavior may be an

1. It is interesting to speculate that the frequency-dependent mating in *Drosophila,* described by Petit (1958) and Ehrman (1969), involves similar fluctuations in competitive advantage. In competitive strains, the less frequent type, especially of males, is more successful in mating. As one genotype increases in number, there is a resultant selection pressure which favors a less frequent genotype and an oscillating polymorphism emerges. Changes in mating advantage may be an evolutionary mechanism to foster polymorphism, and an illustration of shifts in reproductive advantage due to interse and intrase gene competition.

important factor here. In either case, the distribution of genes and the establishment of new colonies assure the continuation of the species and allow genetic differentiation among scattered populations.

Social behavior often appears to be the pivot around which genes spread across the landscape or are lost for all time. Thus, its study, within an evolutionary context, is of enormous importance. To date, however, research psychologists and ethologists who have studied social behavior have not coordinated their efforts, nor have they indicated how species-specific social displays affect the genetic constitution of populations. In short, the outlines of evolutionary progression, so clearly defined by Darwin (1859), Dobzhansky (1970), Mayr (1970), and others, lack information on the behavioral mechanisms that guide much of the destiny of species.

The course of events is changing and will be greatly accelerated in the next quarter century. Remarkably, a growing surge of research on social restrictions of gene flow is following the development of electrophoretic separation of serum and tissue proteins by A. Tiselius in 1937 (*see* Brewer, 1970, for the history of the development). It is now possible to identify a host of isozymes (enzymes of different form which catalyze the same reaction) and designate these as polymorphic markers to study gene frequency and gene flow. Using this simple technique, Selander (1970) and his colleagues have shown that allelic frequency among large numbers of mice (*Mus musculus*), living in barns, is not randomly distributed but shows mosaic clustering. The clustering of particular isozyme patterns appears to correspond to family or tribe unity and is not at all associated with physical barriers. Mice tend to subdivide into inbreeding units consisting of one dominant male, several adolescents, and several submissive males (Reimer and Petras, 1967). Apparently, what Selander is observing is a compacting of related genes by a single male who does all of the breeding and prevents migrants from entering or leaving his territory.

As interesting as these experiments are, the use of genetic markers to determine parentage may have its drawbacks, especially in long-range experiments. Isozymes, enzyme variants which are often considered to be neutral in their evolutionary effect, may be under continual natural selection. In an experiment by Powell (1971), several populations of *D. Willistone* were maintained in cages that had relatively constant or varied environments (e.g., variations in the type of food and temperature). After 45 weeks, 22 protein loci were assessed in these populations by starch gel electrophoresis to assess gene variation. The amount of poly-morphism found in the most homogeneous environment suggested that the degree of genetic variation was proportional to the variable nature of the environment and, hence, to the total strength of natural selection. It is, therefore, possible that group polymorphism may reflect ecological selection pressures more than it does genetic drift and social cast systems. While investigators who are doing short-range laboratory experiments may almost totally disregard selection influences, those doing long-range laboratory experiments or field studies will have to take these into account.

Indeed, laboratory studies are lending verification to what has been seen in the natural environment, namely, that dominant and territorial holding animals regulate the genetic attributes of the population. More-over, these investigations are beginning to pinpoint the details of compe-tion that shift gene frequency and canalize gene flow.

DeFries and McClearn (1970) have recently conducted a provocative study of social dominance in *Mus musculus* that assuredly will become a prototype for future experiments. Triads of interconnected cages were seeded with three males and three females of various strains who were allowed several days to work out a social hierarchy and mate. The strains were selected in such a way that the coat color of the resulting offspring immediately revealed the paternity. After two weeks, the males were re-moved, and the females were allowed to have their litters without inter-ference. Of the several males tested with BALB/c females, including BALB/c, A, C57BL, DBA, I and C3H males, the BALB/c and A animals tended to be dominant. In one reported example, dominance was quickly established, and this ascendency was clearly associated with reproductive fitness. Of the 61 litters obtained, 92% were sired by the dominant male. Replications of this experiment comparing other strains, led to similar results. Based on these findings, the investigators suggest that the *effective breeding population* in demes of mice is equal to one and that the *effective* rate of ingression by subordinate animals may be as low as 3%. As far as I am aware, this is the first controlled experi-ment using a clear-cut criterion of paternity that offers precise estimates of Darwinian fitness in social interactions. No doubt other such experi-ments will begin to provide information about the mechanisms of gene control within, and between, populations.

Dr. Joseph Horn of the University of Texas has recently coupled the use of inbred strains of mice with electrophoretic markers, blood esterase, and hemoglobin in the investigation of social aggression and reproductive fitness (unpublished). Males from RF/J, BALB/cJ, DBA2/J, and C57BL/6J strains are all distinctive in their isozyme patterns and, when mated with C57BL/J females, produce unique electrophoretic bands in F_1 offspring. Thus, when isozymes from the offspring are identified, their paternal origins are immediately known.

When 5 males from each of these 4 strains and 20 C57BL/6 females were placed in a semi-natural environment, it became apparent from isozyme analyses of F_1 pups that RF males sired 97% of the offspring. Also, they engaged in over 42% of all observed fights and won 93% of these. In other words, RF males were the most aggressive and contributed overwhelmingly to the next generation of offspring. Interestingly, when the RF line was not involved, the BALB/c males emerged as most aggressive but, in this case, did not sire any of the offspring. Under these circumstances, high aggression apparently limited the time spent in reproductive activities. Several questions which were generated by these experiments are now under study. In any case, it is obvious that aggression and reproductive fitness are not necessarily identical.

The techniques developed by Horn are indeed portentous for future experiments. While it can be argued that these studies are somewhat artificial and that inbred strains are hardly representative of wild populations, they do offer certain advantages. Genes can be traced through generations with maximal control over the characteristics of the population. It is also possible to study the interactions between aggression, genotype, and Darwinian fitness. It is already clear that social dominance and reproductive fitness are complicated interplays between genotypes and levels of aggression. Additional experiments of this kind will help clarify these relationships and suggest what to look for in the natural environment.

John J. Christian (1970) has recently emphasized the possible influence of social dominance as a stimulus for the migration of subordinate animals and the colonization of new regions. Indeed, "social migration" could be the primary cause of genetic isolation and differentiation in highly mobile species. However, as Miklos Udvardy (1970) points out, unless migratory animals are geographically isolated from the core group, isolation barriers may not be strong enough to prevent reciprocal gene flow and significant genetic mixing.

In fact, the seeming inconsistency of findings between DeFries and his co-workers and Horn and his associates may be explained in this manner. As noted above, DeFries and McClearn found that the BALB strain did a large proportion of the mating; whereas, Horn and his colleagues found that its aggression was so intense that mating was nearly precluded. Had Horn's subordinate males been able to retire to a defined area out of immediate reach of the dominant males, then, perhaps, the BALB males would have been more successful in mating.[2] Before this question and that posed by Udvardy can be resolved, it will be necessary to demonstrate that social behavior can lead to geographical isolation and differential mating.

We have devised a model situation in our laboratory which may help explain how submissive animals become isolated. Essentially, what we have done is to introduce male and female gerbil (*Meriones unguiculatus*) intruders, one at a time, into a territory that is occupied by a resident pair and provide the intruders an opportunity to swim across a water barrier (an aquarium) to a safe unoccupied territory.

What we found is that the test animals will not swim unless provoked by territorial aggression. When the intruder is introduced to the resident pair, fighting immediately breaks out. In two separate experiments involving 48 intruders, we found that approximately 58% migrated within 24 hours, 18% drowned in their attempt, 20% were killed before they could exit, and only about 10% remained in the resident's territory. Even those that remained were still under attack after 24 hours. Clearly, territorial aggression is a potent impetus for migration. From what evidence we have, it would seem that the migrants would never mate in the occupied territory and would remain isolated.

Olfactory cues from the original territory may reinforce this isolation, discouraging the intruders from swimming back. In a replication of the above experiment, we have found that social migrants will avoid odors from the territory they were defeated in. In these experiments, migrants were given a choice between a cage containing soiled shavings and feces from the residents' territory and a cage that contained clean shavings. The interconnected cages were constructed in such a way that the animals could not come into physical contact with the shavings, but could only smell them. Under these conditions, 9 of the 14 migrants nested in the

2. An alternative possibility is that the levels of aggression and reproductive capacity depend upon the genotypic arrangement of the population.

cage containing clean shavings, 2 chose the fouled cage, and 3 others showed no clear choice. Control non-migrant animals that never encountered the residents did not show a preference for either cage. Olfactory signals from territorial-dominant animals may, therefore, reinforce avoidance behavior and help insure that reproductive isolation is complete.

We are continuing our work on isolating mechanisms to more conclusively demonstrate that territorial isolation is equivalent to reproductive isolation. Isozyme variations in plasma and tissue offer markers by which we can identify parents and populations. Using starch gel electrophoresis, we have identified an allelic variant, alpha-glycerophosphate dehydrogenase, which may serve our purposes. Once the mode of inheritance is worked out for this enzyme, it should be possible to track gene flow and differentiation between populations.

There is no clear-cut way to estimate what future research efforts will bring. Almost certainly, though, there will be greater attention given to species-specific behavior in, as well as out of, the laboratory. Precise definitions of reproductive fitness will emerge, and the importance of competition in structuring genetic and phenotypic communities will become more evident. To a great extent, evolutionary principles are already propounded and commonly accepted. What remains to be done is to specify the mechanisms that operate to bring about the end result. More than likely, a search for behavioral variation among individuals and populations which acts to enhance reproductive fitness will allow us to decipher several of the cryptic pathways of evolution.

Future advances will depend heavily on techniques, especially those that allow estimates of gene frequency and those that can code animals for social status and Darwinian fitness. Tracking of animals with radiotelemetry is one such method and will be further exploited. This method, however, is expensive and cannot be used for massive population studies. The labelling of individuals *and* populations is possible with the use of electrophoretically derived isozyme patterns and offers a solid base for future studies. This technique, coupled with coat color markers, the use of homogeneous and heterogeneous populations of animals and the development of other tagging devices, such as the injection of radioactive material and fluorescent compounds, will increase our ability to trace behavior as it shapes the gene pool. Finally, it may become possible to monitor much behavior in the field by electronically recording activity from critical stations within restricted territories. Whatever the future brings in the way of techniques, it is certain that advances will be made to the degree that social status can be detected and individual breeding coefficients determined.

Habitat and Conspecific Preferences as Isolating Mechanisms

Any complete theory of competition and perturbation of gene frequency must take into account the fact that most animals do aggregate peacefully, if only for the purpose of mating. Aggression and competition for resources will parcel genes into distinct configurations, but other forces act to stabilize populations, tribes, families, and cohorts. Clearly, the need for certain food stuffs, an optimal temperature range, shelter, and other physical requirements will act as foci for aggregation. Other than this, however, there is growing evidence that compatibility often hinges on strictly behavioral adjustments. Evidently, normal aggressive tendencies must be in part (and at critical times) superceded by positive attractions to areas and conspecifics.

The further study of habitat selection is likely to reveal reasons why animals congregate in delimited areas and, hence, fail to disperse randomly. For example, Mainardi (1968) and others have demonstrated non-random oviposition in female *Drosophila melanogaster*. This behavior is guided by scents from places where egg laying has occured previously. The net effects are to restrict hatching sites and cause gregarious association among certain genotypes. Harris (1952) and Wecher (1964) also describe habitat selection by *Peromyscus* mouse strains. Prairie and woodland species display a clear preference for an artificial habitat closely matching their natural environment. And, of course, there are numerous examples where prey and predator species select backgrounds where they are least conspicuous (Cott, 1940; Wickler, 1968).

The point is that individuals and species pick environments compatible with their survival and, in doing so, tend to aggregate in circumscribed regions. Gene flow is, therefore, curtailed. There is also a relationship between physical distance and the probability that populations will carry identical genes by descent. This is true in man as well as other species (Cavalli-Sforza, 1959).

We might note that in man the frequency with which marriage partners are born at various distances from one another reflects a dispersal pattern for man that is similar to that of flies. The logarithm of the frequencies of marriage decreases linearly with the square root of distance between the marriage partners. (Wallace, 1968)

Contrary to anecdotal reports, familiarity with conspecifics and environments breeds compatibility, not contempt:

Evidence indicates that attachments within species are deeply influenced by early social experience. Mainardi reported that normal orange fruitflies (*Drosophila melanogaster*) court orange females when given a choice between orange and yellow females. Individuals reared in isolation, however, do not discriminate between orange and yellow females, and court the one as often as the other. Pinckney and Andrews reared guppies (*Lebistes reticulatus*) in groups and in isolation. They found that isolated subjects tended to avoid other fish during the early stages of testing, but eventually they increased the amount of time spent near display guppies and behaved like normal fish. The rat which has been regarded as having a minimal social life, is also not free from the social effects of experience. Latane, observing pairs of rats in an open field test, found that the average distance between the rats of each pair decreased with time. The study confirms others, in which it is consistently found that attraction between rats increases over successive experiences.

While imprinting is more likely to occur as the result of attachment between individuals of the same species, exposures to members of a different species are no less powerful. (Zojonc, 1971)

These illustrations could be multiplied many fold. Ants of various species identify members of their own colony by odors unique to these colonies (Wilson, 1971). Species of voles will choose their own species-specific odors when the odors are presented in a choice situation (Godfrey, 1958). Female mice are attracted to preputial material from males, especially when they have had sexual experience (Caroom and Bronson, 1971). Rats even learn to prefer the music of Mozart or Schoenberg, if they are exposed to the music for long periods of time (Cross et al., 1967). And, humans increase their preference for pictures of strangers and foreign languages as the length of exposure is increased (Zojonc, 1971).

It is also possible to reverse habitat preference and sexual attraction by altering the experience of individuals in early life. Wecher (1964) was able to attenuate the normal *Peromyscus* preference for field environments by raising animals in the laboratory for several generations. When *Mus musculus* are raised with perfumed parents, they tend to prefer similarly perfumed mice at a later age (Mainardi et al., 1965). And, of course, instances are known in which early imprinting on inappropriate species can lead to later sexual abnormalities (Sluckin, 1965). The extreme instance, perhaps, is the demonstration by Cairns (1966) that lambs' affectional responses can be manipulated so that ewes, dogs, and television sets are equally attractive.

Hence, we have strong evidence that species and populations show preference for sites and other individuals in accord with their heritage *and* early experience. Habitat selection can be partially built into the genetic blueprint, and it can be reinforced or attenuated by experience. Similarly, individuals may show a genetically determined attraction for other members of their species, or they can learn to accept strangers. In any case, it appears that individuals, populations, and species are variously programmed to exhibit a high degree of positive affiliation among local members, as well as strong site attachment.

What we do not know is the degree to which these behavioral adjustments stimulate inbreeding and provide genetic insulation between adjacent populations. This would seem to be one of the major problems for future exploration. Territorial behavior and social exclusion may be significant mechanisms for promoting gene flow, but they are also mechanisms for binding individuals to specific locales and individuals. The question still remains as to what effects these activities have on reproductive isolation and gene flow.

Certainly, aggregation not only binds individuals together but also increases hostility between neighboring groups. Wolfe and Summerlin (1968), for example, have shown that captured cotton rats (*Sigmondon hispidus*) show more agonistic behavior toward conspecifics trapped at greater distances from them than toward those trapped at shorter distances. Moreover, we have already discussed the fact that mating frequency between individuals decreases linearly with the square root of the distance between them. No doubt physical distance, site attachment, and group identification act as powerful agents of aggression and gene dispersal, but to what degree is anybody's guess. Can such environmental and social "locks" isolate populations to the extent necessary to cause speciation? Does site attachment result in significant inbreeding depression? And, what are the evolutionary and mechanistic reasons that keep populations isolated, but not completely? Only a fine-grained analysis of social behavior, within the framework of evolutionary theory, will provide the answers.

Aggression and Gene Expression

Relatively few genes participate directly in physiological and behavioral processes. Many are probably quiescent except during critical periods of development or when called upon by specific cellular processes. Periodic gene expression may be the essence of scheduled development and fine-tuning of physiological regulation. Gene flexibility is evident in so many processes that it would not be surprising to find that many behaviors, especially the more volatile ones like aggression, are under the influence of regulatory genes. Some evidence to support this notion is beginning to accumulate although we are a long way from explaining aggression in molecular terms. Nevertheless, as I view the area, the molecular approach represents one of the most promising avenues of exploration.

Several areas of investigation are converging on the idea that the dynamic control of aggression is rooted in gene control. First, there is the substantial evidence that genes determine aggressive differences among strains of mice, rats, and other species, and that aggression can be artificially selected to reach new levels. Second, there is a new surge of research suggesting that the hormones of aggression in mammalian species act by engaging new genes in the central nervous system. Third, there is a growing body of information to link sensory input to the production of unique forms of macromolecules. Fourth, there are several genetic abnormalities known which can change the normal sequence of development and behavior. More than likely, the most profitable research on aggression (as well as related functions) lies in this direction.

Eleftheriou (1971) has recently tied macromolecular changes in selected sites of the nervous system of the mouse to aggression and defeat. Briefly, what he finds in C57BC/6J male mice, subjected to fighting bouts, is an elevation of RNA-ase activity in both the hypothalamus and amygdala. These two areas have repeatedly been implicated in aggression. RNA, on the other hand, drops significantly in these same areas, whereas the frontal cortex and cerebellum display no regular changes in either RNA-ase or RNA. With repeated fighting exposures, there is a tendency for the changes to reverse themselves. It is not clear if the initial periods of aggression affect the genome directly, but that might be the case. With the exception of the cerebellum, all areas exhibited a nucleotide base ratio change. Specifically, there was a decline in the $G + C/A + U$ ratio. Eleftheriou believes that the base ratio changes represent an increased synthesis of messenger RNA, and thus must involve new DNA transcription.

Interestingly, Eleftheriou also implicated dopamine, corticosterone, serotonin, testosterone, and estrogen in RNA-ase, RNA and base ratio changes. In a rather complex way that is difficult to interpret at the moment, all of these biochemicals, when injected, elevated or depressed macromolecular activity. These same bioamines and steroids have been associated with aggression by other investigators (Welch and Welch, 1971), suggesting a chain of action running from aggression to biochemical modification and genetic expression.

The differentiation of aggression by testosterone implies that hormones restructure the brain in profound ways. Edwards (1968) found that 500 μg of testosterone propionate administered to female mice on the day of birth resulted in fighting in over 95% of the females when they were ovariectomized and given testosterone as adults. In a later report by this same investigator (Edwards, 1969), it was found that if the hormone was given on day 10 of life, the organizational effect was much weaker. Bronson and Desjardins (1971) have replicated both of these observations and, in addition, have shown that masculinization of females with testosterone shows a dose-response relation with the amount of hormone injected at birth. As expected, males castrated at birth evidence little aggression, regardless of the presence of testosterone as adults.

Hence, with mice at least, androgen seems to organize the brain in the male direction for aggression in much the same way that it does for sex behavior. A critical period for the effects is evident although the length of this period seems to vary with hormone dosage (Peters, 1972). At this time, we cannot discount the possibility that androgen has significant peripheral effects as well. It is anabolic and could increase body weight and muscle mass to such an extent that fighting is more likely. A similar argument has been proposed for the androgenization effects on penis size and mating ability in rats (Beach, 1971). Nevertheless, the weight of the evidence is toward accepting a central organizing effect of androgen on aggressive and sexual processes.

An extremely exciting possibility is that androgen organizes aggression by affecting gene activity during ontogeny. Bronson and Desjardins (1971) cite evidence that early testosterone treatment in rats produces long-lasting changes in species of RNA and that at least one index of androgenization, absence of ovulation in adults, can be blocked with the early administration of actinomycin D and puromycin along with testosterone. We are a long way from specifying how androgens organize the brain, but we can look forward to more studies which will help reveal the interaction of hormones, gene action, and protein synthesis.

Vale, Ray, and Vale (1972) have approached the problem of sex differentiation from another angle. Capitalizing on the usual genetic differences in aggression found among strains of mice and between sexes, they have attempted to stimulate aggression in females by injecting them neonatally with testosterone. What they found was that the early androgen treatment of females led to male-like aggression in adults but only in strains where the male normally displayed aggression. In other words, the androgen appeared to uncover aggression only in animals that had genes responsive to androgen. Sex differences in aggression may in part be a function of gene differences, but it is also a function of which genes are stimulated to function.

Apparently, similar effects are observable in man. Erhardt and Money (1970) have investigated 10 girls between 3 and 14 years of age whose mothers had been treated during pregnancy with gestogens having androgenic side effects. Regardless of early sex-typing and identification, 9 of the 10 girls were diagnosed as tomboyish. They engaged in more rough-and-tumble activities and showed heightened preferences for boys' toys and outdoor pursuits. These findings are reminiscent of androgenization effects seen in female rhesus monkeys (Goy, 1966). Again, it would appear that the differentiation of sex differences, including aggression, depends upon hormones acting on the genetic substrate.

Finally, it may be informative to cite some recent experiments from our laboratory on territorial scent marking in the Mongolian gerbil (*Meriones unguiculatus*). Gerbils, especially males, scent mark objects in their environment, using a ventral sebaceous gland. The response is androgen-dependent and occurs more frequently in competitive situations. Castration drastically reduces territorial marking and the behavior can be reinstated with implants of testosterone into the preoptic brain area. Here, "territorial brain cells" appear to react to steroids by producing gene products specific to the behavior. Our evidence is incomplete in this regard, but we do know that actinomycin D which prevents the genetic complex from functioning and puromycin, an antibiotic that precludes protein synthesis, prevent the preoptic cells from responding. Moreover, Pauline Yahr and Robert Sanders at the University of Texas have recently demonstrated a qualitative difference in proteins between preoptic tissue under the stimulation of testosterone and tissue which is not exposed to the hormone. It is, therefore, tempting to suggest that the sequence of action leading to territorial behavior involves the activation of specific genetic material in preoptic cells by testosterone and the production of unique proteins.

Whatever the final outcome of such experiments, it is apparent that the genome of an individual sets the ultimate limits of aggression and stipulates the reactions to cellular events. Necessarily, subsequent investigations will focus on regulatory processes that involve transcription and translation of genetic information. Links between hormone induction of gene action, biochemical changes, and behaviors must be completely described. It may be the case that testosterone acts in mammalian species to form new species of RNA which, in turn, specify enzymes involved in the formation of neural transmitter substances and synaptic transmission.

At the heart of the problem, then, is the need to specify the interactions of these various processes. We need to know how the hormone activates or deactivates genes. New species of RNA must be identified, and the subsequent enzyme and neural transmitter functions will have to be clarified. Finally, it will be necessary to discover how sensory information is relayed to sites where hormones act on the genome and motor processes. In short, what must be elucidated in the study of aggression are the same processes that regulate the most fundamental aspects of cellular function.

The progression of research on aggression will no doubt follow the development and application of new techniques. My guess is that DNA-RNA hybridization experiments, coupled with hormone treatment, will tell us something about the kinds of RNA species that are formed. We should also be able to identify and isolate newly-formed proteins in areas of the brain related to aggression. Several of these proteins are likely to be involved in morphological changes in synapses and other neurological structures. Other proteins will probably have enzymatic functions. Once the "proteins of aggression" are isolated, there is the possibility that antibodies can be developed toward them by immunizing rabbits in the usual way. These antibodies can then be tagged with fluorescent complexes and reinjected into animals in order to identify specific cells that form the relevant proteins. More important is the possibility that various forms of aggression discussed in the introduction are managed by different protein complements and that "aggression-specific" antibodies can be developed. If this can be done, then the control of various aggressive acts by administering unique complexes of antibodies which will compete with critical proteins in the central nervous system is only one step further.

Physiological Control of Aggression in Man

In this last section, I would like to point out that human aggression, like that of other animals, is a product of his natural history. As such, it can also be investigated within a biological context. The fact that man is a cultural animal is not opposed to the proposition that he is also controlled by his biological heritage.

> Thus, the argument that we differ from all other species as a result of the triumph of culture over biology I find false, because culture is an aspect of our biological differences from other species. It is the name for a species which ultimately depends on an organ, the brain, in which we happen to have specialized. Thus differences between ourselves and other primates, for example, do not stem from the fact that we have in some way *overcome* our primate natures, but stem from the fact that we are a different kind of nature. At the levels of forms and processes we behave culturally because it is in our nature to behave culturally, because mutation and natural selection have produced this animal which must behave culturally, must invent rules, make myths, speak languages, and form men's clubs in the same way as the hamadryas baboon has to form harems, adopt infants, and bite his wives on the neck. (Fox, 1971)

In my estimation, the cultural approach to the study of aggression in humans can be profitably augmented by greater concern for genetic and physiological processes. In a recent report on television and violence,

"Television and Growing Up: The Impact of Televised Violence," released by the Surgeon General's Scientific Advisory Committee on Television and Social Behavior (American Psychological Association, 1972), a twelve-member committee reviewed 40 original studies in this area and concluded that:

1) There is a preliminary and tentative relation between viewing violence on television and aggressive behavior.
2) There is an indication that television affects some children but not others.
3) There is an indication that television is influential only in some environments.

The committee advocates more research on the role of personality factors, family and peer attitudes, early experiences, and the effects of different media. Indeed, a recent report seems to leave little doubt that the amount of time children watch TV violence is related to later levels of expressed aggression (Eron et al., 1972). It is not clear, however, either from the report by the Advisory Committee or subsequent investigations, what predisposes some children to react aggressively to TV violence and not others. Neither is it known if early expression can alter aggression by changing hormone levels or other physiological processes. It may be that genetic and physiological studies of individuals and families can reveal how early cultural influences have differential effects.

Research cast entirely within the environmentalistic framework has the danger of taking man out of the biological mainstream of life. Of course, the environment acts on man, but it does so within genetically prescribed limits and through physiological mechanisms. He has been biologically constructed to select out only a certain range of sensory information from the nearly infinite amounts that are around him, and he has been constructed to deal with information only in certain ways.

Work with other species has not been hampered by the same attitudes as those affecting man. With the former, evolutionary theory is an accepted format for investigating aggression, and genetic and physiological processes are better understood every day. For this reason, the advancement of knowledge at this level does not depend so much on attitudes as it does on the development of new techniques and a refinement of measurements. With man, in contrast, future advancements hinge on accepting man as a product of natural selection and determining the ways in which experiences interact with genetic elements and physiological processes to stipulate his phenotype. Here is a primary problem for future decades in the search for the reasons of man's aggression.

The understanding of man's brain and its programming ability poses one of the most significant areas of research in the future. Frontiers are being pressed at the moment. For example, several years ago King (1961) described a patient with an electrode implanted into the amygdala who, when stimulated, became verbally aggressive and threatening. Mark and Ervin (1970) have reported similar effects in patients admitted to the hospital for violent episodes. In one case:

> . . . electrical stimulation of the amygdala initiated rage and violence; second: this behavior was preceded by the development of local electrical epileptic seizures. We are not maintaining that the amygdala—nor, indeed, the limbic system—is the only part of the brain involved in violent behavior. Our strands of electrodes are able to give us only a limited view of activity within the central nervous system, and other (perhaps many) areas of the brain must have been involved to produce such well-organized behavioral patterns. However, there can be no doubt that the electrical stimulation of and the abnormal seizure activity from the amygdala preceded and was directly related to Julia's violence. To our knowledge, this is the first time that rage behavior was artificially produced by electrical stimulation in an abnormal brain and used to diagnose the proper placement for a therapeutic lesion. (Mark and Ervin, 1970)

Indeed, when bilateral destruction of the amygdala is accomplished, patients with psychomotor epilepsy and tendencies toward aggressive behavior often show striking improvements. Such operations have now been reported in Japan, India, Mexico, France, and Denmark, as well as in the United States. Both the stimulation and lesion effects are similar to those found in a variety of species by other investigators (Delgado, 1964; Kaada, 1967; Wasman and Flynn, 1962), suggesting that what is found with humans is not unique or limited to abnormal brains.

What is unique in stimulation studies is the content of aggressive expression. Human-like aggression is not evoked by brain stimulation of the cat, rat, or monkey, nor does the reverse obtain. Each species displays its own characteristic form of aggression. Moreover, each individual reacts according to its own background of experience. A socially-submissive rhesus monkey will not direct its attack toward a dominant individual but toward other objects, and a human will attack verbally and behaviorally according to his usual modes of expression. The behavioral content reflects both the genetic blueprint of the organism and the social assimilation of the individual.

Genetic abnormalities which affect sexual differentiation in humans offer additional keys to the understanding of aggression. Several such anomalies exist, one of the most interesting of which is the XYY syndrome. The addition of an extra Y chromosome in male karyotypes not only alters the whole course of development in a significant number of individuals carrying the genotype but also alters a wide array of characteristics. In a well-conducted study of XYY individuals in prisons by Griffiths and his associates (1970), it was found that this chromosome anomaly resulted in reduced verbal and performance IQ, lowered achievement relative to fathers and brothers, asocial and aggressive personality traits, and inclinations toward homosexuality. The control group for this study was an equal number of randomly assigned prisoners. If, as expected, the deviations due to the extra Y chromosome focus around increased secretions of male sex hormones during early or later life, then the wide array of proliferating effects implicates another bridge between gene activity and functional differentiation of aggression (Heller, 1969).

It seems probable that androgen is the hormone that regulates the intensity of sexual drive and aggression in both men and women (Gadpaille, 1972). The relation of androgen to sex behavior is better understood, although future investigations will probably document its influence on aggression as well. It has been demonstrated that the use of androgen-depleting substances, like estrogen, cyproterone acetate, methyloestrenolone, and medroxyprogesterone, decreases aggressive sex drives in male sex criminals (Money, 1970). Should this type of therapy prove beneficial with other types of aggression, the importance of androgen in the regulation of aggression will be established and effective measures for control will be extended.

The above examples are only part of the increasing move toward the study of biology of human aggression. Other brain areas have been explored, and certainly much more of this kind of work will be done. In addition, investigations of the hormonal control of aggression will assume more importance, as will studies of genetic abnormalities, such as with XYY males. Finally, the study of man may eventually reveal the functional significance of aggression and the part it plays in reproduction and gene flow.

References

American Psychological Association. 1972. J. Warren (ed.). *Amer. Psychol. Ass. Monit.*, **3**(3).

Andrewartha, H. G. and L. C. Birch. 1954. *The Distribution and Abundance of Animals.* University of Chicago Press, Chicago.

Ayala, F. J. 1970. Competition, coexistence, and evolution. *In*: M. K. Hecht and W. C. Steere (eds.). *Essays in Evolution and Genetics.* Appleton-Century-Crofts, New York. p. 121-158.

Beach, F. A. 1971. Hormonal factors controlling the differentiation, development, and display of copulatory behavior in the ramstergig and related species. *In*: E. Tobach, L. R. Aronson, and E. Shaw (eds.). *The Biopsychology of Development.* Academic Press, New York. p. 249-296.

Brewer, G. J. 1970. *An Introduction to Isoenzyme Techniques.* Academic Press, New York.

Bronson, F. H. and C. Desjardins. 1971. Steroid hormones and aggressive behavior in mammals. *In*: B. E. Eleftheriou and J. P. Scott (eds.). *The Physiology of Aggression and Defeat.* Plenum Press, New York. p. 43-63.

Cairns, R. B. 1966. Attachment behavior of mammals. *Psychol. Rev.,* **73**: 409.

Caroom, D., and F. H. Bronson. 1971. Responsiveness of female mice to preputial attractant: Effects of sexual experience and ovarian hormones. *Physiol. and Behav.,* **7**: 659.

Cavalli-Sforza, L. L. 1959. Some data on the genetic structure in human populations. *Proc. Tenth Int. Congr. Genet.,* **1**: 389.

Christian, J. J. 1970. Social subordination, population density and mammalian evolution. *Science,* **170**: 84.

Cott, H. B. 1940. *Adaptive Coloration in Animals.* Methuen, London. (Reprinted in 1966.)

Cross, M., A. Holcomb, and C. G. Matter. 1967. Imprinting or exposure learning in rats given early auditory stimulation. *Psychon. Sci.,* **7**: 233.

Darwin, C. 1859. *On the Origin of Species by Means of Natural Selection or the Preservation of Favored Races in the Struggle for Life.* John Murray, London.

DeFries, J. C. and G. E. McClearn. 1970. Social dominance and Darwinian fitness in the laboratory mouse. *Amer. Natur.,* **104**: 408.

Delgado, J. M. R. 1964. Free behavior and brain stimulation. *Int. Rev. Neurobiolog.,* **6**: 349.

————. 1968. Electrical stimulation of the limbic system. *Proc. XXIV Int. Congr. Physiol. Sci.*, **6**: 222.

————. 1969. *Physical Control of the Mind.* Harper and Row, Inc., New York.

Dobzhansky, T. 1970. *Genetics of the Evolutionary Process.* Columbia University Press, New York.

Edwards, D. E. 1968. Mice: Fighting by neonatally androgenized females. *Science,* **160**: 1027.

————. 1969. Early androgen stimulation and aggressive behavior in male and female mice. *Physiol. and Behav.,* **4**: 333.

Egger, M. D. and J. P. Flynn. 1963. Effect of electrical stimulation of the amygdala on hypothalamically elicited attack behavior in cats. *J. Neurophysiol.,* **26**: 705.

Ehrman, L. 1969. The sensory basis of mate selection in *Drosophila. Evolution,* **23**: 59.

Eleftheriou, B. E. 1971. Effects of aggression and defeat on brain macromolecules. *In*: B. E. Eleftheriou and J. P. Scott (eds.). *The Physiology of Aggression and Defeat.* Plenum Press, New York. p. 65-90.

Erhardt, A. A. and J. Money. 1970. Cited by F. Neumann, H. Steinbeck, and J. D. Hahn. *In*: L. Martini, M. Motta, and F. Fraschini (eds.). *The Hypothalamus.* Academic Press, New York. p. 569-603.

Eron, L. D., L. R. Huesmann, M. M. Lefkowitz, and L. O. Walder. 1972. Does television violence cause aggression? *Amer. Psychol.,* **27**: 253.

Fox, R. 1971. The cultural animal. *In*: J. F. Eisenberg and W. S. Dillon (eds.). *Man and Beast: Comparative Social Behavior.* Smithsonian Institution Press, Washington. p. 273-296.

Gadpaille, W. J. 1972. Research into the physiology of maleness and femaleness. *Arch. Gen. Psychol.,* **26**: 193.

Godfrey, J. 1958. The origins of sexual isolation between bank voles. *Proc. Roy. Physiol. Soc., Edinburgh,* **27**: 47.

Goy, R. W. 1966. Role of androgens in the establishment and regulation of behavioral sex differences in mammals. *J. Anim. Sci.,* **25**: 21.

Griffiths, A. W., B. W. Richards, J. Zaremba, T. Abramowicz, and A. Stewart. 1970. Psychological and sociological investigation of XXY prisoners. *Nature,* **277**: 290.

Harris, V. T. 1952. An experimental study of habitat selection by prairie and forest races of the deermouse, *Peromyscus maniculatus. Contrib. Lab. Verteb.,* **56**: 1.

Heller, J. H. 1969. Human chromosome abnormalities as related to physical and mental dysfunction. *J. Hered.,* **60**: 239.

Kaada, B. R. 1967. Brain mechanisms related to aggressive behavior. *In*: C. D. Clemente and D. Lindsley (eds.). *Aggression and defense.* University of California Press, Berkeley. p. 95-133.

King, H. E. 1961. Psychological effects of excitation in the limbic system

In: D. E. Sheere (ed.). *Electrical Stimulation of the Brain.* University of Texas Press, Austin. p. 477-486.

Mainardi, M., D. Marsan, and A. Pasquali. 1965. Causation of sexual preference of the house mouse. The behavior of mice reared by parents whose odour was artificially altered. *Estratto Dagli Atti Della Soc. di Sci. Natur.,* **104**: 326.

————. 1968. Gregarious oviposition and pheromones in *Drosophila melanogaster. Boll. Zool.,* **35**: 135.

Mark, V. H. and F. R. Ervin. 1970. *Violence and the Brain.* Harper and Row, Inc., New York.

Mayr, E. 1970. *Populations, Species and Evolution.* Harvard University Press, Cambridge.

Money, J. 1970. Use of an androgen-depleting hormone in the treatment of male sex offenders. *J. Sex. Res.,* **6**: 165.

Moyer, K. E. 1971. A preliminary physiological model of aggressive behavior. *In*: B. E. Eleftheriou and J. P. Scott (eds.). *The Physiology of Aggression and Defeat.* Plenum Press, New York. p. 223-263.

Peters, P. 1972. Androgen and the development of aggression in mice. Ph.D. Dissertation, University of Texas at Austin.

Petit, C. 1958. *Le Determinisme genetique et psycho-physiologique de la Competition Sexuelle chez* Drosophila melanogaster. *Bull. Biol. France et Belgique,* **99**: 435.

Plotnik, R., D. Mir, and J. M. R. Delgado. 1971. Aggression, noxiousness, and brain stimulation in unrestrained rhesus monkeys. *In*: B. E. Eleftheriou and J. P. Scott (eds.). *The Physiology of Aggression and Defeat.* Plenum Press, New York. p. 143-221.

Powell, J. R. 1971. Genetic polymorphisms in varied environments. *Science,* **174**: 1035.

Reimer, J. D. and M. L. Petras. 1967. Breeding structure of the house mouse, *Mus musculatus. J. Mammal.,* **48**: 88.

Scott, J. P. 1971. Theoretical issues concerning the origin and causes of fighting. *In*: B. E. Eleftheriou and J. P. Scott (eds.). *The Physiology of Aggression and Defeat.* Plenum Press, New York. p. 11-41.

Selander, R. K. 1970. Biochemical polymorphism in populations of the house mouse. *In*: R. J. Berry and H. N. Southern (eds.). *Variation in Mammalian Populations.* Academic Press, New York. p. 73-91.

Sluckin, W. 1965. *Imprinting and Early Learning.* Aldine Publishing Co., Chicago.

Udvardy, M. 1970. Mammalian evolution: Is it due to social subordination? *Science,* **170**: 344.

Vale, J. R., D. Ray, and C. Vale. 1972. The interaction of genotype and exogenous neonatal androgen: Agonistic behavior in female mice. *Behav. Biol.,* **7**. (In press.)

Wallace, B. 1968. *Topics in Population Genetics.* Norton and Co., New York.

Wasman, M. and J. P. Flynn. 1962. Directed attack elicited from the hypothalamus. *Arch. Neurol.,* **6**: 220.

Wecher, S. C. 1964. Habitat Selection. *Sci. Amer.,* **211**: 109.

Welch, A. S. and B. L. Welch. 1971. Isolation, reactivity and aggression: Evidence for an involvement of brain catecholamines and serotonin. *In*: B. E. Eleftheriou and J. P. Scott (eds.). *The Physiology of Aggression and Defeat.* Plenum Press, New York. p. 91-142.

Wickler, W. 1968. *Mimicry.* McGraw-Hill Book Co., New York.

Wilson, E. O. 1971. Competitive and aggressive behavior. *In*: J. F. Eisenberg and W. S. Dillon (eds.). *Man and Beast: Comparative Social Behavior.* Smithsonian Institution Press, Washington. p. 181-217.

Wolfe, J. L. and C. T. Summerlin. 1968. Agonistic behavior of organized and disorganized cotton rat populations. *Science,* **160**: 98.

Wynne-Edwards, V. C. 1962. *Animal Dispersion and Relation to Social Behavior.* Hafner and Co., New York.

Zojonc, R. B. 1971. Attraction, affiliation and attachment. *In*: J. F. Eisenberg and W. S. Dillon (eds.). *Man and Beast: Comparative Social Behavior.* Smithsonian Institution Press, Washington. p. 141-179.

10 The Integrative Approach to Biological Classification

W. FRANK BLAIR
DEPARTMENT OF ZOOLOGY

BILLIE L. TURNER
DEPARTMENT OF BOTANY
University of Texas, Austin

The Past 25 Years

The past 25 years have seen dramatic changes conceptually and in the methodologies of classificatory biology. If we add on about 10 years to take us back to the late 1930s, we can say without exaggeration that in this period there have been more changes in the concepts and practices of systematic phylogenetic biology than there were in the previous history of the science, except for the immediate Darwinian and post-Darwinian period.

There have been parallel advances in evolutionary theory and in the understanding of evolutionary mechanisms, and, in fact, the advances in classificatory biology in this century derive greatly from these and have notably enhanced and broadened its perspective. For example, the concept of the "biological species" (sensu Mayr, 1942 and others) and of isolating mechanisms lays emphasis on a whole spectrum of behavioral and reproductive characters that can be studied and measured only in living specimens, not on preserved specimens in a museum.

However, we are concerning ourselves here with the narrower question of the phylogenetic relationships of the 5 to 10 million species of living organisms. Who is related to whom and to what degree? What is the evolutionary history of the diverse branches of this vast hierarchy? These questions apply at all levels from that of populations, where the question

193

may be one of whether or not two populations may be separate biological species, on up to the higher categories and the degree of their affinity.

Prior to the 1930s, the classification of organisms and the accompanying phylogenetic schemes were based almost exclusively on the degree of similarity of morphological characters of specimens preserved in museums.

The dramatic conceptual change from a classificatory biology oriented toward comparison of readily-observable morphological characters of museum specimens to one that considers the species as a dynamic system (*see* Blair, 1956) and which relies on the measurement of a wide suite of variables in both living and preserved individuals provides the basis for our opening statement about the importance of the past 35 years in classificatory biology.

Significant for the progress of classificatory biology in recent years has been the advance in the technology of measuring various attributes of biological systems. The full list of gadgets and gadgetry would be an impressive one. With respect to the subject at hand, the most significant have been the biochemical techniques of chromatography and electrophoresis for both plants and animals, and for the latter, the techniques of recording vocal signals on magnetic tape and the techniques for quantitative analysis of these signals by oscilloscope and/or sound spectrograph.

New Methodologies

The principal additions to morphological characters in classificatory-phylogenetic studies of animals have been: 1) hybridization experiments to determine the degree of genetic or reproductive compatibility between species and genera, 2) microscopical examination of chromosomes to determine their number and morphology, 3) comparative analyses of various biochemical systems by use of chromatography or electrophoresis, 4) measurement of acoustical signals (= mating calls) and measurement of behavioral responses in those animals which use vocal signals for species identification and as a mate attractant, 5) study of behavioral patterns, especially those related to reproduction, 6) various ecological attributes, and 7) electron microscopy.

For studies of plants the principal methodologies have been: 1) experimental hybridization, 2) chromosomal evidence, 3) biochemical evidence, and 4) the relatively new addition to the list, electron microscopy or ultrastructure.

EXPERIMENTAL HYBRIDIZATION

Experimental garden and laboratory hybridization of both plants and animals has provided much information about degrees of reproductive compatibility, especially as these might relate to genetic differences and similarities.

In general, botanical investigators have had considerably more difficulty than zoologists in applying the results of experimental hybridization to systematic problems, presumably because synthetic crosses are made with relative ease among morphologically remote taxa. In addition, the widespread occurrence of polyploidy in plant groups (Wet, 1970), often of a spontaneous and random nature in an otherwise seemingly homogenous population, makes it difficult to apply compatibility data as an absolute criterion of specific recognition with any degree of conviction. Nevertheless, botanical systematists do use compatibility data, both in experimental crosses and especially as perceived in nature as fundamental to the understanding of species. In short, most plant systematists accept the biological species of Mayr as a conceptual or working base. But they have not been willing to accept the proposal that reproductive compatibilty is necessarily reflective of genetic divergence; indeed, they tend to use the latter as a criterion of speciation, largely for the reasons discussed above and because compatibility in plants may be mediated by single genes, autogamy, facultative chasmogamy and sundry other complicating mechanisms (Grant, 1971).

As with plants, the laboratory hybridization of animals can provide much information about degree of genetic similarity and hence information bearing on phylogenetic relationships. For some kinds of animals (i.e., those with internal fertilization), experimental hybridization involves the action of behavioral-isolating mechanisms as well as the ability of the different genomes to act together to produce an F_1 individual. In some (e.g., many fishes and most anuran amphibians), however, the latter may be tested independently of the former by *in vitro* fertilization since these are normally external fertilizers.

The insect genus *Drosophila* has probably been subjected to the most extensive investigation of genetic compatibility and of behavioral-isolating mechanisms of any group of organisms, thanks particularly to the efforts of J. T. Patterson and Wilson Stone and their students and to those of Theodosius Dobzhansky and his students. For vertebrates the nearest approach would be the work with mice of the genus *Peromyscus* by L. R. Dice (1968) and his students. For vertebrates in which *in vitro* fertilization makes it possible to separate behavioral characters and genetic compatibility, the work of one of us (Blair) and his students has provided a large body of evidence with respect to relationships in anuran amphibians.

A principal result of these hybridization studies has been the identification and confirmation of species groups, the clusters of species that have evolved relatively recently in geologic time. In some instances the results may imply the sequence of separation of species within the species group; e.g., in the *Bufo americanus* group of toads (Blair, 1963b) or the *B. valliceps* group (Blair, 1966).

Another kind of result is the confirmation of affinity and, hence, of evolutionary history of geographically remote taxa. A large group of African toads (*Bufo*) and another group in southern Asia have broad skulls like certain neotropical toads. Does this morphological similarity indicate affinity or convergency? That the African toads have a different chromosome number ($2n = 20$ versus $2n = 22$ in others) might suggest convergence. However, the ability of African and Asian broad-skulled females to produce viable F_1 hybrids when crossed with males of broad-skulled neotropical toads strongly indicates affinity rather than convergence. It now appears that the African and Asian broad-skulled toads represent descendants from an invasion by New World toads in the middle Tertiary (Blair et al., 1972a).

CHROMOSOMAL EVIDENCE

The development of relatively simple squash techniques for the examination of meiotic and mitotic chromosomes during the forties and fifties led to a flurry of cytotaxonomic studies, mostly by botanists since suitable noncultured materials are most readily available in plants. In addition, it became evident, particularly as a result of the detailed chromosomal studies on the plant genus *Crepis* by Babcock (1947) and coworkers, that karotypic information is capable of yielding incisive criteria bearing on the phylogeny of species and genera.

Plant systematists were especially attracted to this approach since one of the first broad compilations of chromosome numbers, *The Chromosome Atlas of Cultivated Plants* by Darlington and Janaki-Ammal (1945), revealed a wide range of chromosomal variation both within and between taxa. Polyploidy, aneuploidy, and karyotypic differences were found in almost every group studied, and the plant taxonomist used these data, in combination with experimental crosses, to construct often sophisticated well-documented generic phylogenies (e.g., on the plant genera *Clarkia,* Lewis and Lewis, 1955; and *Oenothera,* Cleland, 1962). The karyotype in systematics has recently been reviewed by Jackson (1971).

Plant chromosome numbers for literally thousands of species of higher plants have been assembled mostly beginning in the late forties and early fifties (Darlington and Wylie, 1955), by a large number of workers. Publication of annual indices for such counts was soon undertaken (Cave, 1956-64), and these tabulations continue to appear in larger and more prolific editions each year (Ornduff, 1967-69; Moore, 1970-71). At the present writing the junior author estimates that chromosome counts are now available for approximately 40,000 species of plants distributed among more than 6,000 genera.

In general, animal workers have lagged somewhat behind botanists in the systematic application of chromosomal data. But largely due to the introduction of the relatively simple squash techniques for the study of human karyotypes (in part developed on experience with plant materials) by Tjio and Levan (1954), animal systematists have used this approach with increasing frequency.

The greatest amount of usable information in any chromosomes is found in the giant, salivary chromosomes of dipterous flies where it is possible to compare minute details of banding of the chromosomes and to identify rearrangements in the sequence of banding that have resulted from inversions or translocations. Thus, it is possible to trace specific changes (e.g., an inversion) from taxon to taxon and obtain evidence of evolutionary relationship. The powerful tool that this provides for determining relationships of species has been intensively exploited by the "drosophologists" during the past quarter century and to a lesser degree with other groups of Diptera (*see* Patterson and Stone, 1952).

For other kinds of animals, the types of evidence that chromosomes provide include principally: 1) chromosome number, including polyplody, 2) chromosome size, 3) position of the centromere, and 4) position of heterochromatic areas.

The enormous literature on the application of chromosomal data to the systematics of animal groups may be illustrated by reference to the works of White (1954, 1957, 1969 and many others) who has worked largely with Orthoptera. Chromosomes of all major taxa of vertebrates have been investigated, but those of the mammals, lizards, and amphibians have received the most attention. The work with mammalian chromosomes has been summarized in a multi-authored symposium volume edited by Benirschke (1969). The work in anuran amphibians, pioneered by Saez (Saez and Brum, 1959), has been advanced principally by Beçak (Beçak et al., 1970 and various others), Bogard (1967, 1970 and others), and Morescalchi (1968, 1970 and others).

At the very simplest level, the determination of chromosome numbers has revealed dichotomies between morphologically very similar populations. Within the Linnean species *Gryllotalpa gryllotalpa,* populations with 7 different chromosome numbers (2n = 12, 14, 15, 17, 18, 19, 23) have been identified (White, 1957). An isolated Arizona population of the cotton rat (*Sigmodon hispidus*), not morphologically distinct from more eastern populations, has a chromosome number of 2n = 22 versus 2n = 52 in the eastern population and, hence, is considered a separate sibling species (Zimmerman and Lee, 1968), and another southwestern species, *S. ochrognathus,* is considered closest to the eastern population because of its 2n = 52 (Lee and Zimmerman, 1969). Many similar examples could be cited.

The study of anuran chromosomes has also revealed the presence there of polyploidy, common in plants but thought by some (White, 1954 and Dobzhansky, 1951, 1970) to be unsustainable in biparental populations of animals. Seven polyploid species, representing three families of anurans, are now known (Bogart and Wasserman, 1972). An impressive example of the conclusive classificatory evidence that chromosomal study provides is seen in the *Hyla versicolor* group of tree frogs. As defined on morphology alone, *Hyla versicolor* ranges over roughly the forested eastern half of the United States. Blair (1958) noted that there were two call types which overlapped in a narrow zone from the Gulf of Mexico to Canada. C. Johnson (1959, 1963) demonstrated genetic incompatibilty between the two types and Ralin (1968) added to the evidence. Wasserman (1970) discovered that the population which is now known as *H. versicolor* is a tetraploid species which is practically indistinguishable from the diploid species *H. chrysoscelis* except by mating call or chromosome number.

Another kind of chromosomal evidence—heterochromatic areas (secondary constrictions)—has proved useful in tracing evolutionary lines from continent to continent as in *Bufo* (Bogart, 1972).

BIOCHEMICAL EVIDENCE

The biochemical techniques that have been perfected during the past quarter century have permitted a great broadening of the spectrum of evidence available for classificatory biology. These have provided bases for comparison of taxa with respect to character systems which have evolved under independent selective pressures. By this we mean pressures which are independent of those that have produced the morphological characters on which the classification of organisms has been mostly based. In other words, these biochemical characters give a relatively independent basis for assessment of relationships of taxa in addition to simply adding to the total number of characters of whatever type.

Except for serology, however, chemical approaches to taxonomic problems—the newly developed field of chemosystematics—can be said to have begun its ground swell only about 15 years ago, although the potential of the approach has been part of the systematists' thinking for years (Alston and Turner, 1963). As already noted, the development of chromatographic techniques has been largely responsible for the development of this discipline. These techniques, while largely developed by Russian workers in the period 1900-1930, were not applied to systematic studies in biology until the 1950s.

Chemical approaches to systematic problems are varied, but most such studies can be classified according to the kind of molecules under investigation. If the compounds are of relatively low molecular weight such as free amino acids, terpenes, alkaloids, flavonoids, etc., they may be conveniently termed micromolecules. If the compounds are of high molecular weight and essentially polymeric such as proteins (polymerized amino acids), carbohydrates (polymerized nucleotides), etc., they are termed macromolecules. Thus, it is convenient to group chemosystematic studies under micromolecular or macromolecular headings since each of the latter requires different techniques, training, and background, and taken alone, the data are generally applicable to different kinds of problems (Turner, 1967).

MICROMOLECULAR (MONOMERIC) COMPOUNDS

Micromolecular data, assembled more easily and with less expenditure of funds than macromolecular data, were the first to be used extensively in systematic studies. Most of this work has been with vascular plants, probably because such data have proven most useful in resolving problems involving complex hybridization, a not uncommon feature in higher plant groups generally (Alston, 1967; Turner, 1969). More recently micromolecular compounds, particularly terpenoids, have been used quite successfully in the study of infraspecific variation (Turner, 1970) as will be discussed in more detail below.

Among animal groups, the skin secretions of amphibians, with high diversity of compounds, have been of particular value. These have provided evidence of relationship within continentally-limited taxa as in the work of Cei, Erspamer, and Roseghini (1967) with neotropical frogs of the family Leptodactylidae. They have also provided evidence as to evolutionary lines that reflect intercontinental interchange in nearly cosmopolitan groups such as toads of the genus *Bufo* (Cei et al., 1968, 1972; Low, 1972).

MACROMOLECULAR (POLYMERIC) COMPOUNDS

Unlike micromolecules, detailed structural information on macromolecular compounds did not become generally available until about 7 years ago, and even now the accumulation of such data is quite laborious and expensive. Largely because of this, most systematists have turned to gel electrophoresis in the study of protein bands and isozymes. The latter, in particular, have proven popular with evolutionary biologists interested in the structure of populations, especially gene frequencies in the taxa concerned. Some of the more noteworthy studies have been those of Lewontin and coworkers (Prakash et al., 1969) on *Drosophila* and those of Selander and coworkers on the house mouse (Selander et al., 1969); isozyme studies on plants have been fewer, perhaps because of a higher degree of polymorphism in natural populations and the difficulty of working with specific tissue types at a given stage of development in these groups.

The most extensive application of biochemical data to the classification of higher taxa in animals has been Sibley's (1970) study of electrophoretic patterns of egg white proteins in 668 species, representing 60 of the 70 families of passerine birds. In numerous instances, the biochemical data raised questions about family relationships as deduced from other data. Application at levels of inter-species-group relationships within a genus is illustrated by Throckmorton's (1962) comparative study of fluorescing compounds in over 170 species of *Drosophila*. At the level of species comparisons, Johnson and Selander (1971) compared 11 enzymes and 6 non-enzymatic proteins in 11 species of kangaroo rats (*Dipodomys*) and found that the pattern of interspecific relationships differs significantly from those derived from morphological data, but it is similar to that based on karyotype analysis.

Perhaps the most spectacular macromolecular technique developed as an approach to systematics during the past decade has been that in which DNA or RNA is extracted from an organism and made to "hybridize" *in vitro,* presumably through nucleotide-sequence complementations, with the extracted DNA or RNA of another organism. The phyletic implications of this work have been reviewed by several workers (Hoyer et al., 1964; etc.), and it need only be noted here that the approach has not been as systematically rewarding as initial results might have suggested, largely due to the laborious and highly skilled laboratory techniques needed in these studies. It is likely, however, that these routines will be increasingly simplified and combined with new methodologies; the approach should facilitate phyletic studies, particularly those at the generic level or higher.

Many workers have dealt at length with the systematic implications and potential of comparative work on proteins and nucleic acids (e.g., Pauling and Zuckerkandl, 1963; Fitch and Margoliash, 1970), especially amino acid sequence studies of metabolically important enzymes. Undoubtedly the most widely heralded work of this nature has been that on cytochrome *c,* where interpretive studies using probabilistic algorithms and computers have permitted the construction of relatively reasonable phyletic arrangements of the major animal categories. Such data are currently being assembled in several laboratories at seemingly exponential rates (e.g., D. Boulter of Durham University [personal communication] has now worked out the complete amino acid sequence for cytochrome *c* from 25 or more higher plants, including numerous families; when one of us [Turner] reviewed this field in 1967, not a single such example was known for the higher plants), and it appears likely that the most meaningful new biochemical data bearing on the phyletic relationships of relatively remotely-related families, division, and phyla will come out of this approach.

The rationale for the use of metabolically-important enzymes in comparative sequence studies for phyletic purposes rests on the assumption that these enzymes are likely to be widely distributed in both the animal and plant kingdoms; indeed, in the case of cytochrome *c,* a component of the terminal respiratory chain of enzymes in aerobic organisms, its "phyletic history" must predate all multicellular and most unicellular organisms. By inference it appears that:

1) Cytochrome *c* enzymes in all organisms are homologous;
2) by extrapolation, they arise from homologous gene loci;
3) each possesses an evolutionary history;
4) they have diverged from some ancestral prototype;
5) "phylogenies" of proteins can be traced;
6) inferred primitive type molecules can be reconstructed (both on paper and in the test tube); and
7) molecular phylogenies can be tested statistically and possibly experimentally (Pauling and Zuckerkandl, 1963).

Comparative sequential work on selected enzymes is certain to add considerably to our knowledge of phyletic relationships among the higher categories in the near future, for as indicated by Boulter and Thompson (1971), "With the present rapid and reliable sequence methods and with the beginnings of an automated sequenator technology, the bottle-neck in the acquisition of (both animal and) plant cytochrome *c* (and other enzymes) has already become the isolation and purification of the protein itself." Undoubtedly the latter will be resolved through the use of still better techniques and instrumentation so that the systematists can soon expect a deluge of such data, the analysis of which will have to rest largely with the computer.

While much of what's been said above relates to amino-acid sequences in proteins, it is not unlikely that equally important comparative work will be performed on the DNA molecules themselves using a combination of chemical and ultrastructural techniques (much as suggested by Turner, 1967).

ULTRASTRUCTURAL EVIDENCE

The development of electron microscopy during the 1950s and particularly Scanning Electron Microscopy (SEM) during the 1960s has led to the formation of a subdiscipline of taxonomy termed ultrastructural systematics.

Electron microscopy permits the acquisition of character data unobtainable by light microscopy simply because of its extraordinary resolving power. Furthermore, using SEM, even at magnifications in the range of light microscopy, a wealth of new character topology is revealed that promises extraordinary new insights into some of the more intractable problems in micropaleontology, adaptive mechanisms, character homology, etc.

It is clear that data obtained by electron microscopy can be used at almost any hierarchical level, proving especially instructive in the choice of alternatives for the phyletic position of a given taxon. Thus, Skvarla and Turner (1966) were able to place the anomalous genus *Blennosperma* in its appropriate tribe using pollen characters of an ultrastructural nature, and more recently Behnke and Turner (1972) have shown that ultrastructural data from sieve tube plastids can help resolve phyletic problems at the familial level or higher. Indeed, at an even higher level, the ultrastructure of cellular organelles has been partly responsible for profound new insights into the origin of the eukaryotic cell from which it has been postulated that multicellularity is a consequence of the primordial acquisition of symbiotic procaryotes and their subsequent adaptive diversification (Margulis, 1970). Finally, it should be noted that, because of its relatively inexpensive operation, ease of use, and stereoscopic field, data from SEM are likely to prove increasingly popular with systematic workers generally, a trend clearly evident from a recent symposium treating the subject (Heywood, 1971).

REPRODUCTIVE BEHAVIOR

Comparative studies of behavior, particularly of courtship patterns, contribute significantly to classificatory biology. Differences in courtship behavior are especially significant at the species level because they provide a principal means for reproductive isolation of species populations. Additionally, it is possible to trace the evolution of complex behavior patterns through various taxa and hence deduce lines of evolutionary change.

The greatest use of this kind of evidence has been with those kinds of insects that display complex courtship behavior and that are amenable to observation. Spieth (1966, 1968) studied behavior of 40 species of Hawaiian drosophilids and was able to draw conclusions concerning relations of some of the endemic species groups. He also found that "the over-all behavior pattern of the endemic Hawaiian drosophilid species diverges sharply from that of the species seen in most other parts of the world."

Otte (1970) studied acoustical, visual, and tactual communicative signals used in pair-formation, courtship, and aggressive interactions by 117 species of grasshoppers belonging to several families and subfamilies.

Lloyd (1966) studied the flash patterns of 25 of the 31 Nearctic species of fireflies (*Photinus*). These patterns are species specific and act as reproductive isolating mechanisms.

Among vertebrates, non-vocal reproductive behavior patterns are particularly important in lizards and birds. Behavioral patterns have been rather extensively studied in lizards (Carpenter, 1967; Hunsaker, 1962; and others), where head bobbing and other posturing shows species-specific variation and hence provides useful information at species and higher levels.

ACOUSTICAL SIGNALS

It is now extensively documented that several groups of animals use acoustical signals as indicators of species identity at mating time. Males produce the vocalizations; the females home in on the appropriate vocalizations and thus avoid contamination of the genotype where species occur sympatrically.

For groups that use vocal signals as mating calls, the use of acoustical characters as taxonomic characters has permitted extensive refinement of the system of classification. By use of a character (vocalization) that is highly significant to the animals in their partitioning into breeding populations (biological species), it has been possible to uncover many deficiencies and errors in classifications previously devised on the evidence from visual examination of only morphological characters.

A few examples will illustrate the significance of bioacoustical measurements for correcting the classification. A toad that ranges from the southwestern United States down over the Mexican Plateau was long regarded as a single species, with very slightly differentiated northern and southern subspecies. Bogert (1960) compared the mating calls with startling results. The southern population was found to have a call that ranged in length from 12 to 37 seconds, while the northern species had recorded calls ranging from 0.4 to 0.7 seconds in duration (Blair, 1962). The effect of acoustical data on classification of insects that emphasize vocalization as a reproductive signal has been revolutionary. According to Alexander (1962), the number of known species of North American crickets was almost doubled in the 5-year period of 1957 to 1962 after behavioral, principally acoustical, data were applied to the classification. Richard Alexander and Daniel Otte recently spent a year working with Australian crickets and returned with more than 450 species new to science, most of them detected by their vocalizations (Daniel Otte, personal communication).

The impact of bioacoustical research has been greatest, of course, for those groups of animals that use vocal signals as a principal isolating mechanism. These are principally the orthopteran families Gryllidae (crickets) and Tettigoniidae (katydids) and, among the vertebrates, the anuran amphibians and the birds. To review the extensive literature of this period is beyond the scope of this paper. Representative summaries of it include papers by Blair (1958, 1962, 1963a, 1968), Alexander (1962, 1968), and Littlejohn (1969).

OTHER EVIDENCE

Our main thesis is that all attributes of a species, whether detectable and measurable in a preserved specimen through special analysis of a particular tissue or compound or by observation of living individuals, contribute to our knowledge of evolutionary relationships and hence provide classificatory data. We have sampled the main kinds of investigations that have been reported during the last quarter century, but our listing is not exhaustive. For example, chronological attributes may be important as in the time of emergence of 17-year and 13-year cicadas (Alexander and Moore, 1962). Host specificity of parasites, substrate specificity, ecological preferences or tolerances of plants and animals, physiological adaptations—all potentially provide information relative to phylogeny and classification. The problem is the magnitude of the job of obtaining this information for any large group of organisms.

The Team Approach

Although the expansion in the kinds of information about species over the past quarter century has been impressive, results have been limited because of uncoordinated individual efforts. One person might decide to study chromosomal variations in a taxon, and it would be only by chance that another worker would undertake the study of biochemical systems or genetic compatibility or of behavioral phenomena in the same taxon. Thus, the systematist rarely has the opportunity to utilize the evidence from the whole suite of suitable data systems for the solution of any question of evolutionary relationship.

A much more productive approach would seem to be one in which a team of researchers, each skilled in his own methodologies, would undertake the evolutionary study and classification of a particular taxon. Such an approach would permit the immediate balancing of the evidence from one system of analysis against that from all of the others and the production of the best estimate from all systems as to evolutionary history and relationships within the taxon. A few such team efforts have been mounted during the past several years.

Without question, the most extensive and productive team effort with animals has been the work with *Drosophila* and, to a lesser extent, with other members of the family Drosophilidae. Through assignment of specific taxonomic or geographical groups and specific methodologies to graduate students or division of labor among senior investigators, a truly multidisciplinary effort to obtain an understanding of the evolutionary history of these insects has gone forward. Over the past 25 years these studies have involved virtually every pertinent and measurable attribute of many of the some 1000 living species of *Drosophila*. This team approach to the study of the Drosophilidae has proved its worth in the "Hawaiian *Drosophila* Project," largely masterminded by the late Wilson

Stone. Study of the nearly 500 Hawaiian species of Drosophilidae has been a strictly multidisciplinary team effort.

"In such successes as have been achieved to date, serendipity has occasionally played an important role, but the major factors have been the close cooperation and integration of the efforts of all personnel involved in the project. Be that as it may, today probably more is known about the ecology, evolutionary relationships, and cytogenetics of the Hawaiian Drosophilidae than of any other comparable complex of drosophilid species," Carson et al. (1970) conclude.

A somewhat more modest effort has been put forth by one of us (Blair, 1972a) toward understanding the evolutionary relationships of the toad genus, *Bufo*. Parallel studies of osteology (R. Martin, 1972), vocal apparatus and vocalizations (W. F. Martin, 1972), morphology of ancestral forms (Reig, 1972), blood proteins (Guttman, 1972), skin secretions (Cei et al., 1972; Low, 1972), karyotypes (Bogart, 1972), hybridization (Blair, 1972b), and color and shape of the testes (Blair, 1972c) have provided strong evidence for the origin of the genus in South America and for the dispersal of at least two major evolutionary lines northward through western North America, across Eurasia, to Africa.

Team efforts oriented around a particular taxon in plant systematics have been perhaps less impressive than among animal groups generally but at least a few genera such as *Oenothera* (Cleland, 1962; Howard, 1970) and *Baptisia* (Alston, 1967) have been worked on selectively by a generation of doctoral students from several laboratories, and that the team approach is clearly gaining favor among plant workers is implicit in the taxon-centered approach to symposia (Heywood, 1971) and books by recent workers (Harborne et al., 1971).

One of the advantages of taxon-oriented team research is that it provides for an in-depth analysis of problems only hinted at or "skirted over" by the more conventional one-man studies. Thus, the chemically or cytologically oriented workers might provide new information that suggests still other interpretations to existing morphological data. These might then be tested on the spot with appropriate observations and experiments. Interdisciplinary seminars and group discussions may suggest other avenues for investigation and, in general, may catalyze cooperation that might not otherwise exist among the group.

Of course, such team efforts (in this case *organ* centered) are commonplace in medical schools, and our thesis is that organized efforts of a similar nature can be adapted to selected taxa of animals and plants with considerable success. Team efforts can also be quite effective if they are merely discipline-centered, especially where the laboratory and instrumentation necessary for in-depth studies are excessively costly. For example, the comparative phytochemical laboratory at the University of Texas has been developed from both state and federal funds over a 10 year period at a cost of approximately $300,000. This does not include the much greater costs of expendable supplies or the salaries of the professional staff and technicians who maintain and operate such equipment as combined gas chromatography-mass spectroscopy, nuclear magnetic resonance, infra red and UV spectroscopy, amino acid analyzers, computer hardware and computation service, etc. These facilities are all developed around an integrated, highly-interdisciplinary program in plant systematics in which nearly all of the pertinent approaches (cytogenetical, ultrastructural, and ecological) can be pursued by faculty members, staff, and doctorate students. It is this kind of facility and atmosphere that makes for the better-trained systematists of today, however ignorant they may be about taxonomy generally, especially that involving nomenclature and historical knowledge regarding systems of classification and their morphological bases.

Finally, it should be noted that where the team approach is used, the development of a strong computer facility and program for the storage and analysis of data becomes imperative. In fact, we have not treated numerical or computer methods as a *new* approach to systematics generally since in all of the approaches listed above, where data assemblage is considerable and complex, numerical treatment is accepted as part of the parcel. Any good "team" effort will have to have as its central or integrative facility a computer terminal with appropriate staff and programs for its day to day operation.

The past quarter century has seen the development of techniques and metholodology that has brought systematics to the very forefront of biological research. This has resulted, in part, from the dramatic discoveries of the "reductionist" biologists who have come closer and closer to an understanding of the physio-chemical basis of life and life processes. But the answer to systematic problems does not rest there. It takes the study of whole organisms, of populations, and of their place in the ecosystem to complete the picture.

The Next 25 Years

Any guesses as to the future of any particular field of science can be generated only in the context of the past history and of the present status of that field. Historically, the classification of organisms represents the oldest of the disciplines of the biological sciences, and it has predominated through a longer time span than any other discipline. However, the systematist's job of discovering and classifying the diversity of life is far from complete both in terms of discovery and of accurate classification.

The percentage of the 5 to 10 million species of organisms that are estimated to exist today that is actually known to science is remarkably short of the estimated total. In an assessment of "Biology and the Future of Man" (*see* Handler, 1970), a committee of experts provided pertinent estimates: A third or more of the living species of fishes remain unknown to science; of vertebrates, more species remain undescribed than are known to science, and of the 750,000 species of insects already described, 6,000 to 7,000 previously unknown species are being described every year.

Among plants, approximately half a million vascular plants are now known, but probably a quarter-million species remain undetected. In non-vascular plants, especially cryptograms, an assessment is more difficult to make, but the number of described species totals at least 200,000 while the number yet undescribed must number nearly half a million.

Indeed, Raven et al. (1971) and Turner (1970) are quite pessimistic about the systematists' capacity to complete any meaningful inventory of the world's total biota before population growth and technological developments make this impossible. The former state that:

> We have as yet named only about 15 percent of the world's organisms and have no real chance of adding many to the total before the rest become extinct.

This being so, they question the desirability of attempting any such survey except for selected groups such as "flowering plants, butterflies or fleas," concluding that in the future,

> High priority should also be given (i) to taxonomic work that utilizes 'unusual' characters or a broad spectrum of characters; (ii) to the accumulation of information about organisms which does not

seem to have direct taxonomic applicability; and (iii) to the search for original ways of looking at the structure of nature, including new methods of presenting 'taxonomic' information.

The present authors, except for the degree of pessimism expressed, believe these to be reasonable guidelines if appropriate judgement is used in deciding what taxa should be *collected* intensively versus those that should be *studied* intensively. Clearly, team efforts will apply to both, the former through the formation of well-organized, relatively large expeditions for this purpose (such as developed by the New York Botanical Garden for the collection of the relatively poorly known neotropical floristic elements of South America), and the latter by highly developed, interdisciplinary "team" programs.

As we look to the next 25 years, we need to ask the question: Is the effort to discover and describe additional species worthwhile? Is it something that has enough intellectual and/or practical merit for taxonomy to expect its share of the resources which our society can invest in the support of scientific discovery?

Addressing this question first on intellectual/philosophical grounds, the evolution of a system of life partitioned into 5 to 10 million living species or organisms is, for us—one of those species—the most significant thing there is about the planet earth. The more we understand about the complexities of the system, including the degree of diversity in the system, the more basis we have for understanding our own role in the system. The principles and mechanisms that account for this partitioning are intellectually important to man as a sentient being.

On the practical side, it may be that the duration of man's survival as a part of the earth system may hinge on the adequacy of his knowledge of the complexities of the system. In this respect, we take issue with the negative views of some of our colleagues (Raven et al., 1971) concerning the contribution of taxonomic work. They write:

Taxonomic work has helped us only to a limited extent in understanding the functioning of ecosystems, a problem that is of crucial importance for human survival.

Actually, we understand quite a lot about the functioning of subsystems within ecosystems, and the taxonomy of organisms provides a part of the language in which this functioning is described. Secondly, our lack of knowledge of the functioning of whole ecosystems can hardly be blamed on the limitations of taxonomy when, in truth, the lack has stemmed from the unwillingness of ecologists, until recently, to undertake the vast team effort required for investigating and modelling the functioning of whole ecosystems.

As nearly as our crystal ball can forecast them, the next 25 years will be a period in which the impressive new set of taxonomic tools that have been fashioned during the past 25 years will be utilized more- and more effectively both in the description of new taxa and in the perfection of the system of classification. For example, a person who in the future describes a new species of tree frog from deep Amazonas without having tape-recorded and described the physical attributes of its mating call will be doing less than an adequately-scientific job of taxonomic description.

Ideally, the objective will be to obtain information about as many biological attributes of taxa as possible. In practice, some types of data systems will necessarily take precedence over others, depending on the situation. In the example of the tree frog cited above, the character of its vocalization is of major importance with respect to the identification of the species, but its karyotype or a biochemical character may be most important in revealing the degree of affinity with its congenors. With the wealth of disciplinary tools now available and given the demonstrable advantages of a multidisciplinary attack on taxonomic problems, we anticipate that a significant feature of the next 25 years will be the organization of more and more multidisciplinary research efforts by taxonomists. This kind of team effort is proving successful in ecology where analysis of ecosystems poses a much greater problem and requires a much greater diversity of skills and professions than we are discussing here. We recognize the fact that highly competent "loners" exist among taxonomists, just as among ecologists, and that such people will never fit themselves into a team effort. On the other hand, the intellectual rewards and their contributions to society will be greatly enhanced for those who can fit their interests into a team effort.

The greatly-increased amount of information about each taxon, being generated by the taxonomists of the 70s, demands a drastic reappraisal of our methods for storage and retrieval of systematic data.

The museums of the nation and of the world are presently inadequately equipped for the tasks of the coming years. The best are adequately equipped to preserve herbarium sheets of plants, stuffed mammals, pinned insects, and pickled specimens of many sorts. For the most part, they lack the capacity to store magnetic tapes of vocal signals, paper chromatograms, starch gels, and the like. A major revolution in the thinking and practice of museologists, thus seems in order in the coming years.

In reality, the huge quantities of information that we are technologically capable of producing with respect to the attributes of any taxon of plants or animals make it imperative that we look to electronic methods of data storage and retrieval. We predict that the establishment of large data banks for the storage of taxonomic information will be another major feature of the next 25 years. The "Flora North America," sponsored by the AIBS during its conception and now under the aegis of the Smithsonian Institution, represents a tentative first step in this direction.

In conclusion, we believe that the years immediately ahead are crucial ones for man's continuation as a dominant factor in the world's ecosystems. Man continues to increase his numbers in defiance of basic ecological principles of adjustment of population numbers to resource support systems. He expends fossil fuels as energy sources without heed to their irreplaceability. He destroys natural biological diversity in the interest of his own short-term gains. Balanced against these, there may be a plus factor in achieving as much knowledge of the diversity of the system of which he is a part and of the factors leading to that diversity as he can. It is perhaps an understatement to say that in the years ahead man needs all of the pluses of this sort that he can acquire.

There is current talk about a coordinated effort for a 5-year International Environmental Period to start the process of bringing the environment and man into a harmonious state. With only some 15% of the world's organisms known to science and considering the importance of such knowledge for ecosystem management, it seems appropriate that a world-wide effort to increase this percentage might be an important component of this 5-year International Environmental Period. The momentum of such participation could be expected to carry through the next 25 years and more.

References

Alexander, R. D. 1962. The role of behavioral study in cricket classification. *Syst. Zool.*, **11**(2): 53-72.

————. 1968. Communication in selected groups: Arthropods. *In*: T. A. Sebeok (ed.). *Animal Communication*. Indiana Univ. Press, Bloomington, Ind. p. 167-216.

———— and T. E. Moore. 1962. The evolutionary relationships of 17-year and 13-year cicadas, and three new species (Homoptera, Cicadidae, *Maqicicada*). *Misc. Publ. Mus. Zool.*, Univ. Michigan, No. 121. 59 p.

Alston, R. E. 1967. Biochemical systematics. *In*: T. Dobzhansky, M. K. Hecht, and W. C. Steere (eds.). *Evolutionary Biology*. I. Meredith Publ. Co., New York. p. 197-305.

———— and B. L. Turner. 1963. *Biochemical Systematics*. Prentice-Hall, Englewood Cliffs, N.J.

Babcock, E. B. 1947. The genus *Crepis*, I and II. *Univ. Calif. Publ. Bot.*, Nos. 21 and 22.

Beçak, M. L., L. Denaro, and W. Beçak. 1970. Polyploidy and mechanisms of karyotypic diversification in amphibia. *Cytogenetics*, **9**: 225-238.

Behnke, H. D. and B. L. Turner. 1972. On specific sieve-tube plastids in Caryophyllales. *Taxon.*, **20**: 731-737.

Benirschke, K. 1969. *Comparative Mammalian Cytogenetics*. Springer-Verlag, New York.

Blair, W. F. 1956. The species as a dynamic system. *Southwest. Nat.*, **1**(1): 1-5.

————. 1958. Mating call in the speciation of anuran amphibians. *Amer. Nat.*, **92**: 27-51.

————. 1962. Non-morphological data in anuran classification. *Syst. Zool.*, **11**: 72-84.

————. 1963a. Acoustic behavior of amphibia. *In*: R. G. Busnell (ed.). *Acoustic Behavior of Animals*. Elsevier Publ. Co., London. p. 694-708.

————. 1963b. Intragroup genetic compatibility in the *Bufo americanus* species group of toads. *Texas J. Sci.*, **15**(1): 15-34.

————. 1966. Genetic compatibility in the *Bufo valliceps* and closely related groups of toads. *Texas J. Sci.*, **18**(4): 333-351.

————. 1968. Communication in selected groups: amphibians and reptiles. *In*: T. A. Sebeok (ed.). *Animal Communication*. Indiana Univ. Press, Bloomington, Ind. p. 289-310.

————. 1972a. *Evolution in the Genus* Bufo. Univ. Texas Press, Austin, Texas. (In press.)

————. 1972b. Evidence from hybridization. *In*: W. F. Blair (ed.). *Evolution in the Genus* Bufo. Univ. Texas Press, Austin, Texas. (In press).

————. 1972c. Characteristics of the testes. *In*: W. F. Blair (ed.). *Evolution in the Genus* Bufo. Univ. Texas Press, Austin, Texas. (In press).

Bogart, J. P. 1967. Chromosomes of the South American amphibian family Ceratophridae with a reconsideration of the taxonomic status of *Odontophrynus americanus. Can. J. Genet. Cytol.*, **9**: 531-542.

————. 1970. Systematic problems in the amphibian family Leptodactylidae

(Anura) as indicated by karyotypic analysis. *Cytogenetics,* **9**: 369-383.

————. 1972. Karyotypes. *In*: W. F. Blair (ed.). *Evolution in the Genus* Bufo. Univ. Texas Press, Austin, Texas. (In press.)

———— and A. O. Wasserman. 1972. Diploid-polyploid cryptic species pairs: A possible clue to evolution by polyploidization in anuran amphibians. *Cytogenetics.* (In press.)

Bogert, C. M. 1960. The influence of sound on the behavior of amphibians and reptiles. *In*: W. E. Lanyon and W. N. Tavolga (eds.). *Animal Sounds and Communication.* American Institute of Biological Sciences, Washington, D. C., Publ. No. 7.

Boulter, D. and E. W. Thompson. 1971. The amino acid sequence of *Phaseolus aureus* (Mung-bean) cytochrome *c* with reference to phylogeny. *In*: J. B. Horborne, D. Boulter, and B. L. Turner (eds.). *Chemotaxonomy of the Leguminosae.* Academic Press, New York.

Carpenter, C. C. 1967. Aggression and social structure in Iguanid lizards. *In*: W. W. Milstead (ed.). *Lizard Ecology: A Symposium.* Univ. Missouri Press, Columbia, Mo. p. 87-105.

Carson, H. L., D. E. Hardy, H. T. Spieth, and W. S. Stone. 1970. The evolutionary biology of the Hawaiian Drosophilidae. *In*: M. K. Hecht and W. C. Steere (eds.). *Essays in Evolution and Genetics.* Appleton-Century-Crofts, New York. p. 437-543.

Cave, M. S. 1956-1964. *Index to Plant Chromosome Number.* Univ. North Carolina Press, Chapel Hill, N. Car.

Cei, J. M., V. Erspamer, and M. Roseghini. 1967. Taxonomic and evolutionary significance of biogenic amines and polypeptides occurring in amphibian skin. I. Neotropical leptodactylid frogs. *Syst. Zool.,* **16**(4): 328-342.

————, ————, and ————. 1968. Taxonomic and evolutionary significance of biogenic amines and polypeptides in amphibian skin. II. Toads of the genera *Bufo* and *Melanophryniscus. Syst. Zool.,* **17**(3): 232-245.

————, ————, and ————. 1972. Biogenic amines. *In*: W. F. Blair (ed.). *Evolution in the Genus* Bufo. Univ. Texas Press, Austin, Texas. (In press.)

Cleland, R. E. 1962. The cytogenetics of *Oenothera. Adv. in Genetics,* **11**: 147-229.

Darlington, D. C. and E. K. Janaki-Ammal. 1945. *Chromosome Atlas of Cultivated Plants.* G. Allen, London.

———— and A. P. Wylie. 1955. *Chromosome Atlas of Flowering Plants.* G. Allen, London.

Dice, L. R. 1968. Speciation. *In*: J. A. King (ed.). *Biology of Peromyscus* (*Rodentia*). Am. Soc. of Mammalogists, Special Publ., No. 2. p. 75-97.

Dobzhansky, T. 1951. *Genetics and the Origin of Species,* 3rd edition. Columbia Univ. Press, New York.

————. 1970. *Genetics of the Evolutionary Process.* Columbia Univ. Press, New York.

Fitch, W. M. and E. Margoliash. 1970. The usefulness of amino acid nucleotide sequences in evolutionary studies. *Evol. Biol.,* **4**: 67-105.

Grant, V. 1971. *Plant Speciation.* Columbia Univ. Press, New York.

Guttman, S. 1972. Blood proteins. *In:* W. F. Blair (ed.). *Evolution in the Genus* Bufo. Univ. Texas Press, Austin, Texas. (In press.)

Handler, P. 1970. *Biology and the Future of Man.* Oxford Univ. Press, New York.

Heywood, V. H. 1971. *Scanning Electron Microscopy and Evolutionary Applications.* Academic Press, New York.

Horborne, J. B., D. Boulter, and B. L. Turner. 1971. *Chemical Taxonomy of the Leguminosae.* Academic Press, New York.

Howard, L. Z. H. 1970. Biochemical systematic investigations of twenty-one species of the genus *Oenothera* (Onagraceae) emphasizing flavanoid chemisrty. Unpubl. Doctoral Dissertation. The University of Texas, Austin.

Hoyer, B. H., B. J. McCarthy, and E. T. Bolton. 1964. A molecular approach in the systematics of higher organisms. *Science,* **144**: 959-967.

Hunsaker, D., II. 1962. Ethological isolating mechanisms in the *Sceloporus torquatus* group of lizards. *Evolution,* **16**: 62-74.

Jackson, R. C. 1971. The karyotype in systematics. *Ann. Rev. Evol. Syst.,* **2**: 327-368.

Johnson, C. 1959. Genetic incompatibility in the call races of *Hyla versicolor* Le Conte in Texas. *Copeia,* 1959: 327-335.

————. 1963. Additional evidence of sterility between call-types in the *Hyla versicolor* complex. *Copeia,* 1963: 139-143.

Johnson, W. E. and R. K. Selander. 1971. Protein variation and systematics in kangaroo rats (genus *Dipodomys*). *Syst. Zool.,* **20**(4): 377-405.

Lee, M. R. and E. G. Zimmerman, 1969. Robertsonian polymorphism in the cotton rat, *Siqmodon fulviventer. J. Mammalogy,* **50**(2): 333-339.

Lewis, H. and M. E. Lewis. 1955. The genus *Clarkia. Univ. Calif. Publ. Bot.,* **20**: 241-392.

Littlejohn, M. J. 1969. The systematic significance of isolating mechanisms. *In: Systematic Biology: Proceedings of an International Conference.* National Academy of Science., Publ. No. 1692. p. 459-482.

Lloyd, J. E. 1966. Studies on the flash communication system in *Photinus* fireflies. Misc. Publ. Mus. Zool., Univ. Michigan, No. 130.

Low, B. S. 1972. Evidence from parotoid gland secretions. *In:* W. F. Blair (ed.). *Evolution in the Genus* Bufo. Univ. Texas Press, Austin, Texas. (In press.)

Margulis, L. 1970. *Origin of Eukaryotic Cells.* Yale Univ. Press, New Haven, Conn.

Martin, R. 1972. Evidence from osteology. *In:* W. F. Blair (ed.). *Evolution in the Genus* Bufo. Univ. Texas Press, Austin, Texas. (In press.)

Martin, W. F. 1972. Evolution of vocalization in the genus *Bufo. In*: W. F. Blair (ed.). *Evolution in the Genus* Bufo. Univ. Texas Press, Austin, Texas. (In press.)

Mayr, E. 1942. *Systematics and the Origin of Species.* Columbia Univ. Press, New York.

Moore, R. J. 1970-1971. Index to plant chromosome numbers for 1968-1969. *Regnum Veg.,* **68**: 1-130; **77**: 1-132.

Morescalchi, A. 1968. Hypotheses on the phylogeny of the Salientia, based on karyological data. *Experientia,* 24: 964-966.

―――. 1970. Karyology and vertebrate phylogeny. *Bull. Zool.,* **37**: 1-28.

Ornduff, R. 1967-1969. Index to plant chromosome numbers for 1965-1967. *Regnum Veg.,* **50**: 1-125; **55**: 1-126; **59**: 1-129.

Otte, D. 1970. A comparative study of communicative behavior in grasshoppers. Misc. Publ. Mus. Zool., Univ. Michigan, No. 141.

Patterson, J. T. and W. Stone. 1952. *Evolution in the Genus* Drosophila. Macmillan Co., New York.

Pauling, L. and E. Zuckerkandl. 1963. Chemical paleogenetics. *Acta Chem. Scand.,* **17**(suppl. No. 1): 9-16.

Prakash, S., R. C. Lewontin, and J. L. Hubby. 1969. A molecular approach to the study of genic heterozygosity in natural populations IV. *Genetics,* **61**: 841-858.

Ralin, D. B. 1968. Ecological and reproductive differentiation in the cryptic species of the *Hyla versicolor* complex (Hylidae). *Southwest. Nat.,* **13**: 283-300.

Raven, P. H., B. Berlin, and D. E. Breedlove. 1971. The origins of taxonomy. *Science,* **174**: 1210-1213.

Reig, O. 1972. Macrogenioglottus and the South American bufonid toads. *In*: W. F. Blair (ed.). *Evolution in the Genus* Bufo. Univ. Texas Press, Austin, Texas. (In press.)

Saez, F. A. and N. Brum. 1959. Citogenetica de anfibios anuros de America del Sur. Los cromosomas de *Odontophrynus americanus* y *Ceratophrys ornata. Ann. Fac. Med., Montevideo,* **44**: 414-423.

Selander, R. K., W. G. Hunt, and S. Y. Yang. 1969. Protein polymorphism and genic heterozygosity in two European subspecies of the house mouse. *Evolution,* **23**: 379-390.

Sibley, C. G. 1970. A comparative study of the egg-white proteins of passerine birds. *Peabody Mus. Bull.,* No. 32.

Skvarla, J. J. and B. L. Turner. 1966. Pollen wall ultrastructure and its bearing on the systematic position of *Blennosperma* and *Crocidium* (Compositae). *Am. J. Bot.,* **53**: 555-563.

Spieth, H. T. 1966. Courtship behavior in endemic Hawaiian *Drosophila. In*: M. R. Wheeler (ed.). *Studies in Genetics. III, Morgan Centennial Issue.* Univ. Texas Press, Austin, Texas. p. 245-313.

―――. 1968. Evolutionary implications of sexual behavior in *Drosophila. In*: T. Dobzhansky, M. K. Hecht, and W. C. Steere (eds.). *Evolution-*

ary Biology, Volume 2. Appleton-Century-Crofts, New York. p. 157-193.

Throckmorton, L. H. 1962. The use of biochemical characteristics for the study of problems of taxonomy and evolution in the genus *Drosophila. In*: M. R. Wheeler (ed.). *Studies in Genetics. II, Research Reports on Drosophila Genetics, Taxonomy and Evolution.* University of Texas Publ. No. 6205. p. 415-488.

Tjio, J. H. and A. Levan. 1954. Some experiments with acetic orcein in animal chromosomes. *Ana. Est. Exp., Aula De,* **3**: 225-228.

Turner, B. L. 1967. Chemosystematics: present and future applications. *Bull. Natl. Inst. Sci. India,* **34**: 189-211.

————. 1969. Chemosystematics: Recent developments. *Taxon,* **18**: 134-151.

————. 1970. Molecular approaches to populational problems at the infra-specific level. *In*: J. B. Horborne (ed.). *Phytochemical Phylogeny.* Academic Press, New York.

Wasserman, A. O. 1970. Polyploidy in the common tree toad *Hyla versicolor* Le Conte. *Science,* **167**: 385-386.

Wet, J. M. J. de. 1970. Polyploidy and evolution in plants. *Taxon,* **20**: 29-35.

White, M. J. D. 1954. *Animal Cytology and Evolution.* Cambridge Univ. Press, London.

————. 1957. Cytogenetics and systematic entomology. *Ann. Rev. Entomology,* **2**: 71-90.

————. 1969. Chromosomal rearrangements and speciation in animals. *Ann. Rev. Genetics,* **3**: 75-98.

Zimmerman, E. G. and M. R. Lee. 1968. Variation in chromosomes of the cotton rat, *Siqmodon hispidus. Chromosoma,* **24**: 243-250.

11 Evolutionary Biogeography Viewed From Plate Tectonic Theory

DANIEL I. AXELROD
DEPARTMENT OF BOTANY
University of California, Davis

PETER H. RAVEN
Missouri Botanical Garden, St. Louis

Plate tectonic theory provides a reliable basis for reinterpreting major problems of continental and insular biogeography (e.g., Axelrod, 1970, 1972a; Keast, 1971; McKenna, 1971b). At the same time it provides insight into the guiding role of environment in evolution because it illuminates the problem of directional change in adaptation, one of the major features of evolution. Furthermore, it clarifies problems pertaining to diversity and the causes of extinction and replacement. Prior to outlining some of these relations, it is desirable to summarize briefly the nature of plate tectonic theory. Following a review of some conclusions that have been reached concerning its relations to biogeographic and related evolutionary problems, it should be possible to discern paths that may prove most fruitful for future work.

Plate Tectonics

Plate tectonic theory states that the earth's crust (lithosphere) is made up of a small number of rigid plates that are all moving relative to one another, some at rates as high as 10 cm per year. The plates are as few as 6 in some models, and certain investigators recognize a number of subplates as well. Plates are 50 to 100 km thick; they include both ocean basins and continents, and they are generally aseismic except near or at their boundaries where moving plates jostle one another, resulting in intense earthquake activity and vulcanism. Three very different kinds of movements may occur at plate boundaries. First, as major rifting occurs, lavas well up, solidify, and are added to the plate on each side of the rift. As this new crust created by the outpouring basaltic lavas is added to the adjacent plates, they move apart by lateral growth (Fig. 1). As a result, the older sea floor, oceanic islands, continents, and continental islands are rafted to new positions. Second, the moving plates are thrust back into the mantle along linear subduction zones at the site of ocean trenches (e.g., Aleutian trench, Atacama trench) which are usually marked by island arcs typified by active volcanos (Aleutian-Kurile Islands, East Indies) and intense vulcanism. Third, two plates may slide past one another without plate modification, with the zone of movement marked by a major strike-slip fault (e.g., San Andreas fault, California; Alpine fault, New Zealand).

Creation of new oceanic crust may start along a great rupture within a continent, as in the present rift valleys of Africa, or between Africa-South America along a line we now recognize as the mid-Atlantic Ridge. Inasmuch as new ocean floor is constantly being replenished along the

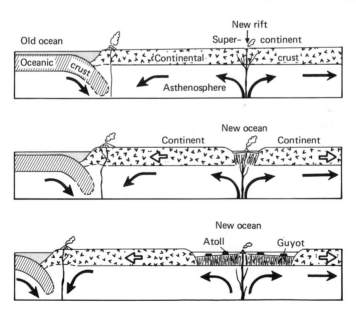

FIGURE 1. Schematic representation of ocean-floor spreading and the rafting of lands to new positions.

mid-ocean rise, it is understandable that nearly half of all the present ocean floor is of Tertiary Age. As lavas well up and solidify at the mid-ocean rise, they become magnetized by the earth's magnetic field which reverses periodically. This reversal results in a distinct pattern of magnetic anomalies which are readily recorded by magnetometer and easily identified. The distribution of magnetic anomalies on the ocean floor has now largely been mapped. They are numbered from 1 to 33, with the higher numbers older, and their ages have been determined by both microfossil and radiometric evidence (e.g., Anomaly 1 = 0.5 m.y.; 5 = 9.5 m.y.; 10 = 32 m.y.; 15 = 40 m.y.; 30 = 70.5 m.y.). By identifying and mapping the dated anomalies, the movement of the plates can be charted. For older rocks, lavas and sediments on the continents are used to determine the magnetic polar positions. By plotting the magnetic poles for progressively older rocks, a "wander-curve" can be reconstructed that shows approximately the changing latitudinal positions of continents. Inasmuch as all plate motions are relative to each other, one area (usually Africa) is anchored for reference.

Plate tectonics thus provides a basis for understanding events that have had a major role in biogeography and evolution. It has already shown that hypotheses that visualize the survival of progressive waves of holarctic groups in the extremities of most southern lands, or radiation of most vertebrate groups from the Old World tropics (Darlington, 1957), or an "Assam to Fiji" heartland for the origin of angiosperms are untenable. As demonstrated earlier by Brundin (1965) in his elegant analysis of the evolutionary relations of the fresh-water midges (Chironomidae), and discussed recently by Keast (1971) and Fooden (1972) for mammals, and by Axelrod (1970; 1972a, b) for angiosperms, the history of global biota must be related to the successive stages of continental fragmentation.

As plates move apart, taxa with formerly continuous distributions become disrupted as when Africa and South America separated in the late Lower Cretaceous (early Albian, 110 m.y.) or when Australia and Antarctica parted company in the Eocene (~45 m.y.). Since isolation frequently provides opportunities for divergent evolution and the emergence of new taxa, lands formerly connected share related taxa which are at the level of species, genus, tribe, or family, depending on the taxon, rate of evolution, and the time involved. If continents are rafted across many degrees of latitude, they move into new climatic belts that provide new opportunities for some, but may result in the extinction of others, as in the case of India moving 50° of Lat. across the tropics and into the northern "horse latitudes" during the Tertiary (Axelrod, 1972b). When plates merge, there is an intermingling of taxa previously separated as when the Australian moved north to meet the Asian plate during the Miocene, creating a zone of mixing along the newly-established Wallace's line (Raven and Axelrod, 1972). On the other hand, as a plate is broken into smaller segments that are rafted to new positions, evolution in isolation will not only result in the emergence of new taxa, but the trend to more equable marine climate may favor the persistence of ancient relicts as in Australasia during the Tertiary (Raven and Axelrod, 1972).

Cretaceous Distribution Patterns

Many existing groups evolved or radiated during the Jurassic-early Cretaceous time when the world was effectively divided into three major segments: Eurasia-North America (Laurasia); Africa-South America (West Gondwana) with a link to western Eurasia *via* Africa; and Australia-Antarctica (East Gondwana) with direct access to South America. There evidently was no broad corridor for migration between North and South America during the Cretaceous (Malfait and Dinkelman, 1972; Fooden, 1972), but migration to South America was possible *via* Laurasia-Africa. This Africa-South American (West Gondwana) ligation was severed in the late Aptian-Albian transition, apparently leaving South America isolated from North America until the late Pliocene except for an archipelago that was a sweepstake route for most animals, but few plants. Migration between Australia-South America *via* Antarctica was possible into Eocene time. Many groups show distribution patterns that correspond to one of the three areas and to the times they were mutually accessible.

1) Among the alliances that seem to have had their primary radiation in Laurasia are the salamanders, emydine turtles, snakes, and most groups of placental mammals (perhaps the entire group), as well as such plant groups as the Pinaceae, Taxodiaceae, Amentiferae (oak, birch, hazel, walnut families, etc.), Magnoliaceae, Ranunculaceae, Berberidaceae, and Apiaceae-Apioideae and Saniculoideae. The deciduous habit among angiosperms evidently evolved first in Laurasia under drought stress (Axelrod, 1966). Herbaceous plants are better represented here than in either

of the two following regions, probably because of its greater seasonality.

2) Some distributions suggest radiation from South America-Africa. These include such animal groups as the primary freshwater cypriniform-ostariophysan fishes, caecilians, pelomedusid turtles, as well as such plant families as Annonaceae, Canellaceae, Myristicaceae, and many others. During early Paleogene time, migration between tropical Asia and Africa was possible for organisms of subtropical habitats. For snakes, many mammals and lizards, and Piperaceae and Lauraceae, Laurasia-Africa constitutes the principal biogeographic unit.

3) Finally, some organisms occur principally on lands that have been connected with Antarctica. These include Winteraceae, Degeneriaceae, Eupomatiaceae, Monimiaceae, Proteaceae, Chloranthaceae, and Apiaceae-Hydrocotyloideae, as well as galaxiid fishes, side-neck turtles, leptodactylid frogs, marsupials, and monotremes. There is a better representation of primitive angiosperms in this group, particularly in Australasia than elsewhere. This region was rafted into increasingly-milder climatic zones as the world climate deteriorated during the Neogene. Thus, their survival may be attributed to a continuously-available equable climate better suited for their persistence.

With respect to Cretaceous and older distributions, biologists should note that some reconstructions (e.g., Dietz & Holden, 1970; Heirtzler, 1971) place Antarctica in a polar position during Triassic and later times. Obviously, the Triassic *Lystrosaurus* fauna (Colbert, 1971; Kitching et al., 1972) recorded from near Lat. 85°S did not live under several months of darkness and low temperature. We are also faced with the problem of the abundant tree ferns and cycadophytes in the Jurassic of Grahamland (*see* Seward, 1941, p. 371). The migration of dinosaurs to Australia in the Cretaceous likewise poses a problem in view of Antarctica's postulated far southern position and the lack of connection with Eurasia at that time. It is doubtful that they could survive the low winter temperatures below Lat. 63°S, and foraging for food during the winter night raises an additional problem. Nor does it seem likely that the evergreen forest (palm, Proteaceae, *Nothofagus*) reported from McMurdo Sound at Lat. 78°S lived at that high latitude. Antarctica more probably moved to its present position since Eocene time, as the Antarctic-Indian Ocean Rise was activated (*see* Veevers et al., 1971, Fig. 7). Some reconstructions (e.g., Dietz & Holden, 1970) also have India in the middle of the Indian Ocean during Jurassic and Cretaceous times. But this ignores the occurrence of large dinosaurs there in the late Cretaceous, sauropods that occur also in South America, Africa, Madagascar, Europe, and the USSR (Keast, 1971, p. 353). India must have been connected with one of the southern lands, probably Africa (Veevers et al., 1971) until at least later-Cretaceous time.

The relatively poor representation of primitive angiosperms in South America-Africa may be consistent with the subsequent evolution of more successful dominant groups in the tropics. In view of this and other qualifications (Axelrod, 1972a), it is unwise to guess where angiosperms may have originated. Although the uplands of tropical Gondwanaland have been suggested (e.g., by Camp, 1947; Axelrod, 1970), the uplands in subtropical Laurasia seem equally plausible because the earliest known fossil angiosperms occur in the north.

Finally, Australia was accessible to immigration from the south *via* Antarctica until approximately 45 m.y. ago. Hence, it has been largely isolated during the main period of evolution of many of its distinctive plants and animals, as discussed below.

Discontinuous Distributions

TROPICAL DISJUNCTIONS

During early Cretaceous time tropical South America and Africa were united. Commencing near the Aptian-Albian boundary (110 m.y.), the sedimentary sequences in each area disclose the gradual encroachment of brackish and thence marine sedimentary environments across areas formerly continental. Fossil pollen floras and ostracod and fish faunas recovered from Cretaceous deposits of both tropical Africa and South America reveal a remarkable similarity although the plants and animals of these tropical lands are very different today.

The Cretaceous and Tertiary separation of Africa and South America by continued ocean-floor spreading accounts for many of the differences between the two areas. Some of the similarities can be traced back to the early Cretaceous. Thus, the primary freshwater cypriniform-ostariophysan fishes of Africa and South America had a common origin at a time when these continents were directly connected by land (Myers, 1967), whereas the snakes and most birds and mammals of these continents were not present prior to mid-Cretaceous time and do not have disjunct ranges between them. Among the amphibians, the caecilians certainly had a

similar time of origin and pattern of dispersal, although their absence
from Madagascar, thought to be joined with Africa into early Tertiary
time, is unexpected. Some groups of frogs probably had a comparable
history. Pelomedusid turtles, common to Africa and South America, are
known from the fossil record at a time when these continents were joined.
A Cretaceous age may also be inferred for lizards of the families Amphis-
baenidae and Leptotyphlopidae now confined to Africa and South America. Many groups of insects that had evolved by Aptian time (Riek,
1970 summarizes the evidence) are now disjunct between these continents, but others, such as Lepidoptera and Isoptera, seem to have been
of Paleogene origin and would not, therefore, be expected to display
analogous disjunct distributions.

Among the angiosperms, a number of families that are preponderantly
confined to the inner tropics occur in both Africa and South America.
These include Annonaceae, Bombacaceae, Burseraceae, Cochlosperma-
ceae, Combretaceae, Connaraceae, Dilleniaceae, Hernandiaceae, Hip-
pocrateaceae, Malpighiaceae, Marantaceae, Musaceae, Myristicaceae,
Ochnaceae, Rhizophoraceae. Furthermore, a number of other pantropical
families that find optimum development and diversity within the tropics
and are represented in temperate regions by only a few small genera, also
link these areas; e.i., Anacardiaceae, Araceae, Bignoniaceae, Ebenaceae,
Elaeocarpaceae, Flacourtiaceae, Icacinaceae, Lauraceae, Leguminosae
(Caesalpinoideae), Loganiaceae, Meliaceae, Monimiaceae, Moraceae,
Palmae, Sapotaceae, Simaroubaceae, Sterculiaceae. There are also some
families that link the African and American tropics, for instance, Canellaceae, Caricaceae, Humiriaceae, Hydnoraceae, Mayacaceae, Rapatea-
ceae, Turneraceae, Velloziaceae, Vochysiaceae. These alliances always
appear to have been basically adapted to warm climates, and most of
them must have attained their distributions before the later Cretaceous
when steppingstones (volcanic islands, microcontinents like Azores plateau) were still sufficiently close to the retreating coasts to enable effective migration between tropical America-Africa.

Many groups of angiosperms now disjunct between these areas thus
attained their disjunct ranges by ocean-floor spreading that separated a
formerly continuous area and not by migration around high latitudes.
This implies that many families of woody angiosperms were in existence
by the middle Cretaceous although few modern genera had yet appeared.
Members of these and other pantropic families that link the American-

African with the Asian tropics extended along the shores of the Tethys during Cretaceous and early Tertiary times.

We emphasize that not all disjunct distributions between South America and Africa have such an ancient foundation, however. Bromeliaceae and Cactaceae, almost entirely restricted to the New World tropics but with one or a few species in the Old World, probably evolved after South America-Africa separated and reached their African stations by long-distance dispersal. The cosmopolitan Typhaceae, first known from the Paleocene and already present in New Zealand by the Oligocene, are especially attractive candidates for long-distance dispersal by wind. In the final analysis, only the fossil record can help us to distinguish with certainty whether the basis for a particular distribution pattern antedates the Tertiary although a helpful clue is provided by the Tertiary radiation of most sympetalous angiosperms (cf. Muller, 1970).

SOUTHERN HEMISPHERE DISJUNCTIONS

Temperate evergreen forests, containing a number of genera of austral gymnosperms together with *Nothofagus* and their associates, occur today in the Tasman region (southeast Australia-Tasmania-New Zealand), in the temperate montane forests of New Guinea and New Caledonia, and also in the Fuegian area (southern Chile, adjacent Argentina). Not only the forest species, but many other plant and animal groups, including marsupials, and certain frogs, turtles, insects, and others, are common to these regions. In addition, some taxa of temperate requirements that occur in southern Africa or Madagascar (e.g., Proteaceae, Cunoniaceae, Podocarpaceae, side-neck turtles, lungfishes, some fresh-water midges, ratite birds) indicate links with both the Fuegian and Tasman regions. As noted above, the relations appear understandable on the basis of the sequential breakup of Gondwanaland, as worked out by Brundin (1965) and considered recently by Fooden (1972) for mammals. As presently understood, New Zealand separated from West Antarctica (an archipelago!) in the late Cretaceous (80 m.y.), and Australia moved north from East Antarctica in the Eocene (~45 m.y.), the last time there was a connection with South America *via* Antarctica. This sequence may account for the absence of marsupials and snakes in New Zealand though water barriers probably were also crucial inasmuch as the region was an archipelago.

NORTHERN HEMISPHERE DISJUNCTIONS

Migration across Laurasia was direct and essentially uninterrupted during much of the Cretaceous, apart from the late Cretaceous (Santonian-
Campanian) sea that bisected North America up the central plains, and
the late Cretaceous to Eocene (Maestrichtien-Lutetian) sea that occupied
the Uralian region. Cretaceous forests were generally similar across the
north but·show regional differences (Muller, 1970, Fig. 4). Migration for
mammals between eastern America and Eurasia continued into the early
Eocene when the corridor was broken as plate movements extended the
Atlantic into the arctic basin. However, forests across the area were
generally similar into the Miocene as shown by the fossil flora of Iceland
that provides many links between western Europe and in eastern North
America. No doubt some of the disjunctions between eastern North
America and eastern Asia result from extinction in western Eurasia rather
than by migration across Beringia; this is clearly a problem for future
study (see Raven, 1972b). The shift from Atlantic to Beringian connections, which may have occurred in Paleogene time (McKenna, 1972a),
and the establishment of islands and other connections in the Bering
Straits area, as North America moved westward, need clarification.

NEOGENE CHANGES IN DISTRIBUTION

Apart from the distributions of Cretaceous-Paleogene age, some of
more recent development involve closely similar or identical species. Some
of these reflect the consequences of plate tectonics, notably the elevation
of high ranges and cordilleras in response to the fusion of plates. The
cordilleras of middle and late Cenozoic age (e.g., Alpine axis from the
Pyrenees to the Himalayas; East Indies arc to New Guinea; New Zealand
Alps; Andes; Alaska-British Columbia-Cascade ranges) not only provided dispersal routes to new areas but also new opportunities for evolution. Such patterns are exemplified by herbs discontinuous between
temperate North America and the Fuegian region (Raven, 1963) (e.g.,
Epilobium, Sanicula, Astragalus, Empetrum) or between temperate Asia
and Australia-New Zealand (e.g., *Epilobium* [independently], *Mentha,
Veronica, Euphrasia*). Their spread down the American cordillera and

across the Oriental tropics was made possible in the first place by the newly-elevated "way-stations" in the tropics. Migration along north-south paths was enhanced by the increased thermal gradient during later Pliocene and Quaternary times which resulted in increased wind velocities and, hence, in the greater probability of seed transport. Also, increased seasonality (= lowered productivity) intensified bird migration leading to more frequent seed transport by regular waves of migrants to austral regions, especially between North and South America. This was primarily a one-way affair since most temperate austral taxa cannot withstand the rigorous northern winters.

The Alpine axis, reaching from the Pyrenees across southern Europe through the Middle East into the Himalayas, is a series of young ranges elevated chiefly during the late Cenozoic. At that time drier climate commenced to spread rapidly over the region, reaching eastward into the western Himalayas and north into central Asia. As a result, the mixed deciduous hardwood forest that had blanketed the lowlands gradually lost broadleaved evergreens (e.g., *Cinnamomum, Magnolia, Meliosma*), as well as conifers and deciduous hardwoods now confined to eastern Asia (e.g., *Ailanthus, Cercidiphyllum, Keteleeria, Pseudolarix*). The mixed deciduous forests that survived in the mountains (Karakorum-Pamir-Hindu Kush, Elburz, Caucasus, Kuzey Anadolu, etc.) are now isolated by hundreds of miles of dry plains covered by steppe, semidesert, or desert vegetation of more recent development. The present taxa in these discontinuous forests are derivatives of deciduous hardwood trees and shrubs that were scattered widely over the lowlands into Pliocene time, notably species of *Acer, Aesculus, Carpinus, Cercis, Cotinus, Daphne, Fagus, Fraxinus, Gleditsia, Ilex* (evergreen), *Pinus, Pterocarya, Quercus, Tilia, Ulmus, Zelkova*. The deciduous forest frequently is bordered at lower altitudes by a woodland of small trees distributed in *Buxus, Juniperus, Nerium, Olea, Pinus, Pistacia, Punica, Quercus*, which also had a wider occurrence into the Pliocene. Related species of many of these genera occur today in these now-isolated mountain regions (Muesel and Schubert, 1971), and similar relations are shown by some snakes, amphibians, lizards, ferns, and mosses. They provide a novel opportunity to study evolution in action; for the period of mountain uplift is known, and many of the ancestral taxa occur in fossil deposits scattered from southwestern Asia into Europe (*see* Tralau, 1963; Florin, 1963).

Survival and Extinction

DECREASE IN DIVERSITY

The fossil record shows that the temperate mixed evergreen dicot and conifer forests that made up the Antarcto-Tertiary Geoflora were rather similar regionally from New Zealand-Australia to Chile-Argentina *via* Antarctica. Genera now confined to one region had wider distributions in the past. *Nothofagus* is recorded on Antarctica; species of the *N. brassii* group, now in New Guinea, New Caledonia, and southern Argentina (van Steenis, 1971), are represented as fossil in Australia-Tasmania-New Zealand; *Araucaria* has been recorded on Antarctica, Kerguelen, and New Zealand, and in India; and *Dacyridium* is known from the mainland of Australia, Kerguelen, Antarctica, and India but survives only in Tasmania.

Today the temperate rainforest of New Zealand is much richer in taxa than that of southern Chile (Godley, 1960). There are 39 angiosperm families common to both areas; 7 in Chile are not in New Zealand, and 24 families in New Zealand are not in southern Chile, including a number of tropical-subtropical alliances: Chloranthaceae, Corynocarpaceae, Icacinaceae, Lauraceae, Meliaceae, Moraceae, Myristicaceae, Palmae, Pandanaceae, Passifloraceae, Piperaceae, Sapindaceae, Tiliaceae. The richer, more diverse forest of New Zealand reflects its different geologic history as compared with that of Chile. The fossil record shows that the forests of each region were relatively similar into Miocene time. Many New Zealand taxa persisted there as climate deteriorated across higher latitudes because New Zealand was being rafted to a more equable marine climate at middle latitudes and was largely removed from the effects of severe cold or drought. At the same time, it was enriched by immigrants from the north *via* new volcanic archipelagos (Solomons, New Hebrides) and also, during Miocene and later times, from the now largely-submerged Norfolk Ridge and Lord Howe Rise. By contrast, the Chilean area has not shifted greatly in latitude, and the forest could not receive new immigrants. As drought spread down the west coast, the forest retreated southward to moister latitudes; relict patches still persist on the fog-shrouded coastal hills well north of Santiago where the trees are mostly small and are surrounded by semiarid scrub. Late Tertiary uplift of the Andes caused the spread of drier colder climate over the Argentine plain, confining the temperate rainforest that had dominated there into Miocene time to the moist upper slopes of the Andes. Following restriction of the rainforest by drought, glacial climate spread along the andine axis and down onto the lowland plains to the east and west, further decimating the remaining forest, and leaving only hardy survivors in the surviving impoverished community.

The much richer representation of archaic plants in Australasia than in South America today does not imply that they have always been absent in South America; some (e.g., *Casuarina* div. *Gymnostomae,* Frenguelli, 1943; L. A. S. Johnson, personal communication; *Acmopyle, Podocarpus* sect. *Dacrycarpus,* Florin, 1963) have already been found there, and others should be sought in the fossil record. Extinction on a continental scale in South America, the amelioration of the climate in Australasia because of its northward movement during the Tertiary, and the greater inaccessibility of Australasia to immigration from Eurasia have all contributed to its existing geographical patterns.

As the Australian plate moved into lower middle latitudes following Eocene time, it entered the permanent high-pressure belt of low precipitation at the south margin of the tropics. As a result, the temperate rainforest, composed of southern beech, araucarias, podocarps, proteads, and other evergreen dicots that had covered much of the continent, was progressively restricted to moist equable southeast Australia-Tasmania. During this movement, many taxa underwent severe restrictions in range, and others must have become extinct. Some that were in the region survive as relicts on offshore lands such as New Caledonia, Fiji, and New Zealand. Eventually, as the Australian plate moved northward and particularly after New Guinea emerged in tropical latitudes, many plants and animals from Asia entered the region for the first time. The rich radiation of elapid snakes in Australia probably dates from the first Miocene contacts with Asia, whereas the colubrids entered much later, judging from their dominance in the world fauna and much more limited radiation. Snakes seem to be a Eurasian middle to late Cretaceous branch of lizards which reached both Australia and South America from the north *via* sweepstakes routes in Neogene time, and Africa perhaps earlier.

Depletion of taxa is also shown by the history of the Indian plate which crossed the wet tropics during the Tertiary and moved rapidly into the dry belt at its north edge by Miocene time (Axelrod, 1972b). Numerous forest trees disappeared, and many others were confined to the moister east (Assam-Malaya) as shown by the nature of the Neogene floras (Lakhanpal, 1970). Relationships with Africa may have been of greatest importance in Cretaceous and Paleogene time (Veevers et al., 1971), those with Asia arising chiefly in Neogene time. India has few endemics as compared with other tropical areas of equal size. Many of those that presumably were there in the early Tertiary probably were eliminated as: a) the plate moved across the inner torrid tropics as b) it was rafted into the drier monsoonal belt and as c) climate changed from equable marine to continental when the Indian and Asian plates collided during Miocene time. The record also indicates that in latest Cretaceous-Paleocene time, when central India was situated near Lat. 30°S, the region supported southern temperate taxa (e.g., leptodactylid frogs, araucarias, proteads, casuarina) that are no longer there. These plants that required generally moist temperate climates probably also became extinct as the plate moved into the torrid tropics because most of the region was low, and mountains of sufficient altitude were not present for their continued survival. *Hortonia,* an archaic angiosperm of monimiaceous alliance, which is the only representative of its family and endemic to Ceylon, evidently is an austral angiosperm that survived on the Indian subcontinent. The paleobiology of India will yield one of the most fascinating Cretaceous-Paleogene sequences anywhere in the world when it has been more comprehensively sampled and worked up.

INCREASE IN DIVERSITY

Rafting lands to new climatic belts has provided new opportunities for evolution. As Australia moved into a zone of warmer drier climate, plant genera such as *Acacia, Eucalyptus, Casuarina, Melaleuca, Hakea,* and *Eremophila,* and animal groups such as the bee family Colletidae and the acridid grasshoppers proliferated into scores of new species adapted to progressively drier, more continental climates. And as drought continued to spread over the interior, new opportunities appeared for temperate austral families which evolved a wholly new flora composed of desert and desert-border alliances restricted to the drier parts of Australia. Some of these groups had earlier evolved sclerophyllous representatives in regions of infertile soil or local aridity. In any case, there were no sources of immigrants for the expanding subhumid and semiarid habitats of Australia—the plants and animals that contributed to this expanding zone were autochthonous. By contrast, the arid flora of India had a very different history. As noted above, during late Cretaceous-Eocene times, the Indian plate was covered with forest and well watered. As it moved across the inner tropical belt and encountered rapidly-spreading aridity during Miocene and later times, its western part was invaded by a flora that had already evolved in response to the dry climate which had appeared over southwest Asia by Eo-Oligocene time. Thus, it is understandable that whereas many of the taxa in the tropical scrub and desert vegetation of India range widely to the west (Afghanistan, Iran, Arabia, Egypt), those in Australia are endemic because they developed and remained in isolation. These relations appear to explain why India, even though isolated longer than Australia, has a relatively impoverished flora and few plant endemics at the familial and generic level as compared with Australia (Axelrod, 1972b).

New opportunities for increased diversity on land also develop when two plates fuse, and a new mountain system is rapidly elevated. During its early northward movement, the leading edge of the Australian plate (e.g., New Guinea) was submerged, but as it encountered the Asian plate during the late Oligocene, land appeared, and the island assumed its present outlines for the first time within the tropical zone. This relatively lowland region was immediately invaded by the rich tropical Malaysian flora. The island was uplifted 4,000 m to over 5,000 m, the altitude of its mountainous backbone, in late Tertiary and Quaternary times. As diverse new tropical montane to alpine zones appeared in response to uplift, numerous taxa diversified in these new montane zones, in such groups as the birds, orchids (2,500 species), *Rhododendron, Ficus,* and many insects. In the same way, rapid uplift of the Himalayas during Pliocene and Pleistocene times has provided a new theater for evolution of scores of new species of *Quercus, Rhododendron, Primula,* and *Pedicularis* which invaded the region from both the moister, more equable east (affinites with China-Japan) and from the drier, less equable west (affinities with taxa in Caucasus, Elburz, Hindu Kush ranges).

In the temperate parts of the Northern Hemisphere, increased diversity is related primarily to the major environmental event of the Cenozoic—the spread of progressively drier and colder climates. This trend, initially ascribed by A. R. Wallace to general continental uplift, mountain building, and withdrawal of seaways from the continents during the Cenozoic, was later "explained" almost wholly by decreased solar radiation. It is now apparent that northward movement of the American plate some 10° to 15° and closing the arctic basin by continental rotation had a crucial role in bringing progressively colder, more continental climates to high and middle latitudes (Crowell and Frakes, 1970). As the interior regions of Eurasia and Noorth America underwent progressive dessication, forests gradually retreated, and patches of prairie in forest-border regions spread gradually to form extensive grasslands and steppes in which there has been a great proliferation of new species and genera. As the northern conifer forests retreated to somewhat lower latitudes and cold increased, tundra plants spread out from earlier localized sites in mountainous areas and gave rise to scores of new races, subspecies, and some species. Another important event that resulted from the glacial climates has been the appearance of mediterranean climate, chiefly in response to colder oceans that developed after each glaciation. These summer dry climates have provided a new theater for evolution, chiefly for herbs and grasses (Axelrod, 1972c; Raven, 1972a). The desert floras, which are primarily post-glacial in their present extent, derived most of their taxa from ancestors in adjacent steppe and border-woodland environments.

The Future

The preceding brief sketch of some of the results and problems raised by an integration of evolutionary biogeographic problems with plate tectonic theory points up some avenues for future work.

1) Inasmuch as the solution to any biogeographic evolutionary problem must be based first on sound toxonomy, taxonomic studies must continue. Monographic studies of natural cohorts, especially well-knit groups including diverse genera, should be especially rewarding when interpreted in terms of earth history.

2) Many problems of biogeography, including the age of taxa, can be clarified by the fossil record. Numerous fossil floras and faunas that have been collected are still undescribed; others need revision by modern methods. In the case of the older Tertiary and Cretaceous floras, investigators should turn to the tropical and temperate regions of the entire world in searching for their taxa before new genera are described. Some floras in critical geographic positions (e.g., Palmer I., Snow Hill I., South Orkeny I., Kerguelen) should be re-collected adequately and described; the associated rocks may yield remains of mammals or other animals.

Study of pollen preserved in old soils between lava flows on oceanic islands can provide critical evidence concerning the composition of Neogene oceanic island floras, and (hopefully) rates of evolution there.

3) The preceding would be facilitated greatly by the compilation of a World Atlas of Palynology for ready reference by all investigators. All palynomorphs should be illustrated by scanning electron microscope photos. This should be a cooperative study, and all illustrations should indicate the source (herbarium sheet number) so that changes in the disposition of species can readily be made. Until such a comprehensive source is available, it will remain virtually impossible to relate many Paleogene and older pollens or spores to their nearest modern relatives.

In addition, a World Atlas of Leaf Morphology, commenced in the days of Ettingshausen, should be completed and illustrated by cleared leaves that show the venation of all genera and many species. With suitable magnification, these can be used for comparison with fossil plants anywhere in the world. This would be of invaluable aid to paleobotanists and also to morphologists concerned with problems of evolution of leaf venation and form. Information on cuticular structure, which has proved so useful in evaluating a number of problems in recent years, should likewise be systematized and made readily available.

4) To aid biogeographers in distributional problems, computerized up-to-date lists of fossil faunas and floras should be assembled at a central repository, available on call by anyone needing data for any region and time (Miocene of Siberia; Eocene of New Zealand, etc.). These could quickly be assembled by specialists in the respective fields and made available by appropriate data processing methodology.

5) From the preceding data, it will be possible to assemble an Atlas of Biogeography. Each natural group should be mapped—and with all maps at the same scale. The data can be programmed, and by using a Calcomp plotter and geographic coordinates, it would be possible to get a print-out of the distribution of a species, genus, tribe, or family—living or fossil—on a world map. Such maps should be assembled for insects, frogs, pines, oaks, earthworms, etc. and should be made available to anyone or to any library. If filed in loose-leaf form, revisions could readily be made to replace older outmoded maps. Such an atlas would be of inestimable value, and many critical relations that have otherwise escaped notice should be readily apparent by mere inspection.

6) To assist in all the above programs, suitable bibliographic refer-

ences must be readily available. These can be placed in a computer bank and called on to give any desired information that may be stored there. This also should be part of an international cooperative program.

The solution of many biogeographic and evolutionary problems is within reach, but requires the assembly of much more comprehensive banks of data so that existing information can be made more readily available. As geological evidence continues to accumulate, the need for accurate and complete biological information will increase exponentially. It is clearly time to lay the foundation that will be necessary if such needs are to be met.

ACKNOWLEDGMENTS

We are grateful for support individually received through a series of grants from the National Science Foundation. Malcolm C. McKenna has kindly reviewed the manuscript.

References

Axelrod, D. I. 1966. Origin of deciduous and evergreen habits in temperate forests. *Evolution,* **20**: 1-15.
*————. 1970. Mesozoic paleogeography and early angiosperm history. *Botan. Rev.,* **36** (3): 277-319.
*————. 1972a. Ocean floor spreading in relation to ecosystematic problems. *In*: R. R. Allen (ed.). *Symposium on Ecosystematics, April 1971.* Univ. of Arkansas Press, Fayetteville, Ark. (In press.)
*————. 1972b. Plate tectonics in relation to angiosperm distribution in India. R. N. Lakhanpal (ed.). B. Sahni Inst. Paleobot. Silver Jubilee Celebration, Dec. 1971. Lucknow, India. *The Paleobotanist.* (In press).
*————. 1972c. History of the Mediterranean ecosystem in California. *In*: H. Mooney and F. Di Castri (eds.). *Evolution of Mediterranean Ecosystems.* Springer-Verlag, New York. (In press.)
Brundin, L. 1965. On the real nature of transantarctic relationships. *Evolution,* **19**: 496-505.
Camp, W. H. 1947. Distribution patterns in modern plants and the problems of ancient dispersals. *Ecol. Monogr.,* **17**: 159-183.
Colbert, E. H. 1971. Tetrapods and continents. *Quart. Rev. Biol.,* **46**: 250-269.

* Indicates works with extensive bibliographies which document much of the data summarized in this paper.

Crowell, J. C. and L. A. Frakes. 1970. Phanerozoic glaciation and the causes of ice ages. *Amer. J. Sci.,* **268**: 193-224.

Darlington, P. J., Jr. 1957. *Zoogeography.* John Wiley & Sons, New York. 675 p.

Dietz, R. S. and J. C. Holden. 1970. Reconstruction of Pangaea: Breakup and dispersion of continents, Permian to Present. *J. Geophys. Res.,* **75**: 4939.

Florin, R. 1963. The distribution of conifer and taxad genera in time and space. *Acta Horti Bergiana,* **20**: 121-312.

Fooden, J. 1972. Breakup of Pangaea and isolation of relict mammals in Australia, South America, and Madagascar. *Science,* **175**: 894-898.

Frenguelli, J. 1943. Restos de *Casuarina* en el Mioceno de El Mirador, Patagonia Central. *Not. Mus. La Plata,* **8**: 349-354.

Godley, E. J. 1960. The botany of southern Chile in relation to New Zealand and the subantarctic. *Roy. Soc. London Proc.,* ser. B, **152**: 457-475.

Heirtzler, J. R. 1971. The evolution of the southern oceans. In: *Research in the Antarctic. Amer. Assoc. Adv. Sci. Publ.* 93. p. 667-684.

Keast, A. 1971. Continental drift and the evolution of the biota on southern continents. *Quart. Rev. Biol.,* **46**: 335-378.

Kitching, J. W., J. W. Collinson, and E. H. Colbert. 1972. *Lystrosaurus* zone (Triassic) fauna from Antarctica. *Science,* **175**: 524-527.

Lakhanpal, R. N. 1970. Tertiary floras of India and their bearing on the historical geology of the region. *Taxon,* **19** (5): 675-695.

McKenna, M. C. 1972a. Was Europe connected directly to North America prior to the middle Eocene? *Evol. Biol.,* **6**. (In press.)

———. 1972b. Biological consequences of plate tectonics. *BioScience.* (In press.)

Malfait, B. T. and M. G. Dinkleman. 1972. Circum-Caribbean tectonic and igneous activity and the evolution of the Caribbean plate. *Geol. Soc. Amer. Bull.,* **83**: 251-272.

Muesel, H. and R. Schubert. 1971. Beitrage zur pflanzengeographie des Westhimalayas. *Flora,* **160** (2): 137-194; (4) 373-432; (6) 573-606.

Muller, J. 1970. Palynological evidence on the early differentiation of angiosperms. *Biol. Rev.,* **45** (3): 417-450.

Myers, G. S. 1967. Zoogeographical evidence of the age of the South Atlantic Ocean. *Stud. Trop. Oceanogr. Miami,* **5**: 614-621.

*Raven, P. H. 1963. Amphitropical relations in the floras of North and South America. *Quart. Rev. Biol.,* **38**: 151-177.

*———. 1972a. The evolution of "mediterranean" floras. *In*: H. Mooney and F. Di Castri (eds.). *Evolution of Mediterranean Ecosystems.* Springer-Verlag, New York. (In press.)

*———. 1972b. Plant species disjunctions: A summary. A.I.B.S. Meetings, Edmonton, 1971.

*——— and D. I. Axelrod. 1972. Plate tectonics and Australasian paleobiogeography. *Science.* (In press.)

Riek, E. F. 1970. Fossil history: In: *Inects of Australia* (C.S.I.R.O.). p. 168-186. Melbourne Univ. Press.

Seward, A. C. 1941. *Plant Life through the Ages.* 2nd ed., reprinted. Cambridge Univ. Press, London. 607 p.

Steenis van, C. G. G. J. 1971. *Nothofagus,* key genus of plant geography, in time and space, living and fossil, ecology and phylogeny. *Blumea,* **19**: 65-98

Tralau, H. 1963. Asiatic dicotyledonous affinities in the Cainozoic floras of Europe, *Kungl. Svenska Vetenskapsakad. Handl.,* **9** (3): 1-87.

Veevers, J. J., J. G. Jones, and J. A. Talent. 1971. Indo-Australian stratigraphy and the configuration and dispersal of Gondwanaland. *Nature,* **229**: 383-388.

12 The Regulation of Human Population

DAVID E. DAVIS
DEPARTMENT OF ZOOLOGY
North Carolina State University

During the next 25 years, the state of the human population will be settled for many centuries in the future. The rapid increase of humans needs little documentation; figures readily available indicate that the population will double in 20 or 30 years, depending on the details of the rate. Continuation of these rates will result in fundamental changes in the nature of the human population (Toffler, 1970) and its relation to the environment. The purpose of this essay is to consider our current knowledge of animal populations to see what insights such information might produce about the future of the human population. Obviously, the basic question is how is the human population regulated? We assume that it *is* regulated and will not increase forever. However, regulation can occur in various ways, and the really important question is whether human populations regulate their own numbers.

Regulation in Animals

The factual information about animal populations has now accumulated to a level that permits generalizations. For the past 25 years, numerous studies using species ranging from yeast to elephants have supplied facts allowing interpretation. The methods have become increasingly complex, starting with simple counting and rather crude measures of birth rates and death rates to elaborate experimental methods in the laboratory and to intensive observational methods in the field. Finally, the use of computer simulation, based on the mathematical models which were originated 50 years ago, has allowed population ecologists to project the changes that occur following variations in birth and death rates. Thus, it can be said that in the last 25 years the study of population dynamics has matured. From these generalizations, some suggestions may be made about the regulation of human populations. Let us now consider animals.

It is, of course, obvious that animal populations are regulated somehow since no population shows a continuous increase for more than a few years. Clearly, an infinite increase would mean that eventually all the protoplasm in the world would be taken up by one species. So, the question becomes: What are the various ways of regulation?

1) As has been noted for many decades, many species, especially primitive ones, are regulated by climatic changes or by exhaustion of resources. Such species increase rapidly under favorable circumstances, and then, when climatic conditions change or the resources decline, the species decreases. While observations of rapid increases and catastrophic declines are numerous, documented histories are rare. Grasshoppers (Birch, 1954) in Australia increase, at least in parts of their range, until some weather condition changes, and the numbers decline. The oak moth (Harville, 1955), in the northern part of its range, increases in several good years and then declines in cold winters. Quail (Errington, 1945) survive in Wisconsin in mild winters but may die out in cold winters. Rabbits, introduced onto Pacific Islands, in some cases destroyed the vegetation and died out but in other cases reached some sort of balance with the growth of plants.

2) Another big category is limitation of population by predation and disease. Under these circumstances, the predators or pathogens increase sufficiently to produce a reduction in the host population. For several reasons, evidence for this type of regulation is rather difficult to describe. Most predator-prey systems are rather well balanced so that the populations change only slightly except when a change in habitat alters the circumstances. Maladjusted predator-prey systems disappear for the obvious reason that one or the other or both become extinct. However, some examples have been adequately documented. A pair of mites form

a predator-prey system on strawberries (Huffaker and Kennett, 1956). If the plants are properly maintained, the mites will remain at reasonable levels. Among mammals, wolves and moose (Mech, 1970) keep in relative balance, and the antelopes of East Africa (Estes and Goddard, 1967) also coexist with various predators. Parasites and diseases, which from the present viewpoint perform as predators, act in much the same manner. The continued existence of parasites attests to their ability to persist in the face of changes in host populations. Proof that a particular parasite or pathogen regulates a particular host is difficult to obtain due to the multiplicity of factors in natural populations.

Introduced predators, parasites, or pathogens frequently bring populations into a new balance. The myxoma virus (Fenner and Ratcliffe, 1965) has literally decimated the Australian rabbit. Insect parasites (DeBach, 1969) have regulated the scale insects on citrus. In some cases, the introduced species has exterminated the prey which, of course, is not regulation since the system can no longer operate.

Sometimes the population changes result in oscillations although the forces of adaptation over the centuries tend to dampen the oscillations so that a truly well adjusted predator-prey system shows rather constant numbers of host and, obviously, of predator.

3) A third category is self-regulation. The term refers to the possibility that populations contain internal mechanisms that allow them to regulate their own numbers. Such mechanisms provide the most complex and highest evolutionary level of regulatory ability. Note that the term "self-regulation" suggests the possibility of purpose or of agreement on a level of numbers. Among animals, no evidence exists that the members of a species have agreed upon a particular level, but it seems clear that survival of groups or of species has favored those populations that by some device maintain their level below the capacity of the environment. Therefore, it is desirable to explore various mechanisms used by animals for self-regulation.

One process which has some aspects of self-regulation is the production of toxic substances. For example, tadpoles (Rose, 1960) excrete chemicals that inhibit the growth of all tadpoles in the pond. Other examples occur in fish. The process is not truly a feedback process but, apparently, simply an accumulation that results in inhibition of growth or reproduction. As far as now known, all individuals are equally inhibited, and social rank, if it exists, does not confer an advantage to the dominant animals. In this arrangement, rank confers no selective value.

To regulate itself, a species might alter the environment or habitat. Few species can change the weather or prevent floods, but many species have circumvented the effects of environment by some device. Construction of nests or burrows and various behavioral activities can mitigate environmental hazards. The relative constancy of temperature in a bee hive is an example of behavioral and constructional adaptation. However, the procedure of avoiding the deleterious impact of the environment promotes survival and increase but does not regulate the species in the sense of preventing excessive numbers.

Another means is the development of physiological mechanisms that have a potential for altering the birth rates and death rates. Presumably, many species, including invertebrates as well as vertebrates, have incipient mechanisms that, at some times, affect birth rates and death rates. However, at the present time, the only mechanism that has been intensively studied is the pituitary-adrenal feedback process in mammals. Therefore, let us consider the mechanism in general terms.

In several species, extensive laboratory work has demonstrated that, as a consequence of aggressive behavior among individuals, the pituitary gland secretes ACTH which stimulates the adrenal cortex to produce corticoid hormones (Christian and Davis, 1964). As a population increases, the amount of fighting increases. Adding tranquilizers to the food resulted in a decline in fighting in colonies of mice (Vessey, 1967) and an improvement in survival of young mice. In lemmings, the percentage of wounded individuals before the peak was 35, at the peak was 55, and after the peak was 19 (Krebs, 1964). Australian rabbits (Myers 1964), at a density of 50 rabbits per acre, showed 2.6 aggressive acts per hour while at 200 per acre showed 18 per hour.

The physiological repercussions of density are now well known. The average size of the adrenal increases, the low ranking animals have the largest, and the secretion of corticoids increases (Christian et al., 1965). The effects pervade many aspects of the animal's life, such as early experience. Consider the exposure of mice to an open field after a treatment of handling in infancy (Chapman et al., 1969). The dominant mice had small adrenals (3.1 mg *vs* 4.2 mg), large seminal vesicles, and high concentrations of fructose. When exposed to an open field, the subordinate mice that had been handled showed great increase in corticosterone in the plasma while the unhandled mice failed to show a difference. Equally complex results occur in relation to the circadian rhythm of ACTH and, consequently, corticoids. Stimulation results in greater response at the trough than at the peaks (Ader and Friedman, 1968), presumably because little further increase is possible. The temporal sequences differ in rats kept 1 or 4 per cage (Plaut and Grota, 1971). The plasma corticosterone, after stimulation, reaches a peak but drops more rapidly in crowded rats.

The corticoids, as well as ACTH, affect reproductive performance (Christian, 1971a) in many ways. The increased levels of adrenal androgens block the production of gonadotropins in the pituitary as shown by use of parabionts. Injection of ACTH in normal and in adrenectomized mice resulted in inhibition of ovarian function. An inhibitory effect was not obtained in male house mice (Lloyd, 1971) but was obtained in male white-footed mice. The reproductive organs and the thymus were inhibited (Pasley and Christian, 1971).

In addition to effects on reproduction, crowding results in change in resistance to infection and also in physiological derangements (Christian, 1963). A frequent result of crowding is inhibition of the thymus which is an indication of lowered antibody function. Experiments with mice showed that low-ranking mice responded weakly to injected beef protein (Vessey, 1964). Reports of effects of corticoids on susceptibility are legion (Kass, 1960; McDermott, 1959). Furthermore, ACTH directly affects the kidneys of house mice and woodchucks causing lesions that may result in death (Christian, 1971b). Increases in mortality occur in rabbits (Myers, 1964) and squirrels.

A final set of repercussions affect the young. Crowding results in stunting in several species (Christian, 1971a; Martinet and Spitz, 1971). Also, corticoids have very complex effects on behavior. Prenatally stressed rats showed a reduction of copulatory behavior when they became adults, but postnatal stress had no effect (Ward, 1972). Corticosterone from pellets implanted during age 2 to 14 days resulted in impairment of fine adjustment of motor control (Howard and Granoff, 1968). Handling rats at early age prepares the adrenal cortex to respond to later stimulation (Levine, 1967).

All these phenomena act to produce a negative feedback process that reduces the birth rate and increases the mortality rate as the density increases.

However, let us consider the situation in other mammals. The existence of self-regulation is clear in certain species, mostly rodents. A comparison of the information about different kinds of mammals is instructive. For the house mouse, the self-regulatory system works smoothly; as the population increases, the birth rate decreases, the mortality rate increases, and the population gradually reduces its growth rate to reach a stationary level which may be maintained for many months, at least under experimental conditions. In nature, house mouse populations, if the habitat is not disturbed, will continue at a rather constant level (Brown, 1953). However, other rodents, especially the microtines, including meadow voles and lemmings, show rather great fluctuations in numbers. Sufficient experimental work has been done to show that the pituitary mechanism operates (Andrews, 1968) but clearly is not able to operate smoothly enough to prevent fluctuations such as the conspicuous cycles of lemmings. The existence of these cycles does not indicate that the mechanism is absent; it simply indicates that the mechanism is not sufficiently tied through negative feedback loops to the population number to provide a close regulation. Furthermore, in microtines, emigration is perhaps more important in regulation than is the case in house mice or in Norway rats. Among deer, which are also herbivores, the meager evidence suggests that the pituitary-adrenal mechanism occurs and does operate (Welch, 1963). However, the adjustment is not adequate to prevent an increase to the level of starvation. Thus, among herbivores, great variation exists in the extent of adjustment through negative feedbacks to the population level. In some species, the adjustment is good, and in others, it is poor.

It is instructive to note that among carnivores the pituitary-adrenal mechanism clearly exists, but evidence concerning the possibility that it operates a self-regulatory mechanism is absent simply because no one has studied a carnivore from this viewpoint. In many cases, carnivores are rigidly territorial, and their abundance is perforce low. Thus, one would not expect that a density-regulating mechanism would occur. (Obviously, species that go in packs, such as wolves, should be carefully studied.)

The conclusions thus far have been derived from rodents and a few other species. In preparation for a discussion of humans, let's consider the possibility of experimentation with primates. Here, rather extensive information has accumulated, especially in the last decade, about the social organization and aggressive behavior of various species, including the apes. However, for practical reasons and also because of lack of interest, no true experiments on the self-regulatory physiological mechanisms have been conducted with populations.

Numerous studies show that primates have aggressive behavior (Russell and Russell, 1968). Crowding increases aggressive behavior but does not alter the social rank (Alexander and Roth, 1971). Transfer of a monkey from a group to isolation results in a decrease of ACTH in subordinate monkeys, and removal of a dominant monkey from a group resulted in a decline of ACTH in the low-ranking monkeys (Sassenrath, 1970).

Controlling Human Population

Now, let us consider the means of regulation of human populations. For thousands of years, the ancestors of humans remained at low numbers, presumably in accord with their environment and probably regulated in much the same manner as are other mammals. Then, about two million years ago in Africa, species emerged which were sufficiently generalized in their habits, especially their food habits, to take advantage of a variety of environmental circumstances. Most importantly, a brain evolved that allowed them to make technical advances. They developed the ability to use fire and to use tools and, thereby, become emancipated to a considerable degree from their local habitat. Thus, the ancestral kinds of man increased in numbers and eventually evolved into man that has spread throughout the world. Surely the numbers of individuals fluctuated up and down but, over the centuries, generally increased (McMichael, 1959). These changes occurred with increasing intensity until the industrial revolution permitted the spurt in numbers that recently has occurred. The number of years necessary for the population to double has changed literally from measurement in centuries to measurement in decades.

The factors that controlled the rate of growth cannot now be determined, but one can examine the history of some islands in the past century. Such histories provide some understanding of population changes in early man. The population of Mauritius increased rapidly from 1760-1860, declined from a severe epidemic of malaria, and then reached a stability (Anderson, 1929) that was maintained until an increase began in 1950 (Brookfield, 1957). The stability was possible because disease and emigration occurred; the recent increase followed a decline in mortality rate. The population of Tikopia increased from 1929-1952 (Bovvie et al., 1957), but the age at marriage and the number of children per female declined. The population of Cyprus increased from 1881-1953, but the rate of increase declined (Taeuber, 1955). The population of Yap actually declined from 1850-1951 (Hunt et al., 1954), in part from complex taboos on coitus. In several societies, increase in number was accompanied by increase in polygyny (Dorjohn, 1958) and a decline in births per female (Muksam, 1956).

During this period of time, humans have developed methods for controlling factors that might limit their numbers. The results of catastrophies, such as floods or drought, have now largely been eliminated although some disasters still occur. Nevertheless, techniques, such as storage and transportation of food or the construction of dams, have largely prevented adverse effects. The level of food supply has long been recognized as crucial. The provision of food, first in the agricultural revolution and then in the industrial revolution, has increased amazingly (Maynard, 1952). Such improvements as the invention of cooking pots (Cowles, 1963) have reduced infant mortality. The splendid supply of energy provided by the potato had decisive influence in various countries, first by its increase and then by its decline (Salaman, 1949). The increased provision of food by diverse means (Harrar, 1955) seems likely to allow interminable increase in population (Cook, 1951) and is only a short-range solution in local areas (Mangelsdorf, 1961) although the birth rate is declining (Kirk, 1955; Dobzhansky, 1967).

The role of disease and predators in limitation of population has become insignificant. Formerly, pestilence was common and, indeed preferred, to other means. In II Samuel 24, it is recorded that King David (for reasons not stated) requested a census of the people of Israel and Judah which totaled 1,300,000 men. Then, Gad, one of David's seers, gave David the choice of: 1) 7 years of famine; 2) flight for 3 months; 3) pestilence. The Lord chose the last, and 70,000 men died. Other episodes, such as the Black Death around 1660, are numerous. The conquest of poliomyelitis is fresh in our memory. While disease and predators are still present, they no longer cause man significant losses.

As in the case of some animals, there is the possibility that direct competition can limit the population. While war for centuries has reduced populations, births have rapidly replaced the losses. In some cases (Vayda, 1961), war provides resources for increase, and in contrast, cessation of tribal warfare allows increase (Bryan and Springfield, 1955). Pressure of one group upon another's territory may push whole tribes into unfavorable climates (Bridges, 1949). Indeed, population increase in a country that will need to expand is everyone's concern (Thompson, 1952). On an individual level, competition effectively reduced the birth rate on farms in Poland around 1870 (Stys, 1957). As population increased, the land was divided into smaller units for distribution among progeny. The age at marriage was negatively correlated, and the number of children born per woman was positively correlated with the size of the farm. Below a critical size, the farmers had to leave.

From these items of information, we see that the usual factors limiting animal populations are not limiting humans—at least not at present. The question now is whether some type of self-regulation exists. A simple example is pollution of the external environment which may have regulated human numbers. However, sanitation systems have generally prevented pollution from preventing increase in numbers.

In considering the possibility that humans can themselves regulate their own population, it is necessary first to determine how data could be obtained. Following the examples from animals, individuals from populations of known numbers could be examined to measure reproductive organs. Experimentally, populations might be artificially increased by the introduction of individuals or decreased by the removal. For example, one could measure the number of individuals in a population for a period of time and then remove half for examination. Subsequently, as the population increased, samples could be taken at suitable intervals. Another technique would be to study humans in the laboratory with various manipulations of organs and innoculations of pathogens. It is perfectly obvious that such experimental approaches to human populations cannot be conducted. Indeed, information about humans is essentially impossible to obtain, even after such natural catastrophies as the typhoon in Bangladesh. Thus, while one can get bits and pieces of information that may agree or disagree with the theory, experimental approaches to human populations cannot be made. One can say that we can never truly know whether human populations can regulate themselves or not since direct evidence can never, for practical reasons, become available. Theoretically, it is possible to design experiments with human populations. Indeed, it is easy to design these experiments, but their completion is not permissible.

There remains, nevertheless, the possibility that man does regulate his own population through some physiological mechanism. Let us consider, in general terms, the pituitary-adrenal feedback, since this is best known and probably the most prominent of the physiological feedback mechanisms occurring in mammals.

For humans, the existence of aggressive behavior needs no documentation; a glance at a school playground at recess (Body, 1955) is ample evidence, and experiments illustrate many aspects (Griffitt and Veitch, 1971). Primitive tribes have ritual performances that settle rank without severe injury, such as the wrestling of Fuegians (Bridges, 1949). Complex and severe ranks are developed in prison camps (McElroy, 1958). Even in polite society, the needs for personal space manifest themselves (Sommer, 1959).

The physiological effects of stress on adrenal function are adequately documented (Estep, 1967). Auditory stimuli increase the levels of cortisol in plasma in normal men and in some types of psychiatric patients (Arguelles, 1967). Pilots showed adrenocorticol response in landing practice (Rubin et al., 1970). Evidence is abundant in man that the physiological consequences inhibit the reproductive organs and increase the susceptibility to infections.

The critical point is that evidence has not yet become available that the aggressive behavior is linked to the reproductive and susceptibility consequences in humans or, indeed, in primates. In mice, the connection is very clear because, experimentally, it can be shown that aggressive behavior is promptly followed by changes in reproduction and in susceptibility, but, as yet, such data are not available for primates. Of course, as explained in detail above, the appropriate experiments have not been done and, fortunately, will not be done with humans. Furthermore, the appropriate experiments have not been done on primate populations largely because of the impracticability of studying appropriate numbers over several decades. However, there are bits and pieces of evidence, such as certain pathological situations in individuals who have been subjected to aggressive stress and such generalized items as the reported increase in mental illness. In addition, there are complex decreases in birth rates associated with crowding in cities but, obviously, confounded by many other factors. These items of information provide a very suggestive possibility that human populations are regulating themselves but do not, by any means prove the point. The difficulty is that these items, although numerous, are only correlations and, thus, do not establish a causal relation. However, a rather clear set of evidence is the documented decline in age at sexual maturity in humans for the past two decades. In rodents, a contrary change is one of the first and most powerful reactions to increase in numbers and causes a significant decline in the rate of increase. Thus, the evidence for humans suggests the absence of a self-regulatory feedback mechanism. Our situation, then, is that we do not know whether human populations regulate themselves or not, and the likelihood of proving the issue one way or the other in the next 25 years seems remote.

Let us return now to the ancestral humans. Apparently, one species of ape man was herbivorous and became extinct, perhaps by force from the other ape men or by environmental changes. The other species of ape men was carnivorous or, at least, omnivorous. We know nothing, of course, about the social organization, but since he lived in groups, we have to assume that some type of dominance order developed, such as occurs in baboons or primitive human populations. Under these circumstances, we see no compelling reason to suggest that the primitive ape man evolved a self-regulatory, pituitary-adrenal mechanism or, for that matter, any other physiological mechanism for self regulation.

The situation is that, although based on meager evidence, we thus far have no indication that man has a physiological self-regulatory mechanism. Many of the ideas are clearly speculative and, in some cases, are proposed principally to stimulate research during the next 25 years. There remains, however, the possibility that man can develop what can be called an intellectual self-regulation. Thus, man has the challenge of considering his own situation and deciding upon rules and regulations that would restrict his numbers.

Let us first consider the prospects of voluntary birth reduction as a means of restricting the world's population. Physiological technics have now been available long enough to permit assessment. The pessimism of early studies (Darwin, 1958) has not been allayed by recent analyses (Bumpass and Westoff, 1970). Indeed, the economic aspects add more problems (Spengler, 1969). While the means exist, the challenge is to gain acceptance. Lack of information, religious taboos, fears of genocide, social suppression, and many other psychological factors prevent acceptance.

Another possibility for voluntary intelligent limitation is death control. At present, the practice of euthanasia is abhorrent, but in some primitive societies, the practice was routine. Recognizing that contraception and abortion are becoming acceptable in our generation, is it not possible that euthanasia will be accepted by the next generation? The application of death control presents even more formidable problems than those of birth control. All the psychologic problems are intensified because the person is a known individual to family and friends. A set of criteria will have to be established and a set of legal procedures prepared. Ask yourself what circumstances and legal procedures would lead you to want your mother euthanazed. Yet, we all know that our civilization is accumulating geriatric cases in hospitals, nursing homes, and mental institutions. Truly, this situation is a challenge for the future.

Another possible alleviation of the population problem is the distribution of people from densely- to sparsely-populated areas. Obviously, this procedure provides only temporary improvement of the problem. Furthermore, what sparsely-populated area (e.g., Australia) will accept a significant number of persons from a densely-populated area (e.g., India)? Redistribution is no solution.

The prospects for intellectual self-regulation seem poor. It is true at the moment that birth rates are declining in many parts of the world, especially among certain groups. However, the declines will have to be much more rapid than declines in the mortality rates to result in a cessation of increase of population. Furthermore, technological advances in food production and utilization of other resources continue to encourage the increase of population, and on the whole, the population is outdistancing the increase in food. Thus, it appears that the human population is not regulating itself in such a manner as to achieve a level below the capacity of the environment. While groups can come to the intellectual conclusion that populations must be regulated and can develop the technological means for reducing the birth rates, the implementation of these ideas seems to elude their proponents.

Thus far, we have considered the possibility that rates of increase can be changed, but we have not considered the quantitative problem of the level. Volumes have been written on the optimum population (Spengler, 1969; Kirk, 1955; Wolstenholme, 1963; Davis, 1955; Osborn, 1953), but the actual number considered optimum reflects the occupation and circumstances of the individual or the group or the nation. The diaper salesman and the wheelchair salesman will suggest different levels for the optimum! Resolution of these conflicts will require new standards for thinking about resources, involving cooperation and sacrifice. The challenge to the biologist and citizen will be to devise objective criteria for determination of an optimum population. The population problem is far more intractable (Nanes, 1971) than is the problem of food supply, and growth of numbers has very deep economic repercussions on the possibilities of self regulation. As social misery continues unchecked, populations—both rural and urban—become increasingly susceptible to appeals to violence. Yet this violence, contrary to the situation in mice, seems not to set in motion a pituitary-adrenal mechanism which results in a reduction in birth rates and an increase in mortality rates. Thus, man, in the next 25 years, has the challenge to imitate the mouse populations that have, through selection, developed a process for self regulation.

References

Ader, R. and S. B. Friedman. 1968. Plasma corticosterone response to environmental stimulation and the 24-hour adrenocortical rhythm. *Neuroendocrinol.,* **3**(6): 378-386.

Alexander, B. K. and E. M. Roth. 1971. The effects of acute crowding on aggressive behavior of Japanese monkeys. *Behav.,* **39**: 73-90.

Anderson, D. D. 1929. The point of population saturation, its transgression in Mauritius. *Hum. Biol.,* **1**: 528-543.

Andrews, R. V. 1968. Daily and seasonal variation in adrenal metabolism of the brown lemming. *Physiol. Zool.,* **41**(1): 86-94.

Arguelles, A. E. 1967. Endocrine response to auditory stress of normal and psychiatric subjects. *In*: Bajusz, E. (ed.). *An Introduction to Clinical Neuroendocrinology.* Williams and Wilkins Company, Baltimore, Md. p. 121-132.

Birch, L. C. 1954. The role of weather in determining the distribution and abundance of animals. *Cold Spring Harbor Symp.,* **22**: 203-218.

Body, M. K. 1955. Patterns of aggression in the nursery school. *Child Develop.,* **26**(1): 3-11.

Borrie, W. D., R. Firth, and J. Spillus. 1957. The population of Tikopia 1929 and 1952. *Pop. Stud.,* **10**(3): 229-252.

Bridges, E. L. 1949. *Uttermost Part of the Earth*. E. P. Dutton Co., New York. 558 p.

Brookfield, H. C. 1957. Mauritius: demographic upsurge and prospect. *Pop. Stud.,* **11**(2): 102-122.

Brown, R. Z. 1953. Social behavior, reproduction, and population changes in the House Mouse (*Mus musculus*). *Ecol. Monog.,* **23**: 217-240.

Bryan, H. M. and H. W. Springfield. 1955. Range management in Iraq—findings, plan and accomplishment. *J. Range Manag.,* **8**(6): 249-256.

Bumpass, L. and C. F. Westoff. 1970. The "Perfect Contraceptive" population. *Science,* **169**: 1177-1182.

Chapman, V. M., C. Desjardins, and F. H. Bronson. 1969. Social rank in male mice and adrenocortical response to open field exposure. *Proc. Soc. Exp. Biol. Med.,* **130**(2): 624-627.

Christian, J. J. 1963. The pathology of overpopulation. *Mil. Med.,* **128**(7): 571-603.

———. 1971a. Population density and reproductive efficiency. *Biol. Reprod.,* **4**(3): 284-294.

———. 1971b. Population density and fertility in mammals. *In*: P. P. Foa (ed.). *The Action of Hormones.* C. C Thomas, Springfield, Ill. p. 471-499.

——— and D. E. Davis. 1964. Endocrines, behavior, and population. *Science,* **146**: 1550-1560.

———, J. A. Lloyd, and D. E. Davis. 1965. The role of endocrines in the self-regulation of mammalian populations. *Recent Progr. in Hormone Res.,* **21**: 501-578.

Cook, R. C. 1951. *Human Fertility: The Modern Dilemma.* William Sloane Associates, New York. 380 p.

Cowles, R. B. 1963. Missiles, clay pots and mortality rates in primitive man. *Amer. Nat.,* **97**: 29-39.

Darwin, C. 1958. *The Problems of World Population.* The Rede lecture. Cambridge Univ. Press, London. 41 p.

Davis, K. 1955. 'Ideal size' for our population. New York Times, May 1. p. 12, 30, 32, 34, 37.

DeBach, P. 1969. Biological control of diaspine scale insects on citrus in California. *Proc. First Internat. Citrus Symp.,* **2**: 801-815.

Dobzhansky, T. 1967. Changing man—modern evolutionary biology justifies an optimistic view of man's biological future. *Science,* **155**: 409-415.

Dorjohn, R. 1958. Fertility, polygyny and their interrelations in Temme society. *Amer. Anthropol.,* **60**(5): 838-860.

Errington, P. L. 1945. Some contributions of a fifteen-year local study of the northern Bobwhite to a knowledge of population phenomena. *Ecol. Monog.,* **15**(1): 1-34.

Estep, H. L. 1967. Neuroendocrine aspects of surgical stress. *In*: Bajusz, E. (ed.). *An Introduction to Clinical Neuroendocrinology.* Williams and Wilkins Company, Baltimore, Md. p. 106-120.

Estes, R. D. and J. Goddard. 1967. Prey selection and hunting behavior of the African wild dog. *J. Wildl. Manag.*, **31**(1): 52-70.

Fenner, F. and F. N. Ratcliffe. 1965. *Myxomatosis.* Cambridge Univ. Press, Cambridge. 379 p.

Griffitt, W. and R. Veitch. 1971. Hot and crowded: Influences of population density and temperature on interpersonal affective behavior. *J. Pers. Soc. Psychol.*, **17**(1): 92-98.

Harrar, J. G. 1955. Food for the future. *Science,* **122**: 313-316.

Harville, J. P. 1955. Ecology and population dynamics of the California Oak Moth *Phryganida californica* Packard (Lepidoptera:Dioptidae). *Microentomol.*, **20**(4): 83-166.

Howard, E. and D. M. Granoff. 1968. Increased voluntary running and decreased motor coordination in mice after neonatal corticosterone implantation. *Exp. Neurol.*, **22**(4): 661-673.

Huffaker, C. B. and C. E. Kennett. 1956. Experimental studies on predation: Predation and cyclamen-mite populations on strawberries in California. *Hilgardia,* **26**(4): 191-222.

Hunt, E. E., N. R. Kidder, and D. M. Schneider. 1954. The depopulation of Yap. *Hum. Biol.*, **26**(1): 21-51.

Kass, E. H. 1960. Hormones and host resistance to infection. *Bact. Rev.*, **24**(1): 177-185.

Kirk, D. 1955. Dynamics of human populations. *Eugen. Quart.*, **2**(1): 18-25.

Krebs, C. J. 1964. The lemming cycle at Baker Lake, Northwest territories, during 1959-1962. Arctic Inst. N. Amer. Tech. Pap. 15:1-104.

Levine, S. 1967. Maternal and environmental influences on the adrenocortical response to stress in weanling rats. *Science,* **156**: 258-260.

Lloyd, J. A. 1971. Weights of testes, thymi, and accessory reproductive glands in relation to rank in paired and grouped house mice (*Mus musculus*). *Proc. Soc. Exp. Biol. Med.*, **137**(1): 19-22.

Mangelsdorf, P. C. 1961. Biology, food, and people. *Econ. Bot.*, **15**(4): 279-288.

Martinet, L. and F. Spitz. 1971. Variations saisonnaieres de la croissance et de la mortalite du Campagnol des Champs *Microtus arvalis. Mammalia,* **35**(1): 38-84.

Maynard, L. A. 1952. Agricultural and industrial possibilities of increasing the food supply. *Fed. Proc.*, **2**(3): 675-680.

McDermott, W. 1959. Inapparent infection. *Pub. Health Rep.*, **74**(6): 485-499.

McElroy, J. 1958. *This was Andersonville.* McDowell Obolensky, New York. 354 p.

McMichael, E. V. 1959. Towards the estimation of prehistoric populations. *Ind. Acad. Sci. Proc.*, **69**: 78-82.

Mech, L. D. 1970. *The Wolf.* Natural History Press, Garden City, N. Y. 384 p.

Muksam, H. V. 1956. Fertility of polygamous marriages. *Pop. Stud.,* **10**(1): 3-16.

Myers, K. 1964. Influence of density on fecundity, growth rates, and mortality in the wild rabbit. CSIRO *Wildl. Res.,* **9**(2): 134-137.

Nanes, A. S. 1971. Beyond Malthus: The food/people ratio. Committee on Foreign Affairs. 96 p.

Osborn, H. F. 1953. *Limits of the Earth.* Little Brown & Co., Boston. 238 p.

Pasley, J. N. and J. J. Christian. 1971. Effects of ACTH on voles (*Microtus pennsylvanicus*) related to reproductive function and renal disease. *Proc. Soc. Trop. Med. Biol.,* **137**(1): 268-272.

Plaut, S. M. and L. J. Grota. 1971. Effects of differential housing on adrenocortical reactivity. *Neuroendocrinol.,* 7:348-360.

Rose, M. S. 1960. A feedback mechanism of growth control in tadpoles. *Ecol.,* **41**(1): 188-198.

Rubin, R. T., R. G. Miller, R. J. Arthur, and B. R. Clark. 1970. Differential adrenocortical stress responses in naval aviators during aircraft carrier landing practice. *Psychol. Rep.,* **26**(1): 71-74.

Russell, C. and W. M. S. Russell. 1968. *Violence, Monkeys and Men.* The Macmillan Company, New York.

Salaman, R. N. 1949. *The History of Social Influence of the Potato.* Cambridge Univ. Press, London. 685 p.

Sassenrath, E. N. 1970. Increased adrenal responsiveness related to social stress in rhesus monkeys. *Hormones and Behav.,* **1**: 283-297.

Sommer, R. 1959. Studies in personal space. *Sociom.,* **22**(3): 247-260.

Spengler, J. J. 1969. Population problem: In search of a solution. *Science,* **166**: 1234-1238.

Stys, W. 1957. The influence of economic conditions on the fertility of peasant women. *Pop. Stud.,* **11**(2): 136-148.

Taeuber, I. B. 1955. Cyprus: The demography of a strategic island. *Pop. Index,* **21**(1): 4-20.

Thompson, W. S. 1952. Population as a world problem. *Ann. N. Y. Acad. Sci.,* **54**(5): 733-741.

Toffler, A. 1970. *Future Shock.* Random House, New York. 561 p.

Vayda, A. P. 1961. Expansion and warfare among Swidden agriculturists. *Amer. Anthrop.,* **63**(2): 346-359.

Vessey, S. H. 1964. Effects of grouping on levels of circulating antibodies in mice. *Proc. Soc. Exp. Biol. Med.,* **115**: 252-255.

———. 1967. Effects of chlorpromazine on aggression in laboratory populations of wild house mice. *Ecol.,* **48**(3): 367-376.

Ward, I. L. 1972. Prenatal stress feminizes and demasculinizes the behavior of males. *Science,* **175**: 82-84.

Welch, B. L. 1963. Psychophysiological response to the level of environmental stimulation. Proc. XVI Int. Cong. Zool. 1:269.

Wolstenholme, G. 1963. *Man and his Future.* Little, Brown and Company, Boston. 410 p.

13 Coexistence of Species

ROBERT MacARTHUR
DEPARTMENT OF BIOLOGY
Princeton University

Introduction

Part of the charm of science is its unpredictability. And one characteristic of the history of ecology is that students tackle completely new and
unexpected problems rather than tidy up those left by their teachers.
Hence, as a teacher charged with guessing the future of ecology, I begin
with two strikes against me. But the science of ecology finally has some
structure, even if not a very orderly structure as yet, and it is from the
shortcomings of its present structure that we can make the safest predictions of the future. I will analyze these shortcomings in some detail
and hazard guesses as to the difficulties in overcoming them.

Since my task is to predict the future, I shall not review details of
the past here. The empirical and theoretical background of this chapter
is discussed in a book that I wrote last summer: *Geographical Ecology*.
Harper & Row, New York. 1972. 287 p.

Scientists are perennially aware that it is best not to trust theory until
it is confirmed by evidence. It is equally true, as Eddington pointed out,
that it is best not to put too much faith in facts until they have been
confirmed by theory. This is why scientists are reluctant to believe in
ESP in spite of indisputable facts. This is also why group selection is
in such dispute among evolutionists. Only when a reasonable theory can
account for these facts will scientists believe them. Ecology is now in

the position where its facts are confirmable by theory and its theories at least roughly confirmable by facts. But both the facts and the theories have serious inadequacies providing stumbling blocks to present progress.

Present State of Knowledge of Coexistence

It is a platitude to say that species do coexist in nature. What is slightly less commonplace is that both early theory and early bottle experiments suggested that coexistence should be difficult. Darwin had resolved the difficulty before it ever arose by noticing that more similar species should compete more and find it harder to coexist. The theory and bottle experiments had treated either very similar species or ones in environments where their differences could not be shown.

The main progress in recent years has been the slow unravelling of the limiting similarity of coexisting species. Even the theory was hard to work out; in its present form, it can be stated in two ways: 1) In an unchanging environment, an arbitrarily large number of *appropriately* selected species could persist (up to the point where some were so rare they went extinct for random reasons). But the closer the species are packed, the more careful must be the choice of new species. A randomly selected one would likely not succeed when packing was close. In these tightly packed communities, all sorts of unexplored phenomena should exist. For instance, there should be cases of "domino extinction" in which elimination of one species results in the loss of a sequence of other species. 2) In a fluctuating environment, there is a distinct limit to the similarity of coexisting species, and it is a limit that is not too dependent upon the degree of fluctuation. Roughly speaking, species cannot be packed much closer than one standard deviation of the utilization curves of separate species.

Our empirical knowledge comes mostly from birds. Closely related species are often found to be doing just one thing different. For instance, pairs of species often forage in the same places and in the same way and differ only in size and, hence, in the size of food or diameter of twig they can perch on. In such pairs of species, the larger one is usually about twice the weight of the smaller. Alternatively, we can sometimes find closely related species that differ not in size but rather in height above the ground at which they forage. Such species usually differ in mean foraging height by about a standard deviation as the theory suggests.

Why are these data largely confined to birds? Partly because birds are easier to census and observe. Perhaps, also, birds are different—maybe they have packed their environment more fully, so that patterns of species packing are more evident. Only time will tell.

Shortcomings of Our Present Knowledge

First, and most interesting, there will be new patterns discovered and described by theory. The present structure is not complete enough to allow any prediction of what patterns these will be. But it is certain that the existence of undiscovered patterns, rather than the beauty of the already elucidated ones, should lure new talent into a field. It is paradoxical that so much talent goes into physics, with its glorious past and uncertain future, when ecology, with a certain future, gets far less talent.

From a view of present theory, it is clear that we know more about overlap of species than we do about their degree of specialization. In the jargon: Why is one species "broad niched" and another "narrow niched"? And why are some species able to adjust niche widths rapidly when put in a new situation while others are rigid? This will certainly be one of the problems occupying critical attention in the future.

Ecology is supposed to be concerned with relations between organisms and their environments, but most ecologists were trained as biologists and have been reluctant to tangle with the complexities of an environment. This has two consequences. First, many ecologists tried to avoid studying the environment by standardizing it in a laboratory situation, and usually by putting organisms into a homogenous medium and, thereby, removing the environmental structure. In these homogenized media, it proved almost impossible to get animals to coexist, in marked contrast to nature. The moral, of course, is that the complex structure of a real environment is essential to the coexistence of species. Therefore, field ecologists must become more concerned with the structure of the environment, and laboratory experiments will more and more be concerned with the effects of different spatial and temporal patterns added to their bottles or cages.

A primary aim of education is to train the student to distinguish the trivial from the profound. The educated theorist thus learns to tell an "interesting" theory from a "trivial" one although the distinction is not easy to spell out. Most interesting theories of coexistence have four shortcomings: 1) The mathematics have a simplified functional form, usually with some linear expressions. Often the equations are explicitly linear and, hence, only valid near equilibrium. 2) They describe populations in a single patch of environment but seldom tackle populations that trickle back and forth between patches. 3) They assume all individuals of a species are identical. 4) They neglect temporal variations in the environment.

These difficulties, coupled with the manifest complexity of nature, have led some good ecologists to doubt that a satisfying theory of ecology is possible. These are largely self doubts. Difficulty in imagining how theory can adequately describe nature is not a proof that theory cannot. People used to believe organic chemicals were too complex to synthesize in the lab on exactly the same grounds.

Philosophical Difficulties

Words are used in two contexts in science. First, when motivating research, or discussing it, or introducing it, one often uses words in a vague but suggestive way to help formulate ideas. When actual data are presented or theories formulated, these vague notions have no place, and all notions must have clear and public meaning. Ecologists have often confused these two uses and tried to give prematurely precise definitions of terms only used in the vague context. At best, this is harmless, while at worst, it is quite misleading. For example, ecologists are quite properly interested in the stability of ecological systems. But there are many different precise meanings for stability, some of them quite inconsistent with others.

The word "niche" is another example. From examination of the theory of species competing along a single resource dimension, it is clear that some definition of niche will be relatable to competition and coexistence, and the word is useful in the vague motivational context. I also believe no present precise definition can be related to competition and that the current precise definitions are premature.

What will the future bring? Clearly it will bring precise definitions of terms like "niche" but only when the time is ripe. Perhaps niche will turn out to be a concept that requires some subdivision into several precise definitions.

Here is a difficulty of another kind.

Ecology stands at a curious crossroads. As a science it is dedicated to reason, the enlightenment it produced, and even to the technological apparatus that make observations and interpretations easier. Yet the "Ecology Movement," to which most scientific ecologists are dedicated, is certainly anti-technological and often in fact anti-intellectual as well. Although individual ecologists resolve the dilemma by one decision or another, the movements do seem to have a fundamental opposition. Unbridled growth of science is certainly correlated with destruction of the environment, and unbridled "ecology" in the popular sense would promote anti-scientific outlooks.

A Long Range Prediction

What I have said so far involves only the short term predictions that can be made with some certainty by examining the weaknesses of present ecology. A longer range prediction must involve more than just the study of species' coexistence, because the long range goals of each ecologist involve the unravelling of a network of relations spanning the whole of ecology. Here I attempt my own prediction of how ecology, especially the ecology of coexistence, will develop; if this deters anyone from following an alternate approach, I will have failed, but if it stimulates people to think about the future without blindly following any course, I will be content.

I predict there will be erected a two- or three-way classification of organisms and their geometrical and temporal environments, this classification consuming most of the creative energy of ecologists. The future principles of the ecology of coexistence will then be of the form "for organisms of type A, in environments of structure B, such and such relations will hold." This is only a change in emphasis from present ecology. All successful theories, for instance in physics, have initial conditions; with different initial conditions, different things will happen. But I think initial conditions and their classification in ecology will prove to have vastly more effect on outcomes than they do in physics. Furthermore, there are many ecologists who, in their education, have been only exposed to one successful bit of science—the DNA, RNA story that proved essentially the same from viruses to mammals. These ecologists are often misled into thinking that viruses and mammals can be utilized equally well to elucidate the same principles of ecology. I will give some examples. First, it seems very clear that predators are very important in intertidal communities and not in terrestrial bird communities. The intertidal is essentially a simple surface, and is easy for a starfish to search effectively; a forest has a very much more complicated geometry, and it would be far more difficult for a hawk to cover it thoroughly. Hence, plausibly the intertidal falls into a classification of environment that tells us to pay special attention to predators, while in the forest community, we pay more attention to competition. Again, bird censuses in a habitat in successive years or in similar habitats in one year are usually very similar, while insect censuses (to the extent they can be taken) seem often to differ dramatically from place to place and year to year. Thus, plausibly in our classification, insects, at least of some kinds, will go into a non-equilibrium category and birds into an equilibrium category. But the classification will be more pervasive than these examples suggest; many morphological, behavioral, and genetic parameters will probably be included.

There has been a biological tradition of searching for the best organism to solve a problem—like Drosophila for chromosome genetics and viruses and bacteria for aspects of molecular genetics. The ecologist should resist this temptation. This is not to say he should not be selective about what he studies—of course he should. Rather, it is to suggest that competition and coexistence must be studied under a very wide spectrum of conditions before we can make the classification. A study of competition in microorganisms is in no sense the slightest substitute for a study in vertebrates —or conversely.

The Training of Ecologists

Ecology as a science is almost always taught in biology departments, giving a natural priority of the organisms over the environment in ecological training. Although most ecologists are exposed to a spread of biological education from biochemistry through subjects closer to their preference, they are seldom exposed to the wide array of subjects that would be much more useful to them than most of biology. How many ecologists have had graduate level training in meteorology and climatology for instance? Or even a respectable training in geology? The cure here is easy: Ecologists should urge their departments to allow the option of substituting, say, geology for biochemistry in an ecologist's education.

But there is another aspect whose treatment is not so clear. How does the ecologist learn what science is? At the undergraduate level, he gets no clear picture from his biology courses, and at the graduate level, he may seldom see his major professor doing research. From the viewpoint of the subject of ecology, it is probably best for a variety of ecologists, with widely divergent backgrounds, to participate, but an open-minded student, wishing the education most likely to be successful, requests a more specific program. What should he be told? As an undergraduate, if he has the talent, I think he should be urged to take several physics courses. Although the actual material may not be applicable to ecology, and physics is not a perfect paradigm for ecology, it provides training in scientific thinking that can hardly be provided in any other way. The problem is more severe for graduate students. I think there is no systematic answer. When many graduate students are good, they reinforce each other.

Ecology has several "schools," at least as recognized by some people. This is all to the good, and we can hope all thrive. Unfortunately, there are propaganda efforts by insecure members of the various schools aimed at others, and it would not be the first time in history if one of these efforts succeeded in temporarily putting one school out of favor. To the extent that the propaganda is positive, it is harmless enough, but most insecure people get their kicks out of attacking others, usually pretending to be logical about it. In the interests of freedom and diversity, even these destructive attacks must be tolerated, but it is well to recognize that they tell us more about the attacker than the attacked. However, it is a pity that several promising young ecologists have been wasting their lives in philosophical nonsense about there being only one way—their own way, of course—to do science. Anyone familiar with the history of science knows it is done in the most astonishing ways by the most improbable people and that its only real rules are honesty and validity of logic, and that even these are open to public scrutiny and correction. For the future, we can hope that fewer ecologists waste their lives.

14 Analysis of Ecosystems

DAVID E. REICHLE
STANLEY I. AUERBACH
ENVIRONMENTAL SCIENCES DIVISION
Oak Ridge National Laboratory[1]

> Actually, as should be apparent, the general problem of ecosystem
> analyses is, with the exception of sociological problems that are
> also ecological, the most difficult problem ever posed by man.
> (P. Handler, 1970)

Introduction

The landscape, when viewed as an abstraction, represents different things
to different people: source of food to the agriculturalist; land for the
developer; places for cities, towns, factories, and parks to the general
population. To the general biologist, the landscape may appear as a complex of organisms influenced by a complex of climatic, edaphic, genetic,
and other interactive factors. To the ecologist, it also appears as a pattern
of interdependent units, or ecosystems, all derived through evolutionary
processes and mediated by climate, substrate, and geography. Examples
of ecosystems are the various types of forests, grasslands, streams, lakes,
deserts, tundras, and oceans which comprise the biosphere. These ecosystems, although part of a larger continuum, possess specific characteristics; some may be unique, others differing between systems only in degree and not in kind.

What is the goal or utility of "understanding the structure and func-

Research supported in part by the U.S. Atomic Energy Commission under
contract with Union Carbide Corporation and in part by the Eastern Deciduous
Forest Biome, US-IBP, funded by the National Science Foundation under Interagency Agreement AG-199, 40-193-69 with the Atomic Energy Commission—Oak
Ridge National Laboratory.

Contribution No. 34 from the Eastern Deciduous Forest Biome, US-IBP.

1. Operated by the Union Carbide Corporation for the U.S. Atomic Energy
Commission.

tion" of ecosystems? Similar to other organisms, man interacts with the other components of ecosystems, affects them, and is affected by them. Attempts to interpret the ecological effects of man's population growth and technological development are showing that simplistic, narrow approaches to assessing environmental impacts are, at best, inadequate. For man to learn to live in and to maintain the quality of his environment, it will be essential to understand ecosystems, their driving forces, their dynamics, and the mechanisms by which they are regulated.

Based upon an historical review of the scientific development of ecosystem analysis and the basic principles of the ecosystem concept, the following sections will illustrate, by means of examples, the potential of the systems approach when applied to the analysis of ecosystems.

Historical Perspective

Recognition of the functional ecosystem approach to environmental problems is commonly credited to Lindeman (1942) and the trophic-dynamic school of ecology (Allee, et al., 1949; Odum, 1957). Perhaps the greatest impetus of this concept as a way of addressing and understanding ecological processes at the landscape level came from the writings of E. P. Odum (e.g., Odum, 1971). Odum and colleagues have demonstrated that ecosystem ecology has an intrinsic intellectual tie to our understanding of nature and the environment. The trophic approach to ecosystem analysis soon associated the flow of materials between system components with the overall metabolism of the ecosystem. It soon became apparent that system metabolism was a measure of the collective processes which served to maintain the integrity and stability of the system.

This analogy to cellular and organism metabolism provided a basis for the application of similar methodologies to ecosystem analysis. Of these, the most powerful were the radiotracers. The theoretical and operational principles had been previously established in physiology (Sheppard, 1962), and the advent of radioecology, with its applied mission for determining the fate of radioactive elements released to the environment, provided both the impetus and the tools for testing these concepts. The principles, techniques, and analytical power of radiotracer methods to quantify trophic dynamics were demonstrated by Davis and Foster (1958), Auerbach (1958), Crossley and Howden (1961), and other early radioecologists. Application of transfer coefficient matrices in ecosystem modeling by Olson (1965) illustrated the potential for applying advancements in systems analysis, using the electronic computer to provide solutions to problems of complex ecosystem interactions.

Computer development in the late 1940s was followed by a growing recognition among biologists of the power of the computer for manipulating large data sets which are characteristic of ecosystem research. By the early 1960s, a small number of ecologists had begun to apply this data-handling capability of the computer to the solution of long-standing (but unresolved) problems, such as predator-prey interactions (Holling, 1966), populations and their exploitation (Watt, 1963), and ecosystem dynamics (Olson, 1965).

The potential of the computer in large-scale ecosystem studies awaited recognition of the need for a new level of formal theory. Based on an ecosystem level of analysis, an understanding of mathematical and numerical analysis, and an appreciation of the magnitude of the problem, ecologists (Olson, 1963; Van Dyne, 1966; Watt, 1966; Patten, 1971) began to write convincingly of the need for application of systems analysis procedures to ecology and, in fact, developed the field of Systems Ecology. Currently, the Biome programs of the International Biological Program (IBP) have further stimulated the application of systems analysis to the understanding of complex ecosystems (Reichle, 1970).

Ecosystem Ecology

The goal of ecosystem analysis is to develop a quantitative ecosystem science which may provide new theoretical insights into the organization *and* function of natural systems at their most complex level. One of the basic hypotheses being tested is whether the landscape is organized in logical patterns of self-sustaining, dynamic, and internally regulated components. Because of the complexity of interactions and variables involved, the question is: "How can the ecologist approach the quantitative analysis and interpretation of ecosystems?" From development of conceptual, and then mathematical, models and their subsequent validation, the ecologist strives to acquire a formalistic basis for dealing with complex sets of interacting variables. Subsequent simulations which involve manipulation of model parameters may be used to test hypotheses of system behavior and regulation—and to derive inferences at different levels of scale.

Holistic models are often required to deal with a scale of the landscape

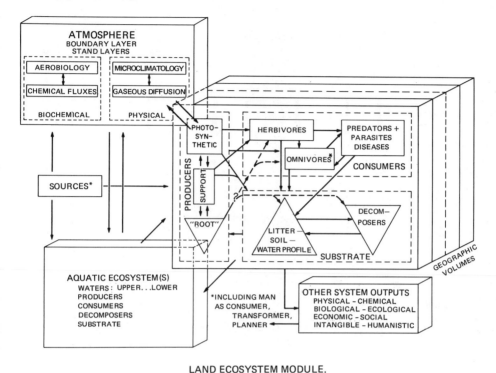

LAND ECOSYSTEM MODULE.

FIGURE 1. A diagramatic representation of a land ecosystem module, inter-
faced with atmospheric and aquatic systems to represent an integral segment
of the landscape. This concept of the environment recognizes the coupling
between ecosystems in time and space. The hierarchical organization of ecosystem attributes reflects the interaction of system components at several
scales by resolution. (modified after Olson, 1970).

considerably more broad and generalized than the precise levels of resolution necessary to understand the underlying ecological mechanisms. The
biosphere may be examined at various levels of resolution, depending
upon the complexity of the problem and the kinds of couplings between
ecosystems (Fig. 1). Specific ecosystems also may be subdivided into a
hierarchy of subsystems based on internal mechanisms (or processes).
These may be basic processes of energy transformation, such as production, mortality, and decomposition of green plants, or related functional
processes, such as nutrient cycling (Likens et al., 1970).

The ecosystem is conceptually defined (Figs. 1 and 2) as a functional
entity with internal homeostasis, identifiable boundaries, and recognizable

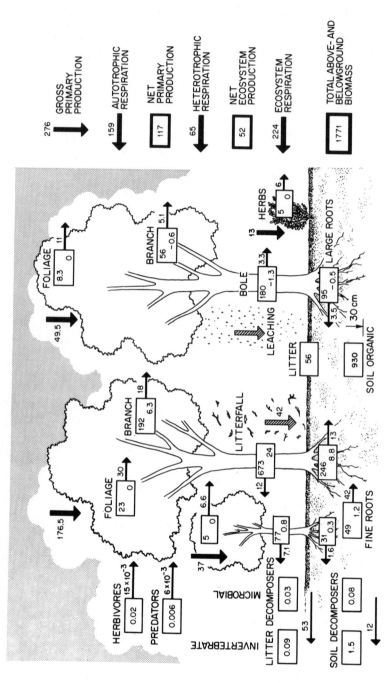

FIGURE 2. Pictorial presentation of the carbon cycle in a mesic hardwood forest ecosystem at Oak Ridge National Laboratory. Structural components of the ecosystem have been abstracted as compartments, with the major fluxes through the system illustrated by arrows. Values in compartments are annual standing crops and those in parentheses are annual increments. Units of measure are 10^5 grams per hectare and 10^5 grams per hectare per year for fluxes on arrows; e.g., value for litter is equivalent to 5600 kg ha^{-1} or 560 g m^{-2}. Summaries of ecosystem metabolism are shown to the right of the figure. (constructed from Sollins, 1972).

relationships between subcomponents. System boundaries are established to minimize or maximize transfers across them (to optimize analytical evaluation) and must contain a complete set of ecosystem processes and their interactions (Smith, 1970). Let us consider a specific example by examining the biological cycle of carbon in the biosphere, proceeding from global budgets to ecosystem cycles and related ecological processes.

Among the ways of functionally linking the world's regional and local systems to one another has been the unifying consideration of the circulation of carbon through a common atmospheric pool. Rather simple mechanistic models (e.g., Olson, 1970) have been sufficient to assess recent trends of carbon exchange and to extrapolate a few years into the future. Even now, we are not certain how important terrestrial ecosystems, especially forests, are in modifying or stabilizing these cycles, but

TABLE I. *Net Annual Carbon Fixation in Primary Production and Standing Crop of Carbon in Biomass for Terrestrial Ecosystems of the World.*[*]

	Area 10^4 km^2	Net Primary Production of Carbon NPP ton/km^2/yr	10^9 tons	Live Carbon Pool		
				Tons km^2	10^9 tons	NPP pool
Woodland or forest						
temperate "cold-deciduous"	8	1,000	8	10,000	80	0.10
conifer: boreal and mixed	15	600	9	8,000	120	0.075
rainforest: temperate	1	1,200	1.2	12,000	12	0.10
rainforest: tropical, subtropical	10	1,500	15	20,000	200	0.075
dry woodlands (various)	14	200	2.8	5,000	70	0.04
Subtotal	48		36		482	
Wetlands, thickets	1	2,000	2	5,000	5	0.40
Nonforest						
agricultural	15	400	6	1,000	15	0.4
grassland	26	300	7.8	700	18.2	0.43
tundra-like	12	100	1.2	600	7.2	0.17
other "desert"	32	100	3.2	287	9.2	0.29
glaciers	15		0			
Subtotal	100		18.2		49.6	
Average/continents	149	380	56.2	3,700	544.6	
Average/ocean	362	61	22	8	3	
Total Biosphere	511		78		548	

[*] Carbon data and geographic estimates of ecosystem area updated by Olson from Table 3 (Olson, 1970). (Courtesy Springer-Verlag)

data suggest that their importance may have been underestimated in the past (Table I). Current information is insufficient to assess the atmospheric impact (and indirect effects on local ecosystems as well as the biosphere) of excess carbon dioxide released from the burning of fossil fuels and land clearing which releases much carbon from humus and dead trees. Better understanding of the internal processes of aquatic and terrestrial ecosystems is essential before we can extend predictions to the decades ahead.

Systems Approach to Studying Ecosystems

Systems ecologists' heritage in trophic dynamics and the flow of energy through ecosystems has resulted in a concern primarily for ecosystem processes rather than for species components. Research on transport mechanisms, such as food chains, relates not only to system components (organisms) and their interactions but also to those physical and biological factors which control the rates at which ecosystem functions occur. This approach has resulted in an interpretation of ecosystem dynamics in terms of the structural and compositional attributes affecting internal transport of materials (carbon, mineral elements, etc.). Ultimately, the ecosystem ecologist is concerned with both system dynamics and system strategies which provide a basis for synthesis of the contributions from both functional and structural fields of ecology.

Since environmental factors themselves are part of ecosystems, the distinction between dependent and independent variables becomes obscure. This feature necessitates varied and innovative approaches to the analysis of ecosystems (Goodall, 1970). *Experimentation,* to cover a broad range of relevant component combinations, may be equally as valuable as the usual effort devoted to replicate sampling for statistical precision. *Observation* of the behavior of components of ecosystems under different conditions gives breadth to the standard experimental approach. In addition, historical information may show that key variables and infrequent events have greater control over the long-term behavior of the system than the normal ranges of obvious variables.

Morton (1964) has suggested that systems analysis is, in effect, the scientific method itself which ensures an organized approach to examination of complex systems. In the study of ecosystems, the modeling activity is of great importance since a model which accurately represents the real system can itself be utilized for experimentation as well as to provide early identification of key variables, parameters, and linkages between subsystems. In the analyses of ecosystems, five sequential operations (objective, conceptual, modeling, empirical, and analytical) are fundamental to both the research and modeling efforts (Dale, 1970; Reichle et al., 1971).

The carbon cycle in deciduous forests can be used to illustrate these facets of environmental systems analyses. From examination of the carbon pools and turnover rates in deciduous forest ecosystems (Fig. 2), the relative contribution of various system components to carbon dioxide exchange with the atmosphere is apparent. The greater percentage of aboveground respiration resulting from autotrophic (green) plants comes from metabolically active tissues, such as leaves and bark of branches and twigs rather than the bulk of the biomass represented in wood. Well over one-third of the total ecosystem respiration of 224×10^5 grams per hectare results from the decomposition of detritus in the soil carbon pool. The subsequent model of decomposition will serve to illustrate one aspect of ecosystem dynamics and continue our analysis of the carbon cycle.

To examine the dynamics of the soil and litter carbon pool, Sollins (1972) developed five linear differential equations describing the organic detritus component of the forest carbon model (Fig. 2). Conceptually, the forest floor was partitioned into two litter layers (0_1 and 0_2) and two mineral soil layers (0-10 cm and 10-60 cm depth). Modeling the system consisted of specifying the mechanisms by which the decomposition processes occurred and writing the system equations. Concise and realistic definitions had to be made for each compartment and for all transfer pathways in the model. As an instructive example, let us examine the equation describing changes in compartment size of the fast decomposing component of 0_1 litter:

$$O_1 = (L_o + L_u + L_g) + C(1\text{-}a) - [O_1(R_{o_1} + \beta)K] + \pi$$

where $L_o = \lambda_1 Q_1 = $ (overstory leaf fall) (kg m^{-2} yr^{-1})

$L_u = \lambda_2 Q_2 = $ (understory leaf fall) (kg m^{-2} yr^{-1})

$L_g = \lambda_3 Q_3 = $ (ground flora leaf fall) (kg m^{-2} yr^{-1})

and λ_i's are the respective litterfall rates (yr^{-1}) which operate only during the dormant season and Q_i's are the respective foliage biomasses (kg m^{-2})

where $C(1 - a) = $ frass influx (kg m^{-2} yr^{-1}) to forest floor and

$C = $ insect feeding flux (kg m^{-2} yr^{-1}) and

$a = $ proportionality constant for digestive assimilation

where $O_1(R_{o_1} + \beta)K$ = decomposition losses of litter and

O_1 = weight of O_1 litter (kg m^{-2}) and

R_{o_1} = respiratory carbon losses (yr^{-1}) and

β = transfer rate of O_1 litter to O_2 horizon and

K = a dimensionless temperature-moisture coefficient

= 0.2 ($^\circ$ C $\times$ % moisture in litter)

where π = the input of the rapidly decomposing component of litter other than leaves (e.g., reproductive parts) (kg m^{-2} yr^{-1}).

After such mathematical representations of system processes have been developed, the important analytical aspects of quantifying coefficients and investigating model responses remains. Mean standing crop of litter in the forest was 540 g m^{-2} (Fig. 2). Total annual litterfall averaged 420 g m^{-2} yr^{-1} plus 100 g m^{-2} yr^{-1} branch and bole wood. Insect frass (and aphid honeydew) amounted to 10 g m^{-2} yr^{-1}. Respiration accounted for a total litter (0_1 and 0_2) weight loss of 530 g m^{-2} yr^{-1}. Soil organic matter has been estimated to accrue at 100 g m^{-2} yr^{-1} (Sollins, 1972). Consequently, estimated root dieback of ~350 g m^{-2} yr^{-1} was found to be a significant input to soil and litter detritus, heretofore not fully appreciated.

Since models are often constructed from existing data bases, their realism needs to be tested by comparison with other independent data bases to avoid circular reasoning. A high degree of realism implies that the model resembles the real system for the range of system variables relevant to the problem at hand (Walters, 1971). Accuracy of model simulations is not necessarily synonymous with model complexity (O'Neill, 1972). Many mathematical and systems analysis techniques are available for evaluating model performance, but the ecologist must supply the objective criteria to be tested. The model remains not a product in itself but an experimental tool for data synthesis and interpretation. In this final stage, the results of model analyses are applied as the best assessment of the performance of the system. (The entire sequence is iterative.)

Analysis of an Ecosystem

Just as the organism is more than its component tissues and cells, so the whole ecosystem is more complex than the sum of its constituent parts. In ecosystem analysis, however, the challenges lie in interfacing processes to construct total systems. New system properties arise from interactions, feedbacks, and synergisms between individual components.

Total system attributes and perspectives, forthcoming from analysis of ecosystem studies, can be exemplified by again considering the example of energy flow and productivity in a forest ecosystem (Fig. 2).

In this analysis, net primary production (NPP) is obtained by direct measurement of ecosystem components, but evaluation of autotrophic respiration (R_{sA}) is necessary to calculate gross primary production (GPP) and assess the metabolic "costs" of radiant energy conversion via the photosynthetic process. Net ecosystem production (NEP) or the accumulation of organic biomass by the system, however, requires that total ecosystem respiratory losses (including heterotrophic respiration, R_{sH}) be known. New properties for the ecosystem begin to emerge which are aggregates (but not necessarily simple algebraic sums) of its components and presumably relate to the strategy by which the *system* has adapted to its variable environment.

Consider the relationship among parameters of the whole ecosystem (Fig. 2). Can these attributes contribute toward a general set of ecosystem principles? Do the ratios of R_{sA}/R_{sE} of 0.71 and R_{sH}/R_{sE} of 0.29, which compare the autotrophic respiratory energy losses, provide a clue to the efficiencies of anabolism and catabolism in the ecosystem (Reichle et al., 1972)? How do the metabolic costs of ecosystem production ($NEP/R_{sE} = 0.23$) and the size of ecosystem increments relative to standing crop ($NEP/NPP = 0.44$) relate to patterns of structure, composition, and age of different ecosystems (Jordan, 1971; Sollins, 1972)? Are these attributes always proportioned in a fixed 1.0 to 0.35 ratio between above- and below-ground components as in the forest ecosystem example (Fig. 2), or do they vary in accordance with unappreciated patterns of ecosystem dynamics? While pattern is beginning to unfold for components, little is known of the quantitative similarities and differences in function between ecosystems. There is a need to explore what these analytical measures contribute toward our understanding of the living environment. They reflect a deeper and more complex nature of the ecosystem, and pragmatically, they lead to examination of an entirely new series of questions.

The methods of systems analysis have been developed to apply to man-designed systems; e.g., transportation networks, economic systems, and industrial production. Ecosystems are the product of biological evolution and display inherent strategies and mechanisms for self-perpetuation and reproducibility. Ecological concepts derived from the analysis of ecosystems may offer significant new contributions to our knowledge about systems theory.

SYSTEM DYNAMICS

There are many alternative routes for the cycling of materials via the biogeochemical cycle. The importance of any particular pathway in the ecosystem at any single point in time (e.g., transport at what rates and along which one of the myriad of food chains) is an intricate and dynamic property of the system. Hence, the seemingly unpredictable dispersion of many toxic substances in the environment. This is a problem area particularly suitable for examination by critical pathway analysis (Booth et al., 1972).

REGULATING MECHANISMS

Some species in ecosystems that are either rare or contribute insignificantly to cycling of elements or flows of energy may have considerable import in the regulation of system processes. What kinds of negative feedback loops, such as seed consumption (Janzen, 1971) or limiting nutrients (Whittaker, 1970), exist as regulatory mechanisms? How many unanticipated system attributes might be exposed through use of systems analysis techniques, such as control theory and optimization?

STABILITY OF SYSTEMS

Analysis of ecosystems can contribute knowledge of the homeostatic mechanisms which ensure self-perpetuation. What are the structural and functional characteristics of ecosystems which contribute to stability (Woodwell and Smith, 1969)? Here the methodology of sensitivity analysis (Smith, 1970) becomes a powerful analytical tool. The means by which ecosystems persist may differ from those of species components and may even occur at the expense of certain species.

ADAPTIVENESS OF SYSTEMS

If ecosystem evolution, as well as species evolution, has been shaped by selection pressures for existence, then the system strategies which have occurred to effect these objectives may provide significant insights for ecosystem analyses. Is the diversity in ecosystem structure unexplainable or simply an array of alternatives for exploiting dissimilar environments with similar strategy? What is the ecological significance of evergreenness (Monk, 1966)? Are many constituents of ecosystems relatively insignificant in the steady-state dynamics of the system? Does this diversity represent the "buffer" mechanism which permits ecosystems to respond to change? Perhaps ecosystems have evolved structures with concomitant internal dynamics which are geared to the most efficient transfer of energy rather than to maximum energy transfer (Odum and Pinkerton, 1955). The strategies of ecosystems may not always be inferred from the strategies of species; optimization of system properties does not necessarily follow from maximization of internal processes. Is man consistent with these principles in his concepts of management of the environment (Van Dyne, 1969)?

Future Role of Ecosystem Analysis

The world-wide recognition that environmental problems transcend, not only political, but also intellectual boundaries which have segregated many scientific disciplines, is resulting in the emergence of the environmental sciences as a broad, interdisciplinary field of endeavor. Within this context, ecosystem analysis may provide both a conceptual and an operational framework for linking the research of various environmental disciplines, such as meteorology, geophysics, soil chemistry, and hydrology. Each of these disciplines has much to contribute toward an unraveling of the complex environmental processes that must be understood if we are to solve such pressing problems as the maintenance and conservation of renewable resources and pollution, as well as to provide the predictive capability for assessing the consequences of manipulating these systems.

ENVIRONMENTAL IMPACT OF TECHNOLOGY

The National Environmental Policy Act (NEPA) of 1969 requires assessment of both the short- and long-term environmental impacts of technological developments. This Act requires consideration of alternatives in design, engineering, construction, operation, application, or even

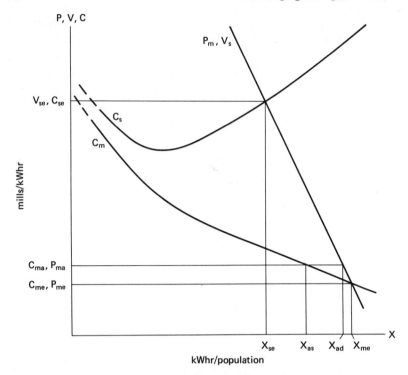

FIGURE 3. Market cost and social equilibria associated with energy production by stationary power plants. Vertical axis represents power costs, and horizontal axis represents per capita power production. (after Chapman and O'Neill, 1970).

$$C_m = \text{Market cost function}$$
$$P_m = \text{Market demand function}$$
$$C_{me} = \text{Market equilibrium cost}$$
$$P_{me} = \text{Market equilibrium price}$$
$$C_{ma} = \text{Cost of actual supply}$$
$$X_{me} = \text{Market equilibrium output}$$
$$X_{ad} = \text{Output demand at price } P_{ma}$$
$$C_s = \text{Marginal social cost function}$$
$$V_s = \text{Marginal social demand function}$$
$$C_{se} = \text{Social equilibrium cost}$$
$$V_{se} = \text{Social equilibrium marginal value}$$
$$P_{ma} = \text{Price of actual supply}$$
$$X_{se} = \text{Social equilibrium output}$$
$$X_{as} = \text{Output actually supplied}$$

new location. Preparation of these statements has required unprecedented effort by ecologists in analysis and synthesis of environmental data. Weaknesses which have become evident are a lack of relevant data and adequate capability to analyze and synthesize for assessment of potential risks. Ecosystem analysis, with its built-in requirement for the structured synthesis of multiple parameters associated with large bodies of quantitative environmental data, will lend itself to effective interpretation of research on ecological processes. Information derived from these efforts is needed to develop ecological criteria as a basis for impact evaluations.

The conflict between demands for increased power production and improved environmental quality can be approached by integrating economic and ecological theory in a functional systems analysis. Consider the current problem of "blackouts" or "brownouts" in major cities (Fig. 3), as evaluated through a socioeconomic model by Chapman and O'Neill (1970). Intersection of the market supply and demand functions defines the market equilibrium, X_{me}, with price P_{me}. Environmental impact of power generation, as perceived by society, causes a new (social) equilibrium, X_{se}, defined by the intersection of the marginal social cost and marginal social value functions. Differences between equilibria create conflict between construction plans of power companies and conservation groups. At the total power production from plants actually built, X_{as}, the utility incurs market costs, C_{ma}. The regulatory agency requires the utility to set its market price, P_{ma}, at or near C_{ma}. With price, P_{ma}, public consumption demands quantity, X_{ad}, which is substantially in excess of the amount, X_{as}, that can be supplied. This study illustrates how the energy production/utilization system is coupled in such a way that demand can exceed supply and cause brownouts.

Ecosystem analysis, dealing as it does with the structure and function of landscape components, will find valuable application to other aspects of technological development. The orderly arrangement of hierarchical data sets describing the landscape (Fig. 1) must be coupled with human ecology (socioeconomic, demographic, and political aspects) to form arsenals of models which can be used to analyze the consequences of new technologies on large landscape regions. Ecosystem analysis will be a powerful tool for evaluating and selecting sites for stationary power plants, industrial facilities, and new cities. The need for this capability is already rising from the nation's developing energy crisis. The location of the large number of electric generating stations that will be required in the next few decades is already posing serious questions of land use allocation and environmental quality.

ENVIRONMENTAL QUALITY

As the earth becomes more populated and as societies move toward global energy-dependent economies, it will be necessary to establish internationally accepted criteria for dangerous pollutants. A concomitant need will be prediction of the behavior and long-term fates of toxic materials in the environment. There is already an urgent need to identify sensitive ecological parameters which can give early warning of ecosystem degradation.

An example is the simulation model of DDT and DDE movement in human food chains developed (O'Neill and Burke, 1971) for the Environmental Protection Agency, Advisory Committee on DDT, to forecast pesticide concentrations in man under alternative assumptions for application levels in the United States. The model consisted of a set of ordinary differential equations to express pesticide concentration changes through time.

$$F(t) = 54 - 7t$$

$$\frac{dx_1}{dt} = a_1F(t) - b_1x_1 \qquad b_1 = 1.014$$

$$\frac{dx_2}{dt} = a_2F(t) - b_2x_2 \qquad \begin{aligned} a_2 &= 0.0247 \\ b_2 &= 0.0507 \end{aligned}$$

$$\frac{dx_3}{dt} = a_3(x_1 + x_2) - b_3x_3 \qquad \begin{aligned} a_3 &= 0.1430 \\ b_3 &= 0.4740 \end{aligned}$$

where x_1 and x_2 are food items contaminated directly by spraying and indirectly from the environment, respectively, and x_3 is the concentration in human adipose tissue. The constants a_1 relate rate of input to magnitude of the source and the b_1's are biological elimination coefficients for DDT/DDE. After 1966, no direct spraying of the food supply was permitted, and no value for a_1 could be estimated.

Source terms used in the model and comparison of model simulations and actual pesticide concentrations in man are given in Table II. If DDT usage had continued at the 1966 level, the model extrapolates that concentrations in man approach an asymptote at some value above 6.7 ppm around 2022. Simulation with DDT usage, decreasing at the present rate of about 7 million pounds per year, shows decreasing levels (1 ppm by

TABLE II. *Source Terms Utilized for Modeling DDT and DDE Movement Through the Human Food Chain and Comparison of Model Output with Residue Levels Monitored in Human Adipose Tissue.*

Year	DDT Usage (10^6 lb)[a] $F(t)$	DDT + DDE in Diet (mg/kg)[b] $(x_1 + x_2)$	DDT + DDE in Human Adipose Tissue (ppm)[c] x_3 observed	x_3 model predicted
1965	53	0.031		
1966	46	0.040		
1967	40	0.026	4.65	5.02
1968	33	0.019	5.61	5.57
1969		0.016	5.22	5.42
1970		0.015	5.27	5.14

Data sources: a) USDA Pesticide Review, 1969; b) FDA analyses of food at the market place; c) Human monitoring survey.

2006) but with measurable concentrations still remaining after 50 years.

Traditional concepts of simple biological indicators are not sufficient to detect effects on ecological systems or on their internal processes until we know how species are coupled within ecosystems and how changes wrought in the species composition or population levels reflect damage to the total system. Additional information will be required about the fundamental processes (food chain mechanisms and related biogeochemical cycles) which transform and disperse these materials in the biosphere. Assessment of potential long-term environmental degradation from pollutants requires an understanding of ecologic processes at the ecosystem level. Our stewardship of the biosphere may depend on sophisticated application of the principles of ecosystem analysis.

LAND USE

A national land use policy will require a profound understanding of the landscape and its component processes. The capacity of natural and managed ecosystems to produce food and fiber, with optimized inputs of energy and material resources, needs to be seriously examined. Similarly, ecosystems need to be studied at a number of levels of resolution to derive a more fundamental understanding of how much, if any, of man's indus-

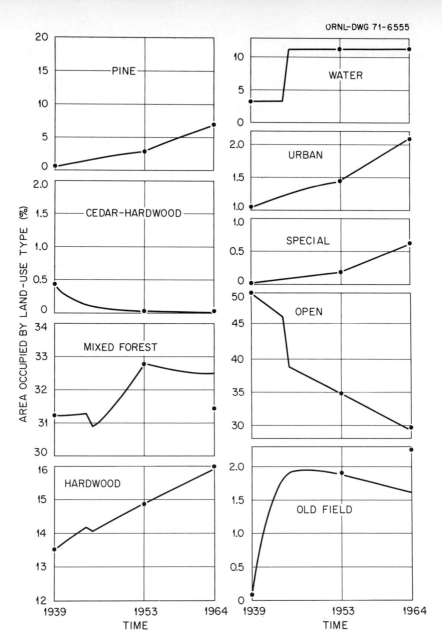

FIGURE 4. Results of a land-use simulation model predicting the time response of land use categories (curves) compared to observed land use patterns (solid points). The nine categories are: open (primarily agricultural); old field (abandoned farm land); pine (plantation); mixed forest (conifer and hardwood); cedar-hardwood forest; hardwood forest; water (impoundments and rivers, but excluding small streams); urban; and special (e.g., quarries, power line right-of-ways, etc.). (after Hett, 1971).

trial, domestic, and agricultural by-products can be accommodated, recycled, or otherwise disposed of without detriment to the environment.
There is growing recognition that current land use patterns throughout
the country do not always represent the best mix of urban, rural, and
recreational allocations and that these uses often undergo rapid and
dramatic changes. This capability to forecast land-use changes will involve a substantial input from ecologists since the landscape is a mosaic
of natural and managed ecosystems, each influenced by ecological events
as well as human activities.

Recently, collaborating scientists from the International Biological Program and the Tennessee Valley Authority (TVA) examined the changing land-use patterns in eastern Tennessee (Hett, 1971). A simulation
model was developed, based upon known plant succession for the region
and land use trends derived from aerial photographs spanning 25 years.
Predictions were made of the rates of change of various landscape categories for a five-county region (Fig. 4). The rates of change for different
vegetation types are related to the rates of plant succession and can be
evaluated using empirical data from the field. The annual loss of non-
forested land for the five-county area was 5.28 km^2 per year, of which
2.39 km^2 per year represented an increase in forested land (primarily
due to the influence of a paper mill on the establishment of pine planta-
tions) and 2.85 km^2 per year was irreversibly lost to reservoirs (TVA
dams in the Valley) and urban development.

Expansion of simplified man-made agricultural ecosystems has renewed
the question of whether or not these systems are increasingly vulnerable
to biological insults and increasingly costly to maintain in terms of direct
energy expenditures or requirements for energy-dependent products, such
as fertilizers and insecticides. The future will see more research on landscape dynamics and interactions to determine how best to organize natural and managed ecosystems. Agricultural systems of the future might
be mixes of large and small monocultures intermixed with heterogeneous
crop and forest ecosystems to maintain the gene pools necessary to ensure
genetic variability and landscape viability. The data and understanding
required to lead logically to this development will draw heavily on advancing knowledge of ecological processes operative within these systems.
Ecosystem analysis can provide the conceptual and mechanistic framework to integrate these findings into meaningful syntheses and predictions
of environmental phenomena at landscape levels of resolution.

References

Allee, W. C., A. E. Emerson, O. Park, T. Park, and K. P. Schmidt. 1949. *Principles of Animal Ecology.* W. B. Saunders Co., Philadelphia. 837 p.

Auerbach, S. I. 1958. The soil ecosystem and radioactive waste disposal to the ground. *Ecology,* **39**: 522-529.

Booth, R. S., S. V. Kaye, and P. S. Rohwer. 1972. A systems analysis methodology for predicting dose to man from a radioactivity contaminated terrestrial environment. *In*: D. J. Nelson (ed.). *Symposium on Radioecology.* USAEC CONF-710501. (In press.)

Chapman, D. and R. V. O'Neill. 1970. Ecology and resource economics: An integration and application of theory to environmental dilemmas. ORNL-4641, Oak Ridge National Laboratory.

Crossley, D. A. and H. F. Howden. 1961. Insect vegetation relationships in an area contaminated by radioactive wastes. *Ecology,* **42**: 302-317.

Dale, M. B. 1970. Systems analysis and ecology. *Ecology,* **51**: 2-16.

Davis, J. J. and R. F. Foster. 1958. Bioaccumulation of radioisotopes through aquatic food chains. *Ecology,* **39**: 530-535.

Goodall, D. W. 1970. Studying the effects of environmental factors on ecosystems. p. 19-28. *In*: D. E. Reichle (ed.). *Analysis of Temperate Forest Ecosystems.* Springer-Verlag, Berlin-Heidelberg-New York. 304 p.

Handler, P. 1970. *Biology and the Future of Man.* Oxford University Press, Oxford. 471 p.

Hett, J. M. 1971. Land-use changes in East Tennessee and a simulation model which describes these changes for three counties. International Biological Program, Eastern Deciduous Forest Biome. ORNL-IBP-71-8, Oak Ridge National Laboratory, 56 p.

Holling, C. S. 1966. The functional response of invertebrate predators to prey density. *Mem. Entomol. Soc. Can.,* **48**: 1-85.

Janzen, D. H. 1971. Escape of *Cassia grandis* L. beans from predators in time and space. *Ecology,* **52**: 964-979.

Jordan, C. F. 1971. A world pattern in plant energetics. *Amer. Sci.,* **59**: 425-433.

Likens, G. F., F. H. Bormann, N. M. Johnson, D. W. Fisher, and R. S. Pierce. 1970. Effects of forest cutting and herbicide treatment on nutrient budgets in the Hubbard Brook Watershed Ecosystem. *Ecol. Monogr.,* **40**: 23-47.

Lindeman, R. L. 1942. The trophic-dynamic aspect of ecology. *Ecology,* **23**: 399-418.

Monk, C. D. 1966. An ecological significance of evergreeness. *Ecology,* 47: 504-505.

Morton, J. A. 1964. From research to industry. Int. Sci. Technol. May 1964. p. 82-92, 105.

Odum, E. P. 1971. *Fundamentals of Ecology*. 3rd ed. W. B. Saunders Co., Philadelphia. 574 p.

Odum, H. T. 1957. Trophic structure and productivity of Silver Springs, Florida. *Ecol. Monogr., 27*: 55-112.

———— and R. C. Pinkerton. 1955. Times speed regulator, the optimum efficiency for maximum output in physical and biological systems. *Amer. Sci., 43*: 331-343.

Olson, J. S. 1961. Analog computer models for movement of isotopes through ecosystems. p. 121-125. *In*: V. Schultz and A. K. Klement, Jr. (eds.). *Radioecology*. Reinhold Publ. Corp., New York. 746 p.

————. 1965. Equations for cesium transfer in a *Liriodendron* forest. *Health Physics, 11*: 1385-1392.

————. 1970. Carbon cycle and temperate woodlands. p. 226-241. *In*: D. E. Reichle (ed.) *Analysis of Temperate Forest Ecosystems*. Springer-Verlag, Berlin-Heidelberg-New York. 304 p.

O'Neill, R. V. 1972. Error analysis of ecological models. *In*: D. J. Nelson (ed.). *Symposium on Radioecology*. USAEC CONF-710501. (In press.)

———— and O. W. Burke. 1971. A simple systems model for DDT and DDE movement in the human food chain. International Biological Program, Eastern Deciduous Forest Biome, ORNL-IBP-71-9, Oak Ridge National Laboratory. 18 p.

Patten, B. C. (ed.). 1971. *Systems Analysis and Simulation Ecology*. Academic Press, New York. 607 p.

Reichle, D. E. (ed.). 1970. *Analysis of Temperate Forest Ecosystems*. Springer-Verlag, Berlin-Heidelberg-New York. 304 p.

————, R. S. Booth, R. V. O'Neill, P. Sollins, and S. V. Kaye. 1971. Systems analysis as applied to ecological processes. p. 12-28. *In*: T. Rosswall (ed.). Systems Analysis in Northern Coniferous Forests—IBP Workshop. Bull. No. 14, Ecological Research Committee, Swedish Natural Science Research Council, Stockholm.

————, B. E. Dinger, N. T. Edwards, F. W. Harris, and P. Sollins. 1972. Carbon flow and storage in a woodland ecosystem. In: *Carbon and the Biosphere*. Brookhaven Biology Symposium. No. 24. (In press.)

Sheppard, C. W. 1962. *Basic Principles of the Tracer Method*. John Wiley and Sons, New York. 282 p.

Smith, F. E. 1970. Analysis of ecosystems. p. 7-18. *In*: D. E. Reichle (ed.). *Analysis of Temperate Forest Ecosystems*. Springer-Verlag, Berlin-Heidelberg-New York. 304 p.

Sollins, P. 1972. Organic matter budget and model for a Southern Appalachian *Liriodendron* forest. Doctoral Dissertation, University of Tennessee, Knoxville.

Van Dyne, G. M. 1966. Ecosystems, systems ecology and systems ecologists. ORNL-3957, Oak Ridge National Laboratory.

——. (ed.). 1969. *The Ecosystem Concept in Natural Resource Management.* Academic Press, New York. 383 p.

Walters, C. J. 1971. Systems ecology: The systems approach and mathematical models in ecology. p. 276-292. Chapt. 10. *In*: E. P. Odum. *Fundamentals of Ecology.* W. B. Saunders Co., Philadelphia. 574 p.

Watt, K. E. F. 1963. Mathematical models for five agricultural crop pests. *Mem. Entomol. Soc. Can.,* **32**:83.

——. 1966. *Systems Analysis in Ecology.* Academic Press, New York. 276 p.

Whittaker, R. H. 1970. The biochemical ecology of higher plants, p. 43-70. *In*: E. Sondheimer and J. S. Simeone (eds.). *Chemical Ecology.* Academic Press, New York. 336 p.

Woodwell, G. M. and H. H. Smith (eds.). 1969. Diversity and Stability in Ecological Systems. Brookhaven Nat'l Lab. Publ. No. 22, Upton, New York. 264 p.

15 Whither Tropical Ecology?

DANIEL H. JANZEN
DEPARTMENT OF BIOLOGY
University of Chicago

Preamble

There are few things more presumptuous than a U.S. scientist holding forth on the future of tropical ecology. The easy defense is that AIBS asked for it. The much less palatable answer, but one that must be faced squarely in the future of tropical ecology, is that I am here by default. The fantastic diversity of resources and cultures in the tropics is singularly lacking in indigenous scholarly exposition on the ecology of the tropics. I must be quick to add that a description of site resources is in itself not an ecological study. This apology aside, my goal is to generate a dialogue on tropical ecology, not offer a definitive treatise on the future of tropical ecology. The tropics are far too diverse for one person to absorb and relate to as one can to the Rocky Mountains, the Mediterranean coast, or the Russian steppes. The literature must itself be the clearing house and collating device.

Introduction

The only justification for a non-medical terrestrial tropical biology is in the area of ecology, whether it be applied (agriculture) or esoteric,*

Current address: Department of Zoology, University of Michigan.

* As used in this essay, "esoteric" refers to scientific investigation conducted purely in the pursuit of knowledge for its own sake, with no practical justification intended (i.e., "basic" in pre-1970 terminology).

and I will restrict myself to that area. The major unsolved ecological problem in the tropics is the gross failure of the decision-making processes in tropical countries to incorporate what the aggregate scientific and folklore community already knows about tropical ecology and its application. This problem will not be much alleviated by further research of the type classically conducted by tropical scientists, and therefore, the content of classical tropical research will not be the subject of this essay.

The tropics are many things to many people, and tropical ecology is headed in many directions. This heterogeneity is based on four phenomena: 1) There is far more basic diversity of habitats and resource bases between the tropics than outside of them. 2) These habitats and their indigenous cultures have been invaded by a wide variety of cultures and economic practices evolved to deal with the seasonal pulsed energy systems of extra-tropical regions. 3) There are two conflicting goals in planning for resource use: Is the tropical country to be treated as a primarily self-contained ecosystem, or is it to be treated as a collection of components of a global ecosystem and, therefore, available for competitive exploitation? 4) Tropical environmental predictability (and often a lack of extremes) at any particular site allows an array of solutions to resource use, each of which is approximately as profitable as the other, and thereby, allows greater variance through personal idiosyncracies.

And what are the tropics? To adopt a definition approximately congruent with current usage, they are those areas with moderately predictable major weather events and year-round strong solar radiation. This definition underlines the precaution often voiced by researchers in the tropics—some temperate habitats are as predictable as the majority of tropical habitats, and some tropical habitats are extraordinarily unpredictable. Unfortunately, this definition also bolsters a grossly-erroneous impression held by most temperate zone scientists and policy makers; their decisions reflect a strong bias toward thinking of the tropics as a unit rather than as a collection of problems and resource bases easily as diverse as occur in temperate zones. The ecology of droughts, subsistence agriculture/trans-Amazonian highways is as dissimilar from that of rubber/paddy rice/herbicides as the ecology of grapes/tourists/Mediterranean winter rains is from that of Douglas fir/SST/rainforest.

We may also offer two pragmatic descriptions of the tropics. When in a relatively undisturbed state, the tropics is a fantastic natural laboratory for the generation of ideas in the esoteric pursuit of understanding the interaction of organisms with their biotic and physical environments in all parts of the world. On the other hand, the tropics is a set of habitats already converted in great part to a living machine that maximizes (with varying success) the sustained production of human desiderata from fossil fuel, sunlight, water, and inorganic ions. Obviously for any given piece of terrain, these two descriptions are only very marginally compatible, if at all. I shall discuss them separately in this essay and adopt the general philosophy that the only real decision left is how much of the tropics' habitat shall be allotted to land fitting either description.

And what is tropical ecology? It is ecology as practiced in the tropics. Here we encounter a second major area of heterogeneity that is strongly interwoven with the four points stressed earlier. The high diversity of tropical organisms and interaction systems maximizes the opportunity for the development of polarization between those researchers whose primary goal is to understand nature (esoteric ecology), and those who wish to manipulate it. (Let us not quibble over the obvious fact that manipulation requires partial understanding, and understanding derives only from partial manipulation). Between these two camps lies a host of opportunities for splinter groups to form and retain their identity. Heterogeneity in tropical ecology is also maximized by the fact that peer judgement, that bastion of quality control in science, is a nearly useless tool owing to the paucity of peers. It is rather easy to be an unquestioned world "authority" on the ecology of Central American acacia-ants, the silviculture of mahoganies, or the foraging behavior of weaver finches when you are the only scientist in the country with first-hand experience with the subject.

And where is tropical ecology going in the next 25 years? Some say "back to the temperate zones"—they clearly have the goal of understanding nature uppermost in their priorities. The National Science Foundation, the Institute of Ecology, and many other planning agencies, both temperate and tropical, want to see temperate zone dollar resources pumped into tropical research—they appear to have the goal of manipulating nature uppermost in their priorities. Why they wish to manipulate it had better be left for another essay.

Tropical Ecology as a Manipulatory Science

Let us for the moment be quite cynical and assume that nearly all of the esoteric research in tropical ecology (as, for example, reported in the pages of *Ecology, American Naturalist, Evolution, Journal of Ecology, Journal of Animal Ecology, Journal of the Zoological Society of London, Oikos, Oecologica,* etc.) will have little or no direct impact on the rates, directions, and quality of the conversion of tropical natural habitats to living machines for the production of society's desiderata. We may then safely assume that the primary input to habitat manipulation will come from the application of resource management technologies, ranging from age-old farming traditions to the integration of genetic and biological control programs, to technological innovations such as converting wood from rainforests into cattle feed. So what's new? Sounds just like the temperate zones.

This leads me to realize that the primary problem area is not whether the ecological rules for manipulating complex natural systems have a very large potential future use in the tropics; this may be safely taken for granted. The hitch comes in identifying a mechanism to insure the incorporation of these ecological rules into the socio-economic decision-making processes and in deciding which of several possible technologies should be used to generate the particular ecological recipes for manipulating any particular habitat.

INCORPORATION OF ECOLOGICAL RULES

Peoples of temperate zone countries generally feel that it is out of ignorance that tropical countries apparently disregard ecological principles in habitat exploitation. This condescending elitist view results directly in the "developed" country being very susceptible to the argument that it should fund research to produce the information that the "uninformed" tropical government "must be lacking." (Let us leave for later the question of what part of this information is already known elsewhere in the world but not immediately available to the tropical person making a decision.) What is clearly missing is the proof that lack of ecological planning is not simply due to an imbalanced exploitation program which is to the immediate advantage of the person with the power to control it. For example, the administration may be much more concerned with meeting the press of immediate produce needs than with producing longer range sustained (and generally lower) yields and higher standards of living. We then have the consequence of Nobel prizes being given for "green revolution" strains of grain. A second example, often discussed by Latin American politicians, is the excellent game and timber harvest laws that are on the books of many neotropical countries. These are rarely if ever enforced, and then generally only when to the advantage of the economic power directly concerned.

I think that we can safely assert that much of the disregard for ecological principles in tropical habitat manipulation is due to asking tropical habitats to produce yields incompatible with sustained yield levels or quality. This applies at all levels, from the farmer who wants cash for a new radio up to the government that wants to convert its forest reserves to cash for guns to protect its borders from a country that some years ago converted *its* forests to cotton fields.

So, what can be done to interest tropical decision-makers in the incorporation of sustained yield systems into their agroecosystem* development plans? (Please note that at this point I am not arguing for anything even remotely resembling conservation of natural systems.) As a predictor of the future, I cannot help but be cynical if I look around me in the tropics; planners will become aware as the agroecosystem in each tropical country degenerates until the lack of ecological planning is felt strongly and identified. At that point, the economic-social system will begin to incorporate its own checks and balances. The carrying capacity (*n* people at *x* standard of living) will be at some low level, depending on the intensity of destruction of natural capital up to this time. It is most likely that no semblance of natural habitats will remain even as national reserves. The critical question, then, becomes how much of the natural capital has been permanently destroyed, requiring a permanently lower human population density for a given standard of living. But need I paint such a gloomy scenario? Probably yes, but that should not obscure the obvious fact that there are positive ways to locate the carrying capacity of a habitat without such a dramatic country-wide or global experiment. As will be a recurring theme throughout this essay, I would like to emphasize that these positive ways are where the first priority should be in funding.

Even our crude level of understanding of tropical ecology is quite adequate to recognize major areas where money invested would yield very heavy returns:

1) Tropical decision makers are usually very provincial in their first-

* "Agroecosystem" as used here refers to all types of land or water use where organisms are manipulated to produce products desired by humans.

hand experience with agroecosystems. When they have the opportunity
to study abroad, it is generally in temperate zone countries. They should
have the financial means to view and work with those few functioning
sustained-yield harvest systems that are scattered about the tropics.

2) Tropical decision makers are likewise unfamiliar with the ways
that tropical agroecosystems outside their own country have repeatedly
gone awry. They are badly in need of an educational system that com-
municates and produces scenarios based on real examples drawn from
around the tropics. Farvan and Milton's "The Careless Technology"
(1972) is a long overdue start in this direction. For example, must each
country have its own failures at official land colonization by settlers
drawn from urban slums? Must each country rediscover the interaction
between large-scale cotton growing and insecticide resistance in tropical
insects?

3) When tropical biologists travel abroad for advanced training,
they return home to a governmental hierarchy badly in need of Ministers
of Agriculture, Department Chairmen, Bank Vice-presidents, etc. who
have technical expertise coupled with a broad education. They are
quickly led or forced out of applied research itself, and into administrative roles, substantially weakening the educational-research structure at
its base. Funding is badly needed to bolster job security and other rewards for the first-class researcher or teacher when doing the job he was
trained for. Suggestions are also in order, but beyond the scope of this
essay, for ways to minimize the administrative loads of tropical countries.

4) The directors and assistant directors of tropical agricultural field
stations, potentially the most important roles in the tropics, generally
regard the job as a hardship post. It often becomes a nine to five job or
less and is viewed as a necessary evil in the steps to becoming the Min-
ister of Agriculture or other top government official. We can hardly
expect such a person to take a truly active interest in the integration of
the results from his station's research into the agricultural ecosystem
that surrounds him. Conversely, the director can hardly be expected
to search out actively the needs of his surrounding agricultural ecosystem and pursue them with research. Funds are badly needed to make
this position an honorable and pleasant one which holds the best people
for long periods.

5) Schools are devices for transmitting the rules that run our socie-

ties. We teach math, biology, chemistry, languages, etc. because these abilities will presumably be needed in the years ahead as the child grows. The teaching of the socio-economic rules of a steady-state, non-expanding economy, attuned to the concept of living within the carrying capacity of the country's or region's resources, is an equally important subject from the first year in school.

TECHNOLOGY OF GENERATING RULES FOR ENVIRONMENTAL MANIPULATION

We must recognize the existence of an extremely important dichotomy in the philosophy of tropical applied ecology. The arguments are essentially as follows:

The Ecosystem Model Hypothesis (EMH).

We should attempt first to devise a general model of tropical ecosystems. Such a model would contain subsystems of such detail that current knowledge is inadequate to detail them. Once generated, this model would be used to predict the effects of various environmental perturbations on a local basis and, therefore, would be of great use in planning and carrying out the development of sound tropical ecosystem management/manipulation.

The Regional Development Hypothesis (RDH).

We should establish agricultural experiment stations for each of the major ecosystems on a regional basis, working toward a pragmatic set of sustained-yield solutions for each major region. The basic ecological background that is currently held in aggregate by the global scientific and folklore community is considered an adequate knowledge base to initiate such a program. Detailed information would be obtained as needed through direct large-scale experimentation at the station and on sub-leased neighboring land. Under this approach, each tropical agro-ecosystem is treated as relatively unique. Scientific linkage among the agroecosystems would be provided through publications and a greatly-increased exchange of personnel among field stations rather than through a formal model.

The philosophies underlying the above dichotomy deserve considerable discussion. As will become obvious, I feel the first hypothesis to be unnecessary and feel that the future in tropical applied ecology lies in the second hypothesis.

The EMH assumes that there is a thread of generality among the planning and development programs for a wide variety of tropical sites, a thread of generality that is not already known to the scientific community and that is not functional without formal incorporation into a model. I cannot disagree with the first assumption but have yet to see any evidence for the latter pair of assumptions. RDH, on the other hand, assumes that each site has very unique aspects; to make an *a priori* overall model detailed enough to deal simultaneously with all sites would require an inordinate amount of time to produce and maintain in the face of changing needs and technologies. In view of the extreme heterogeneity of tropical systems, such a model may be impossible even with the worldwide time and money resources available. In short, I feel that global heterogeneity within the tropics is so extreme that the pragmatic returns will be far greater through ecologically-sound regional development than development of overall ecosystem models.

By the fact of its attempted generality, the EMH appears to require extensive study of natural and quasi-natural ecosystems. A good deal of attention is given to documentation of community-wide energy flow, productivity, maintenance metabolism, etc. It is highly questionable that any of the general statements (e.g., "tropical lowland rainforest has the highest productivity of any habitat on earth"—which may well not be true, incidentally) produced by such a study, even when well documented by numbers, are relevant in any useful way to the development of a specific sustained-yield agricultural ecosystem. As a Southeast Asian biologist recently said: "but how important is productivity? The productivity of a crop plant is only of importance in so far as it affects the yield of the economic part of the crop. The padi (rice) planter is interested only in the harvest of rice grain, the rubber planter in the yield and quality of latex and the oil-palm grower in the yield of palm oil. Whether these plants come from plants (and I may add, communities) with high or low general productivity is immaterial." (Bullock, 1969.)

There is no evidence that an optimization of productivity of man's desiderata at various item- and system-specific levels will be a solution that even approximates the ecosystem structure and parameter values being examined in the development of ecosystem-wide models of natural communities in the tropics. If there is anything at all in common between natural and quasi-natural systems, and agroecosystems, it is the individual control mechanisms and their principles; these are the very aspects of ecosystem models that receive the least attention. To use a temperate zone example, the highly successful agricultural ecosystems of temperate zones were developed with virtually no understanding of natural systems. To maximize stable corn production in Iowa, a knowledge of undisturbed prairie productivity is probably unnecessary.

Even a complete Tropical Ecosystem Model in hand could be a very obstructive device. Its structure would necessarily be based on statements of central tendency, as its predictions would be. Tropical man's needs have a habit of lying many standard deviations from means determined by averages taken over all the energy flows or units in the ecosystem; this, of course, is not to say that the optimal human system cannot be a sustained-yield system. I merely wish to stress that natural solutions, or models based on natural solutions (systems), are very likely not to be optimal for man, and adherence to such models is likely to greatly delay the development of innovations (such as converting forest to cattle food directly). This adherence is especially likely in tropical economic-social systems where "elegant science" with all its trappings of prestige (computers, foreign aid programs, big name scientists, elegantly-illustrated publications, new equipment with sophisticated technology, etc.) is often treated with greater reverence than merited by its information content or pragmatic value. Further, the presence of such an official "solution" causes researchers to try to use it (much as there is the temptation to use a faulty tool rather than to construct a new one) and, thereby, become distracted by the inability to apply a technique rather than focusing on the true problem at hand. The highly formal educational systems of many tropical countries also generate a predilection for this error in tropically-trained technicians.

Viewed overall, the tropics has a tremendous heterogeneity of optimal solutions for any given site; this heterogeneity of optimization is aided by the diverse needs of a tropical country and especially by the world market in aggregate. A rainforest in Nigeria may be best maintained on a 50-year shelterwood cutting cycle for furniture, construction, and veneer stock; a rainforest in Costa Rica may be best converted to secondary vegetation to be processed directly to cattle feed; a rainforest in Sarawak may be best converted to paddy rice. Or a given rainforest may be best converted to all three or more. I maintain that the choices can only be identified through an active regional experiment station seated in the local agroecosystem that contains the rainforest. The station will have to assess the kinds of use to which its forest can be put (through experiments and through observation of other current forest uses, experimental or otherwise) and the world and local needs that have an impact on the local ecosystem. There is no evidence that the scientific and agricultural community at large does not already possess the needed technological information to conduct such an evaluation. And where the information is lacking, this information is of sufficient specificity that it will have to be generated by specific and directed experiments set up for local conditions, species, labor forces, etc.

It should be obvious that we are discussing a system where the conclusions of a regional experiment station can neither be taken lightly nor lightly made. Further, for it to develop a viable sustained-yield program over a large area, it or its agents will often have to have the power to overrule private interests; for example, such would be the case in an attempt to control insecticide resistance in cotton insects through sequential cotton-free years on a regional basis. It is also obvious that such a station must be managed by dedicated persons commanding the respect of scientists, local land owners, and the political powers of the country itself. Such a state of affairs would be at the extreme opposite end of the spectrum from the current status of most tropical experiment stations.

The system being proposed here is very susceptible to biological imperialism from well-meaning, but nevertheless destructive, temperate zone countries. Major sets of policy decisions must be made as to whether the regional experiment station is to aid and abet a maximally self-contained agroecosystem, with most of the produce of the region going to raise the standard of living of that region or its immediate political superior, or whether it is to produce an ecosystem highly integrated with the world ecosystem. A clear example is whether to generate a coffee-based economy, and use the cash to provide goods and services, or to go to a much more diverse agriculture and land-use program that will have little output to temperate-zone countries. When providing economic or educational assistance, it is extremely difficult for temperate-zone countries to avoid the temptation of structuring their aid in a manner that will destroy self-sufficiency on the part of tropical ecosystems.

Tropical Ecology as Esoteric Research

The esoteric research yet to be done in tropical ecology, as in temperate ecology, will have little or no direct impact on the development of sustained-yield tropical agroecosystems. This annoying statement requires elaboration. Under the rubric "esoteric research," I include those studies that are usually justified (if at all) by a general statement such as "tropical ecosystems are the most complex on earth, and man surely has something yet to learn by understanding how they function." ("Tropical ecosystem," as used here, is almost always an erudite synonym for "undisturbed lowland tropical rainforest.") Or another view states that "diversity enhances stability, and since we are after stability, we must study diverse ecosystems." Such studies are usually done on habitats nearly or totally undisturbed by man. Even when organisms or systems of economic importance are studied, the structure of the study is usually the same as if it were in an undisturbed habitat. As mentioned earlier, the results are generally reported in a set of journals regarded as prestigious. The results, wishfully, tend to increase our general understanding of ecological processes and the patterns they generate and, thereby, raise the quality of education of future biologists/ecologists whether they be esoteric or applied researchers.

But here is where my pessimism appears. I have seen no evidence to suggest that increasing the amount of ecological understanding of the tropics through more esoteric research would increase the speed with which high-quality sustained-yield agroecosystems will replace the exploitative-expansionist systems currently operating in most of the tropics. There are vast amounts of basic ecological knowledge stashed away in the world's journals and in scientists' heads that is never brought to bear on the decision-making processes or, once there, is rejected by those making the decisions. The same may be said of the agricultural folklore that is rapidly becoming extinct as subsistence agriculture is replaced by cash crops and land "development." On the other hand, once one has focused on a particular tropical agroecosystem, one can very quickly identify a large number of applied research projects which would be clearly of use in improving that particular agroecosystem. Further, one can often identify the bottle-neck in the absorption process where money should be applied to get the information taken up by the administration, rather than using that money to generate more information to pile up behind the obstruction.

It is quite obvious that esoteric research in tropical ecology will occasionally come up with a fact or process that is of use to the person putting together a sustained-yield agroecosystem. Aside from the problem that such information is generally inaccessible until it has filtered through the educational digestive system, there is a very grave danger in its use and interpretation as science is currently practiced. As mentioned earlier, one of the criteria of good esoteric research in ecology is the general applicability of the study being reported. For example, we may have a study that shows that in tropical deciduous forest, a large proportion of the insect community passes the dry season as active adults concentrated in the humid shade of riverside (riparian) forests. When the rainy season starts, they move back into upland pastures, fields, and forests. Two agricultural predictions follow. First, with an insect community of this type, dry season irrigation may greatly increase the pest problem by providing a finely-reticulate network of dry season refugia. Second, we should destroy the riparian forest through clearing or stream diversion. The careful agroecosystem planner cannot afford to be satisfied with this kind of average information. Each of these conclusions may be invalid for any given agroecosystem, depending on the exact behavior of the precise pest species *vis à vis* dry season refugia.

Only a minuscule fraction of a natural tropical insect community falls in the pest category, and it is unreasonable to expect those pest species to always behave as the average insect does. If the planner is alert and has good ecological training, he will know that insects migrate, diapause, are generally host-specific, require moisture, and vary at the species level in their behavior. This knowledge should be adequate input to cause him to have a brief study conducted for his own particular ecosystem and its pests and, thereby, decide the fate of the forests that constitute dry season refugia for his insects.

I think that we must recognize that esoteric tropic ecology is essentially an art form. Like all such complex intellectual human endeavors, it occasionally generates a useful overview and, more rarely, some specific bit of information that is of use to applied ecology. Its most important potential is the dual role of its practitioners who simultaneously serve as teachers of general ecological principles to up-and-coming applied persons. A second important task is in stimulating more experienced people through presentation of a fresh view or an intellectually-titillating solution to an esoterically-complex problem. It is my opinion that funding of esoteric tropical ecology should be restricted to the best artists and to those who are also willing to put in the time and emotion to share their studies extensively with those who choose to work with construction and maintenance of tropical agroecosystems.

A substantial part of current "ecological" tropical research does not fit in either category. Several examples might be illustrative. During the past 10 years, there have been at least 25 studies in major journals describing this or that piece of undisturbed to lightly-disturbed tropical forest; these studies were not aimed at bolstering our conceptual framework of tropical ecology, and they do not achieve that goal by accident. They will be of little or no use to a carefully-managed regional experiment station developing an agroecosystem. This is true even for the forestry portion of that program. The station director will have to gather on the spot his own information in the format that he needs. As a second example, productivity studies are clearly on the rise, with one focus on mangrove swamps. We hear that the goal is to determine the impact on marine productivity of the removal of mangrove vegetation. Unfortunately, some ecologists have decided that the way to get at this is to measure photosynthetic productivity of the crowns of mangrove plants. When we consider the incredible network of control loops and compensation systems between the crowns of mangrove trees and the actual amount of useful fish caught by the fisherman, it seems obvious that the only productive experiments may be those similar to the ones already kindly provided free of charge by Uncle Sam (though unfortunately lacking controls).

Our goal should be to understand tropical nature, not to describe it. This understanding can have intellectual justification and/or enhance habitat manipulation. With infinite time, resources, and interest, we could simply let the description roll on, and eventually understanding would come out of it, though one could also envision the description becoming so mammoth that we would have to do research on it to rediscover it—in short, the tropical world as it functions is the epitome of a pragmatic description. Our goal is to reduce it to workable size.

This seems the best point to bring up conservation of tropical habitats. At present, most of the acres of most tropical habitats have been mildly to severely altered by man's recent activities. Many of the animals and plants still remain (though often not as breeding populations), but the interaction systems that produced and maintained them through natural selection are often gone; much of the tropics has been converted to a haphazard zoo and botanical garden. There seems to be an alternative. Throughout this essay, I have been arguing for development of carefully-planned and tropical-regional agroecosystems. If intellectually-stimulating or aesthetic experience is not regarded as useful produce from such an agroecosystem, then there is very unlikely to be justification for inclusion of natural habitats. There is a substantial part of any tropical flora and fauna that man can outcompete and do without. If this is carried out well, as I predict it will be, then the conservationist should prefer the currently mismanaged tropical lands, as dismal as they may appear. Brushy cattle pastures (the haphazard zoo mentioned earlier) and weedy fields support a very large flora and fauna that will definitely be missing from carefully managed pastures and fields.

It seems that the best the esoteric ecologist can ask for is small bits of strategically placed and carefully chosen undisturbed natural vegetation on which to practice his art. The careful agroecosystem planner will probably give him vegetation types that are representative of those from which his fields, pastures, and forests are derived. It is obvious that once the society changes to where undisturbed habitats are regarded as having aesthetic value in their own right (rather than being the environment against which man competes as is currently the view in most of the tropics), the amount of land under this type of use may be legitimately increased. This is, of course, provided that there has been a large enough piece retained as a reservoir of participants.

Most of the classical non-aesthetic arguments for the preservation of unmanipulated tropical forests appear to be specious. As stressed earlier, there is no *a priori* basis for assuming that stable natural communities are ideal for high output sustained yields. Further, to be stable, a cleverly manipulated community need be neither natural nor diverse to the extent found in nature. There is no obvious reason why man should not competitively displace a large part of the natural tropical community and yet keep it in balance. Nature is probably not a realistic gene pool for future agricultural marvels; when a new strain of corn, beans, cacao, or ginger is needed, the plant breeder turns to the variability expressed in domestic plantings rather than putting on his pith helmet and heading for the jungle. To be sure, the forest is a seed source for lumber and drug species, but it hardly needs to be undisturbed to produce seeds. To a minor extent, the forest may contain phenotype pools in the form of undomesticated plants and animals, but the cogent evidence is very weak that contemporary tropical man has a shortage of useful phenotypes or is interested in filtering such phenotypes out of natural vegetation; it would have to be a rather highly specialized phenotype for man to have missed it already. Such plants are usually of value only for their secondary compounds. Biosynthesis being what it is today, it seems rather unlikely that there is a huge store of valuable compounds sitting there to be discovered. For such obvious things as erosion control and timber, undisturbed forests can be replaced with diverse ones of much greater direct value and still provide game cover and erosion control.

Recommendations

This essay is not intended as definitive. Rather, I wish to make explicit an unpalatable view that floats in the backs of many ecologists' minds but is carefully suppressed owing to its obvious threat to both our material livelihood and our intellectual egos. However, it seems better to discuss it explicitly among ourselves than to have our credibility gap progressively widen. I have been rather negative to this point. Can I make some positive suggestions?

I have referred constantly to the concept of regional experiment stations for major agroecosystems. It should be emphasized that these are not just stations for breeding better strains of corn, cotton, etc. They would be expected to have the personnel and resources to investigate and develop all aspects of the agroecosystem, in many ways filling the combined roles of the United States land grant colleges of agriculture, fisheries, forestry, the associated state experiment stations, the U.S.D.A., and some private companies. I suggest that temperate-zone funding in the tropics could be far better spent in aiding and abetting such field stations than through the current vogue of funding large conferences where the same tired questions (e.g., "are tropical soils fragile?"; "is subsistence agriculture consistent with modern society structure?") are pontificated on by various people with a few years' experience in the tropics. Any competent director of a tropical experiment station could sit down for an afternoon and draft the same list of questions while looking out his office window. What he needs is the funding, equipment, and innovative scientific manpower to get to work on these questions for his own specific region. I suggest that we stop planning the solutions of the tropics' problems from our temperate zone offices and start returning some of the resources we have ripped off the tropics over the past 400 years in the form of hard cash and technical expertise directly to the development of regional sustained-yield agroecosystems. This should not require planning conferences at all except perhaps among the tropical countries on the general philosophical underpinning to be discussed below. The details of the research should be the subject of discussions by the field station directors, staff, and whatever imported personnel are interested in direct involvement. If it is felt that block funding cannot be trusted to a particular experiment station, then, some sort of review process could be generated whereby the reviewers at other experiment stations would participate, with occasional input by esoteric and applied ecologists the world over.

But this would not be enough. The governments of tropical countries obviously have to come to grips with several policy questions before a steady-state agroecosystem can develop. First, a decision has to be made about the average standard of living and the frequency distributions of the individual standards of living. Further, the currency units in which it is to be expressed (income, suicide rate, education level, immigration rate, etc.) must be identified. Second, once this is done, planning councils can decide relatively easily how many persons the region can support and determine the needed intensity of birth control.

A second major change is also needed. I think we should undermine the current concept that, to be really elegant, applied research must also deal with fundamental or theoretical ecological ideas. Vice versa, we need to undermine the idea that there is such a thing as an overall, general-purpose ecological study which will maximize practical results and contribute to sophisticated ecological theory as well. Very often the gathering of "basic" ecological data during applied studies dilutes the applied study almost beyond usefulness.

References

Bullock, J. A. 1969. Producibility of the rainforest ecosystem. *Malayan Nature J.*, **22**: 198-205.

Farvar, M. T. and J. P. Milton. 1972. *The Careless Technology*. Natural History Press, New York. p. 1030.

16 Contaminants and Recycling in Relation to Biogeochemical Cycles

ORIE L. LOUCKS
INSTITUTE FOR ENVIRONMENTAL STUDIES
University of Wisconsin

Pollution and recycling appear to be the watchwords of the 1970s. Even a brief survey of the recent work on cycling of pollutants and resources should take several chapters. Perhaps another author, uninhibited by data, could describe his view of the future directions of research on pollution and recycling more easily than he could describe the present, but I cannot. My objective is, therefore, more modest: to try to highlight what seem to be the most substantive problems, in a generic sense, and to point to the great opportunities and obligations of biologists to contribute to the evolution of these relatively new areas of science.

John R. Platt (1969) is one of few authors to have offered a new dimension for outlining priorities in research over the next 5 to 50 years. Using an exponential scale of the technological problems facing man, he listed "destruction of biological and ecological balance by pollution" as the second most important problem facing both the United States and the world, superseded only by total annihilation. In taking this view, Platt seems to have in mind the long-term effects observable in biological systems due to addition of almost innocuous quantities of persistent materi-

Some of the work reported in this paper was sponsored in part by the National Science Foundation under Interagency Agreement AG-199, 40-193-69 with the Atomic Energy Commission, Oak Ridge National Laboratory.

als to the world biosphere. The best known examples include DDT, mercury, and radioactive wastes, but there is evidence indicating we will soon know more about others.

One of the failures of biology over the past 25 years was in not fully recognizing the potential for biological concentration of these materials by selective uptake and retention in food chains. Part of the reason is because cycling of materials in the biosphere involves many more disciplines than biology, and at that time, we were too interested in subject matter problems to consider a question of major inter-disciplinary dimensions.

However, little can be learned from passing judgements with the benefit of hindsight. Our role now is to use all the experience we have to look ahead. The important question is how do we mount the research needed today to assure that, within one or two decades, we will have the understanding to anticipate and substantially reduce unintended effects from the use of contaminating substances. Demands are being made for more and more precise statements of the thresholds where a material (such as waste heat) that is usually a normal constituent of the environment has to be recognized as a pollutant. These studies are not clearly a part of any existing discipline. Many areas of science, including biology, will be modified as we respond to the need for new and precisely defined programs. Biology will be a prominent part of this process, and I shall try to show why.

At this point, let me define both "contaminant" and "pollutant." The American Chemical Society (1969) offers one of the most quantitative approaches to these widely used terms. A *"contaminant"* can be defined as anything added to the environment that causes a deviation from mean geochemical composition, an average prior to human activity. In this view, a contaminant is considered a *"pollutant"* only if it adversely affects something that man values and is present in high enough concentrations to do so. Thus, contaminants can include natural phenomena, such as the products of a forest fire or the silt from a collapsing river bank. As common a material as water vapor can be a pollutant if the local concentration (as from a cooling tower) is sufficient to induce fog and affect highway safety. I am also adopting the broad generic term "material" to describe all types of products produced naturally, or by man and released into the environment. Included are all synthetic chemicals, metals, radioactivity, and energy, the latter largely in the form of waste heat.

The changes in our definition and conceptualization of safe materials, or safe quantities of materials, and the new understanding of the human value system that causes some materials to be viewed as pollutants, indicate that research in this area will become more complex and more interdisciplinary with time. In my opinion, this work probably will continue to follow the four lines that can be recognized in the new and ongoing programs of environmental research and monitoring:

1) physical and chemical characterization of the contaminants;
2) evaluation of biological responses in various forms of biota;
3) pathway mechanisms for redistribution of persistent materials in the biogeochemical cycles of the earth;

and

4) studies of resource (waste) recycling to prevent concentration of the contaminants in those resources.

The specific objective of this chapter will be to comment on some current research trends that illustrate the areas of growth I expect to see.

Chemical and Physical Characterization

The research on radiation hazards over the past 30 years has shown that the most systematic approach to undertaking and anticipating effects of significant deviations from mean geochemical or geothermal balance rests with precise chemical and physical characterization of the potential contaminants. Ten broad categories of natural and man-made materials with a potential to qualify as pollutants are listed in Table I. The properties of many of the materials in these classes are reasonably well known, but others are unknown. Even the natural transformation of inorganic mercury to methylmercury in lake and river sediments is a recent discovery (Wallace et al., 1971). The characterization of synthetic organic compounds used as food additives and in pharmaceuticals is almost a discipline in itself.

The program of research on radioactive substances and radiation effects sponsored by the U.S. Atomic Energy Commission since its inception is an example of what could have been done and can yet be done for

TABLE I. *Broad Categories of Both Natural and Man-made Materials That Enter the Environment and Which Often Qualify as Contaminants or Pollutants.*

---

1. Metals and related elements (e.g., heavy metals, asbestos)
2. Naturally-occurring organics (e.g., O_2-demanding wastes), including oil spills
3. Synthetic organic compounds (e.g., plastics, food additives, etc.)
4. Biocides (e.g., rodenticides, insecticides, herbicides)
5. Waste gases (e.g., CO, CO_2, SO_2, NO)
6. Cycling cations and anions (e.g., calcium, fluorides, nitrates, and phosphates)
7. Particulates (e.g., dust, smoke particles, silt)
8. Radioactive substances (e.g., ^{90}Sr, ^{131}I, ^3H)
9. Ionizing radiation (e.g., alpha particles, X-rays, gamma radiation)
10. Thermal energy (e.g., power plant waste heat)

---

each of the other classes of materials in Table I. Numerous reviews of the AEC-sponsored research are available, but the summary of results on turnover and concentration of radionuclides in food chains by Reichle et al. (1970) is worth particular attention. The results of work on nine of the most significant radionuclides are shown in Table II. The biological concentration factors from one trophic level to the next is still unknown for many elements at certain levels in the food chain. The wide range in values for both aquatic and terrestrial food chains is largely due to the great differences from one life-form to the next, and the authors note that the studies are still incomplete for many forms of animal life.

In addition, the biological turnover time varies widely from one element to the next and from one life-form to the next. These authors conclude that considerable additional effort is needed for "characterizing the effects of environmental factors on radionuclide cycling in selected ecological systems, particularly in highly populated riparian and coastal areas." One hundred radionuclides were considered significant for the models of potential radionuclide transport in the marine environment around Amchitka Island (Bloom and Raines, 1971).

The basic studies of the characteristics of DDT and other persistent pesticides (Mrak, 1969) provide another example of a problem-oriented research program that may be needed for other compounds. The most important physical and chemical characteristics of DDT and its closely

TABLE II. *Food Chain Concentration Factors for Nine Elements in Aquatic and Terrestrial Systems.**

Trophic level	Element concentration factors**						
	Ca	Cs	Mn	Fe	H	P	I
Aquatic systems							
Water	1.0	1.0	1.0	1.0	1.0	1.0	1.0
Algae & higher plants	1-400	50-25,000	700-35,000	2,400-200,000	—	36,000-50,000	60-200
Invertebrates							
Saprovores	16	60-11,000	6,000-140,000	—	—	2-100,000	20-1,000
Herbivores	—	600	—	125	—	2,000	—
Fish							
Omnivores	—	125-6,000	—	10,000	—	3,000-100,000	25-50
Carnivores	0.5-300	640-9,500	—	—	—	—	—
Terrestrial systems							
Plants	1.0	1.0	1.0	1.0	1.0	1.0	1.0
Invertebrates	0.1-18	0.1-0.5	—	—	0.6	11-18	—
Mammals							
Herbivores	—	0.3-2.0	—	0.8	0.6	—	0.5
Carnivores	—	3.8-7.0	—	—	—	—	0.1

* From Reichle et al., 1970.

** Ratio of element level in consumer to element level in food-chain base, with base value normalized at 1.0.

related analogs are extreme insolubility in water, high solubility in lipids (whether in water, in air, or in a digestive tract), and resistance to chemical breakdown in most environments (Woodwell et al., 1971). The resistance to chemical breakdown leads to persistence which, with the long-overlooked capacity to vaporize and ability to be selectively retained by higher trophic levels in food chains, provides, in a single compound, almost all the undesirable chemical characteristics of a contaminant.

The extent of basic chemical and physical studies needed is apparent from any of the current surveys of needs for testing the new materials being developed by our technology. The report on toxic substances by the Council on Environmental Quality (C.E.Q., 1971) indicates that 300 to 500 new chemical compounds are introduced into commercial use annually. About 9,000 synthetic organic compounds were in commercial use by 1968. The synthetic (man-made) organic chemicals (Table III) are of special concern as contaminants because they are usually alien to the natural environment, but the large quantities of metals in use indicate the need to be concerned about transformation and biogeochemical cycling of these materials as well. The effort needed to characterize these chemicals and anticipate their breakdown products or movement in the

TABLE III. *The Major Metals and Synthetic Organic Compounds Considered to be of Potential Concern to the Public.* Total Consumption and Release is Increasing from 2% to 20% Each Year.*

Metals	Estimated U.S. Consumption in 1968 (tons)	Synthetic Organic Chemicals**	Estimated U.S. Consumption in 1968 (10^6 lbs.)
Arsenic	25,000	Dyes	226
Barium	1,590,000	Flavors and perfumes	117
Cadmium	6,664	Plastics and resins	16,360
Chromium	1,316,000	Plasticizers	1,331
Copper	1,576,000	Elastomers (synthetic	
Lead	1,328,790	rubbers)	4,268
Manganese	2,228,412	Surface active agents	3,739
Mercury	2,866	Miscellaneous***	67,525
Selenium	762		
Vanadium	5,495		
Zinc	1,728,400		

* Council on Environmental Quality, 1971. ** Exclusive of medicinals and pesticides. *** Cleaning solvents, aerosol propellants, alcohols, etc.

environment is almost overwhelming. However, the work has been done for radioactive substances, and I believe we will see no less for other potentially-hazardous contaminants.

Biological Responses to Environmental Contaminants

The more interesting questions for biology, however, are the responses generated in living systems by the materials used or released in the environment. The spectrum of biological responses is almost as broad as biology itself. Effects are discernible: 1) as damage to genetic material; 2) as upsets in enzyme reactions; 3) as mortality or morbidity of whole organisms; 4) as an effect on whole populations; and 5) as a modification of the structure of natural ecosystems. All five levels of effects have been investigated for DDT (Harrison et al., 1970), and several levels are involved for each class of material in Table I. As we come to use the current experience of experimental biology and environmental systems methods for investigation of the effects of a contaminant on organisms, we will, more and more, begin by considering the chemical and physical properties of the contaminant and of its metabolites and proceed to investigate the responses that appear to be attributable to these properties. In the following four sections, we will consider the types of research which can be expected to develop in the respective areas of biological concern.

MORTALITY AND MORBIDITY FROM ACUTE TOXICITY

Relatively few contaminants in the environment will ever produce demonstrable mortality of humans, we hope, although releases of mercury through historical times have been notorious killers. During the 1950s, industrial mercury contamination of the aquatic food resources of Minamata Bay in Japan (Wallace et al., 1971) led to the deaths of 41 people and to the poisoning of many others. Such incidents are not likely to recur with mercury, but the metabolism and redistribution of other heavy metals are not yet well enough known to assure the safety of man and natural resource species.

In any case, the effects of contaminants will be viewed more often in terms of some very low probability of mortality of either plants or animals and a somewhat higher possibility of morbidity effects from chronic

TABLE IV. *Daily Intake of Mercury and Associated Mercury Concentrations in Blood and Hair of Humans.**

Case	Daily intake (μgHg)	Mercury in blood corpuscles (ppm)	Mercury in hair (ppm)
4 normal persons (Sweden)		0.006	1.35
83 normal persons (Sweden)	10	0.010	
51 fish eaters (Sweden)	44	0.058	7.9
20 fish eaters (Finland)		0.196	17.3
8 afflicted persons (Sweden)	204	2.59	36.1
Diseased Japanese (Minamata)		2.40	500.0

* From Wallace et al., 1971.

toxicity. The most vexing question that will have to be resolved for a large number of contaminants is that of permissible tolerances in food and water. The work on mercury summarized by Wallace et al. (1971) is still the best example of a pattern we can expect more frequently. The data in Table IV illustrate the relationship between mercury in the diet, mercury in the bloodstream, and long-term accumulation in hair. Obviously, a diet restricted to slightly contaminated foods leads to a significant risk of illness not shared by people using a more mixed diet.

The established tolerance of 0.5 ppm of mercury for fish in the United States has meant the withdrawal of much tuna and swordfish as a food resource although the high levels in these species seem likely to be normal for carnivores at the top of the food chain in a marine environment. Further research can be expected to identify numerous other toxicants in natural foods (Stokinger, 1971) that are acceptable as part of a mixed diet but which may have to be regulated. Neither science nor society has really faced up to the broad implications of "safe" tolerances as yet, but both will have to within the next 10 years. A major research effort will be needed to provide evidence instead of emotion in the forthcoming dialog.

MUTAGENIC, TERATOGENIC, AND CARCINOGENIC EFFECTS

Within the past few years, much of the scientific community and the public have come to accept the principle that virtually every material added to the human diet or used in health care should undergo extensive testing for its potential carcinogenic, teratogenic, or mutagenic effects. Epstein (1970) is one of a number of qualified scientists who have expressed concern about increases in certain diseases that have been linked to the presence of contaminants in air, water, and food. Although this evidence is preliminary, it raises questions concerning the thoroughness of the work done in the past and present in determining approvals for the use of new chemicals.

Epstein believes that, even before testing is planned, we should first begin by asking questions as to the efficacy of a proposed chemical, and whether it will serve a socially- and economically-useful purpose. Second: He believes that metabolites of the chemical should be characterized and examined for toxicity as well as the source chemical itself. He draws particular attention to the problem of toxic impurities in some compounds that make evaluation difficult or misleading. The presence of trace quantities of dioxins in the herbicide 2,4,5-T is a well known example. One of the major reservations presently being attached to the use of nitrilotriacetic acid (NTA) is the absence of data on intermediate pathways and reaction products during biodegradation.

Third: Epstein suggests that the question of the predicted degree of safety attached to the use of a chemical—presently in use or proposed—should be based on a balance of systematic toxicology, considering acute and chronic toxicity *per se* (including carcinogenicity, teratogenicity, and mutagenicity), and model ecological studies for prediction of environmental concentration mechanisms. He proposes a program of monitoring for the chemicals *and* their metabolic degradation products, particularly in areas of high risk.

However, the views expressed by Epstein need not be taken as support for a literal interpretation of the Delaney Amendment to the Federal Food, Drug, and Cosmetic Act. The thinking of many scientists, such as Stokinger (1971), will receive increasing attention if an orderly approach to the balancing of risks and benefits is to be achieved. He suggests seven strict rules which, if followed, will provide objective criteria for judging the seriousness of potential health hazards. At the same time, new efforts will have to be directed to improve experimental procedures for testing teratogenicity and mutagenicity of chemicals. The question of mutagenic effects on native species in wild habitats is still being passed over as relatively insignificant and, also, will receive much more attention in the next decade.

POPULATION RESPONSES

The effects of some contaminants are hardly detectable from observation of individual organisms. However, significant effects are often observed on population levels over the period of a few generations. Very careful studies are needed to relate the observed population response to an effect of a contaminant, but this has been done to the satisfaction of most scientists in the case of DDT effects on the reproduction and population levels of the peregrine falcon (Hickey, 1969) and a number of coastal fishery species (Goldberg, 1971).

Population effects are equally observable in response to the additions of nutrients to aquatic systems, particularly phosphates. The addition of waste heat also has a variety of effects on populations in aquatic systems (Krenkel and Parker, 1969). Both thermal energy and nutrients operate to stimulate growth of certain aquatic organisms for which the enriched environment is favorable, but at the same time, heat depresses the growth of other species for which the environment is less favorable.

Beeton (1969) has investigated the levels of contaminants and the associated changes in the biology of the Great Lakes over the past 70 years. Many aspects of the Lake Erie environment, in particular, have changed, and the shallow western basin has been modified most of all. He notes that total phosphorus concentrations doubled between 1942 and 1958 and that total nitrogen increased about 3-fold between 1930 and 1958. Between 1919 and 1963, the abundance of phytoplankton increased 3-fold, and different genera became dominant. Decomposition of the increased growth has led to an almost 10-fold increase in oxygen demand and a periodic anoxic condition that now limits some of the species stimulated by the earlier changes. The nymphs of mayflies (*Hexagenia*) have almost disappeared from the western Lake Erie basin, and oligochaetes are now dominant. The fishery has shifted from lake herring and blue pike around 1900, to blue pike, whitefish, and walleye in the 1940s, and yellow perch, smelt, and sheepshead by 1965.

Our current research on lake systems, under the sponsorship of the Deciduous Forest Biome, United States International Biological Program (IBP), is an example of a probable trend toward more intensive investigation of the effects of man-modified environments on populations of aquatic biota (Loucks, 1971). Recent results have demonstrated that precise measurement of the observed responses of biota in the lake, when related quantitatively by means of systems models to observations on the levels and turnover rates of nutrient contaminants, provides an understanding of the causes, effects, and interactions that was not previously possible. Some significant theoretical analyses have been made possible, particularly on the principles of species differentiation and tactical utilization of the aquatic environment. One hypothesis suggests that the rise of blue-green algae in over-fertilized lakes may be due to the selective advantage of nitrogen-fixing species in systems where a nitrogen deficiency has been generated by comparative phosphorus abundance. The systems approach is providing evidence for a major growth in theoretical biology as it relates to the response of competing wild populations in modified environments.

EFFECTS ON DIVERSITY AND STABILITY OF ECOSYSTEMS

Until the 1950s, few people believed that any chemicals could be introduced into the environment in sufficient quantity to threaten the characteristics of an entire ecosystem. Even when the persistence of DDT began to be more fully understood, there remained questions as to whether there would ever be evidence indicating the extent of an ecosystem upset.

A number of analyses now have been completed that show the results of whole system upsets and the types of evidence needed to document them. Woodwell (1970) and Odum (1970) reported on studies of the effects of a radiation source on a forest ecosystem, and Harrison et al. (1970) have used systems methods and the results of studies of DDT effects on populations to examine whole ecosystem response characteristics. These upsets have to do with large-scale changes in population levels of certain species and their replacement by other species, or their complete elimination. Both studies indicate a trend toward simplification of the system when placed under the stress of a contaminant, but the long-range effects of such simplification cannot yet be evaluated. We will undoubtedly see much more macroscale experimental and theoretical study of the effects of ecosystem simplification within the next 10 to 20 years.

An equally significant study of a whole ecosystem response is the rehabilitation of Lake Washington (Edmondson, 1970). This initiative depended on a prior understanding of ecosystem modification by nutrient contaminants and demonstrates the way in which studies of the departures from normal biogeochemical cycling can lead to alleviation of large-scale environmental problems. Lake Washington is only one system in which recovery through control of the sources of contamination has now been demonstrated. Tens or hundreds of other examples can be expected to follow in the next 25 years, each involving different types of problems.

We will also see much more work on examples of potential ecosystem upsets, on the role of native species diversity in maintaining the stability of these systems, and on the long-range effects of the trend toward simplification. These studies will involve a major infusion of systems methods and a new theoretical biology of ecosystems, but the groundwork for these developments is already apparent from other chapters in this volume.

Biogeochemical Cycling of Contaminants

The processes by which contaminants move in the environment from points at which they are applied to other sites where a biological response is produced are subjects that frequently have not concerned biologists, other than indirectly. The movement of fluorides, lead, or DDT in the atmosphere, transformation and transport of mercury in lake and stream sediments, and the potential contamination of deep groundwater resources by ill-chosen surface or underground waste disposal sites are all primarily concerns of the physical sciences.

However, utilization of the principles of hydrologic, meteorological, and geological cycling has become an integral part of biology over the past 20 years. The best examples of this fruition are the Hubbard Brook project in New Hampshire (Likens et al., 1970) and the Deciduous Biome watershed projects of the US-IBP (Reichle and Auerbach, 1972).

In my opinion, the next 10 years will see an increasing proportion of biologists collaborating closely with scientists from other disciplines in research on the movement of contaminants in the earth. The system-coupling techniques being developed by the US-IBP ecosystem programs (Loucks, 1971; O'Neill and Burke, 1971) are examples of the innovations in systems methods that will become more prevalent within the next decade. As mentioned previously, a body of new theoretical foundations is being developed that is likely to modify greatly our very concept of pollution. It is entirely probable that many of these studies will be part of a new "environmental science," if such develops and in 10 years may not be recognized directly as biology. If not, biology will have lost, for the research and its interpretation will involve significant numbers of biologists.

Recycling of Resources: Natural Process or Source of Contamination

Considerable attention is being given to the long-range potential of complete or partial recycling of certain resources, particularly metals, paper products, wood, glass, and thermal energy. The goal is obviously desirable, and some of the studies to date (ORNL, 1971) indicate that, in certain areas, large-scale collection, processing, and re-use are technically and economically feasible. However, the extent of contamination of solid wastes during manufacture and use seems likely to lead to aberrations of biogeochemical cycles that will require intensive monitoring and evaluation.

One example of the problem comes from the efforts to recycle paper. Until relatively recently, small quantities of methylmercury were used in pulp bales to prevent fungal growth. The remanufacture of pulp from paper containing the fungicide involved washing and release of the mercury to the aquatic environment. Compost from domestic refuse has been widely used in parts of Europe (Marx, 1971), but the larger proportion of "compost reject" material in American cities presents a problem. Digested sludge from sewage waste disposal plants may be dangerous for use as an agricultural fertilizer because of the trace quantities of toxic metals that enter the sewage systems. Trace element tolerances that attempt to prevent serious contamination of soils and crops have been set for irrigation waters (FWPCA, 1968). Marx (1971) also discusses the pathways that may link chemical waste disposal, recycling, and human disease.

If extensive recycling of wastes is to be achieved, even within 50 years, including the removal of excess nutrient from waste waters, large-scale removal of contaminating chemicals will also be necessary. The technology to do it is not yet available; the research to develop the capability is hardly underway. The understanding that biologists are now developing with respect to contaminants in biogeochemical cycles seems likely to play a major role in the new recycling technology. During the next two decades, I expect considerable expansion of research on the problems in this area (jointly with engineering studies of collection and processing methodologies) and increased participation by biologists.

Biologists in Future Environmental Problem-Solving

Biologists have a long history of successful problem-solving in the areas of agriculture, fisheries, and forestry. The next 25 years are likely to bring about a similar problem-solving focus on preventing or alleviating biological upsets due to contaminants in the environment.

It is now also becoming clear that the legislative intent of the National Environmental Policy Act (NEPA) of 1969 will be enforced by the federal courts. Two of the purposes of the Act are worth quoting:

> To promote efforts which will prevent or eliminate damage to the environment and biosphere and stimulate health and welfare of man; and to enrich the understanding of the ecological systems and natural resources important to the nation.

The Act further provides that the federal government shall use all practical means to

> fulfill the responsibilities of each generation as trustee of the environment for succeeding generations; attain the widest range of beneficial uses of the environment without degradation, risk to health or safety, or other undesirable and unintended consequences; and enhance the quality of renewable resources and approach the maximum attainable recycling of depletable resources.

As the means of reaching these goals, the NEPA provides for filing and evaluation of environmental impact statements for proposed construction, diversions, spraying programs, etc., and the assembling of evidence to assure that no significant violation of the above goals is anticipated or allowed. The problem to date has been the lack of widespread access to understanding of the long-range effects of shifts in material balances implicit in some projects. The recent interpretations by the federal courts have made clear that this statute will not be ignored, unless it is seriously amended (Gillette, 1972). Within a very few years, most biologists can expect to participate to some extent in the preparation, review, or evaluation of impact analyses.

The past two years have seen a major increase in emphasis on applied science by some of the federal granting agencies, as well as by private foundations. There has been a popular demand, nationally, that we use the present scientific state of the art to address the problems of man and recommend solutions. This is a departure of some consequence to many scientists and is one that will be uncomfortable to a few. However, both physical and biological applied science has been accepted as an essential part of university and governmental agency research since the beginning of these institutions, and adjusting to the new forms of applied science should present no serious difficulties.

Problem-solving on the scale of large biogeochemical systems will change the outlook of almost all areas of science in the next two decades, and in the long run, these changes will be more important than the new developments in experimental technique and subject matter. All scientists, however, are trained to promote and accept new developments and should look forward to the relatively sharp turn toward problem-solving. This certainly should be the outlook for biologists contributing to solution of contamination and recycling problems.

References

American Chemical Society. 1969. Clean our environment: The chemical basis for action. A Report by the Subcommittee on Environmental Improvement, Committee on Chemistry and Public Affairs. Washington, D.C.

Beeton, A. M. 1969. Changes in the environment and biota of the Great Lakes. In: *Eutrophication: Causes, Consequences, Correctives.* Proceedings of a Symposium. National Academy of Sciences. Washington, D.C. p. 150-187.

Bloom, S. G. and G. E. Raines. 1971. Mathematical models for predicting the transport of radionuclides in a marine environment. *BioScience,* **21**: 691-696.

Council on Environmental Quality. 1971. Toxic substances. U.S. Government Printing Office, April.

Edmondson, W. T. 1970. Phosphorus, nitrogen and algae in Lake Washington after diversion of sewage. *Science,* **169**: 690-691.

Epstein, S. S. 1970. Control of chemical pollutants. *Nature,* **228**: 816-819.

Federal Water Pollution Control Administration (FWPCA). 1968. Water quality criteria. Federal Water Pollution Control Administration Report

Gillette, R. 1972. National Environmental Policy Act: How well is it working? *Science,* **176**: 146-150.

Goldberg, E. D. 1971. Chlorinated hydrocarbons in the marine environment. National Academy of Sciences, Washington, D.C.

Harrison, H. L., O. L. Loucks, J. W. Mitchell, D. F. Parkhurst, C. R. Tracy, D. G. Watts, and V. J. Yannacone, Jr. 1970. Systems studies of DDT transport. *Science,* **170**: 503-508.

Hickey, J. J. 1969. *Peregrine Falcon Population: Their Biology and Decline.* University of Wisconsin Press, Madison.

Krenkel, P. A. and F. L. Parker (eds.). 1969. *Biological Aspects of Thermal Pollution.* Vanderbilt University Press, Nashville, Tenn.

Likens, G. E., F. H. Bormann, N. M. Johnson, D. W. Fisher, and R. S. Pierce. 1970. Effects of forest cutting and herbicide treatment on nutrient budgets in the Hubbard Brook Watershed-Ecosystem. *Ecol. Monogr.*, **40**: 23-47.

Loucks, O. L. 1971. Models of land-water interactions in the Lake Wingra Ecosystem Study. INTECOL Symposium: *Interactions between Land and Water.* Leningrad, USSR, August. (In press.)

Marx, W. 1971. *Man and His Environment: Waste.* Harper and Row, New York.

Mrak, E. M. 1969. Report of the Secretary's Commission on Pesticides and their Relationship to Environmental Health. Parts I and II. U.S. Department of Health, Education and Welfare.

Oak Ridge National Laboratory. 1971. The environment and technology assessment. Progress Report, June-December 1970. ORNL NSF-EP-3.

Odum, H. T. (ed.). 1970. A tropical rain forest. A study of irradiation and ecology at El Verde, Puerto Rico. Division of Technical Information, U.S. Atomic Energy Commission.

O'Neill, R. V. and O. W. Burke. 1971. A simple systems model for DDT and DDE movement in the human food-chain. Eastern Deciduous Forest Biome, Oak Ridge National Laboratory Report, ORNL-IBP-71-9.

Platt, J. R. 1969. What we must do. *Science*, **166**: 1115-1121.

Reichle, D. E., P. B. Dunaway, and D. J. Nelson. 1970. Turnover and concentration of radionuclides in food chains. *Nucl. Safety*, **11**(1): Jan.-Feb. p. 43-55.

———— and S. I. Auerbach. 1972. Analysis of ecosystems. *In*: J. A. Behnke (ed.). *Challenging Biological Problems: Directions Toward Their Solution.* Oxford University Press, New York.

Risebrough, R. W., D. B. Peakall, S. G. Herman, M. N. Kirven, and P. Reiche. 1968. Polychlorinated biphenyls in the global ecosystem. *Nature*, **220**: 1098-1102.

Stokinger, H. E. 1971. Sanity in research and evaluation of environmental health. *Science*, **174**: 662-665.

Wallace, R. A., W. Fulkerson, W. D. Schults, and W. S. Lyon. 1971. Mercury in the environment: The human element. Oak Ridge National Laboratory, ORNL NSF-EP-1.

Woodwell, G. M. 1970. Effects of pollution on the structure and physiology of ecosystems. *Science*, **168**: 429-433.

————, P. P. Craig, and H. A. Johnson. 1971. DDT in the biosphere: Where does it go? *Science*, **174**: 1101-1107.

17 Ecological Management of Pest Systems

CARL B. HUFFAKER
INTERNATIONAL CENTER FOR BIOLOGICAL CONTROL
AND DIVISION OF BIOLOGICAL CONTROL
DEPARTMENT OF ENTOMOLOGY AND PARASITOLOGY
University of California, Berkeley

Introduction

It is proper that in this volume consideration be given to pesticides, the environment, and ecology, for great changes in this area have been wrought in the 25 year period this volume commemorates. Shortly after World War II, with the immediate and spectacular success of DDT and other synthetic broad-spectrum insecticides, some entomologists confidently looked to the day when there would be few economic insect problems requiring major research attention. Smith (1941), however, in his Presidential Address to The American Association of Economic Entomologists, had warned of the insects' potential for developing resistance to insecticides and of the consequences of an insect control regimen omitting consideration of other control tactics.

The correctness of Smith's prophetic counsel was not long in surfacing, as we have seen on every hand. Over 200 examples of resistance are now known. The consequences of the era of the narrow-chanelled prophylactic pattern of insect control through calendar-scheduled treatments with an assortment of insecticides have caused a profound shaking and awakening of all those engaged in insect control. New avenues are being feverishly explored, and old ones, formerly abandoned (or never really given a fair trial), are being looked at again with renewed enthusiasm and insights. This has not come too soon!

313

Disturbances in terrestrial environments from use of insecticides, as well as the advantages of their use, have been extensively described. Also, significantly, the National Academy of Sciences volume (1971) "Chlorinated Hydrocarbons in the Marine Environment" stresses the accumulation of chlorinated hydrocarbons in the sea and calls for immediate ". . . massive national effort . . . to effect a drastic reduction of the escape of persistent toxicants into the environment." I see no means of solving this problem compatible with the demands of pest control unless a massive effort is made to develop alternatives to conventional insecticides.

Our expanding world population requires an increasing supply of food (and fiber) and its protection from insects. Great increases in food have been achieved in recent years through improved varieties, methods of culture, and pest control. The demand for pest control and the consequences of current pesticides usage mean that agriculture must seek a more lasting, effective, and ecologically-compatible pest control technology. Two of the major advances increasing crop yields have been pursued largely with indifference to ecologically-inherent, potentially countermanding consequences. First, narrowing of the genetic base, including the growing of a narrow spectrum of varieties, thus aiming only at high yields, implies a reduction in genetic factors for resisting pests for the crop area as a whole. For example, the southern corn blight outbreak in 1970 was the greatest single catastrophe of its kind in the history of agriculture (Smith, 1972). Second, the remarkable, but foredoomed, success with insecticides following World War II led to an era when chemistry and merchandising of toxic chemicals (spreading also to acaricides, nematocides, fungicides, herbicides, etc.) soon replaced biology in this essentially biological discipline. There was general disregard of the fact that even the simplest agricultural system presents a maze of delicately balanced ecological intricacies. Both approaches ignore the complexity of agroecosystems, and both of them ignore the two main mechanisms of nature's own system of pest control, i.e., natural enemies and evolved plant resistance. Moreover, the third of nature's great triumvirate in insect containment, adverse meteorological conditions (not directly manipulatable) had long been used by man in the form of cultural practices exposing pest insects to greater rigors of the environment, but this tactic has also been neglected.

Since the objective of the unilateral broad-spectrum chemical approach to insect control was total and lasting destruction of the pests, irrespective of effects on other species far or near, serious disturbances arose. The story of disturbing effects from general use of broad-spectrum insecticides has been frequently told. Included are development of resistance, release of target species to rapid resurgence and of minor or innocuous ones to serious pest status, and increasing dosages and more kinds of, and more frequent, applications of chemicals, leading to pesticide addiction and problems of residues, hazards to workers, and serious environmental effects at places far removed from treated areas. This has led to public clamor against all pesticides. But our insect problems would not simply disappear if we stopped using insecticides. Contrariwise, the consequences could not be quite as catastrophic or prolonged as some would have us believe! As the new era of a more enlightened insect control develops, we must move cautiously; insecticides remain our most reliable tool as an *immediate* solution to an insect problem.

The revival of an abandoned era when insect control was largely ecologically oriented has come at a time when ecology itself has greatly advanced, and a unifying philosophy or strategy (discussed below) has developed, supported by a substantial array of promising and intriguing tactics and advanced skills. Not all of these tactics, however, are likely to prove compatible with the others or with the goal of reducing the use of polluting insecticides, and herein lies the need for caution.

The indicated strategy or goal is *containment* or *correction* of insect pest populations, not their *prevention* or *eradication*. This is the strategy of integrated control. The tactics embrace all ecologically-compatible measures, centered around nature's two principal *manipulatable* mechanisms of insect containment: vastly tested and proved plant resistance and biological control by parasites, predators, and pathogens. These are truly natural mechanisms, operating in their natural biological way. Certain other biological processes or principles may be used by man in insect control, but their use is in unnatural ways and to obstruct the natural sequences of population events; hence, I do not look at them as "biological control."

Strategy and Tactics

Chant (1964), Watt (1963), and others have discussed the question of strategy and tactics in insect control. The National Academy of Sciences,

National Research Council (1972) has assembled a multi-authored volume on this subject. Terminology, however, has been vague. "Strategy" in military usage connotes the overall game plan, including the combining of all the methods (tactics) available. The central strategy might be, however, the destruction of central resource in the enemy's capacity for making war. The various tools and details of operation of *how* this is to be accomplished are referred to as the tactics." Since tactics are employed in any strategy, the two are commonly interrelated, but a component tactic is not a strategy. In insect control and the research necessary to this end, "strategy" refers to the choice of basic approach, and "tactics" refers to how this is to be achieved. There would seem to be two basically different strategies or philosophies of insect control: 1) the *preventive* or *eradicative* approach, and 2) the *containment* or *corrective* approach. In practice, our control efforts have not fallen exclusively in either of these strategies, nor should they. For example, when an insecticide is used in a purely prophylactic fashion (by calendar dates), it is employed in the preventive strategy, but if it is used properly and only when pest densities are threatening, this is containment or corrective strategy.

A third philosophy or strategy might be to take the view that natural forces will always right affairs and *to do nothing,* accepting whatever losses may occur. This is an unacceptable alternative as an overall strategy with reference to the whole complex of insect pests on a crop, but as a tactic in the strategy of the containment approach, it may wisely be employed at a given time with respect to one or more pest species among a complex, for to take action could cause more problems than would be solved. The decision would, of course, be based on estimates of losses under the two alternatives, considered over a reasonable interval of seasons (not just the crop year at hand).

The typical employment of the preventive approach has been to treat each pest as an isolated matter and to use a broad-spectrum chemical on a prophylactic basis, thus, hopefully, preventing the development to pest status of other species as well. This approach is thus simple in conception as it requires only limited knowledge. No effort is made to determine the factors that tend to regulate, or to affect variably, densities of the target pests or other species under undisturbed or commercial conditions, and to utilize this knowledge in the control design for the whole complex of pests and potential pests. In fact, as Doutt and Smith (1971) noted, spray schedules are commonly fixed by calendar without regard to target pest densities, influences on its natural enemies or on other pest species and their natural enemies. It should be noted that *if* this method would remain effective at allowable cost and *if* it did not result in significant additional problems (mentioned above), it would be superior. It would demand no extensive outlay of effort to gain the necessary knowledge for, and to manage, an alternative program.

The philosophy of integrated control relies on containment strategy. With respect to a key pest on a crop, however, it would include preventive action selectively applied (e.g., the growing of a crop variety on which the species could not develop) or the pest's actual eradication from the environment. Eradication of species that have only gained an initial foothold is the first consideration, but this does not normally form a part of an overall integrated control effort.

The strategy of integrated control relies upon an analysis of the biological and economic system of pest control and crop production. This embraces all significant factors acting on the complex of real pests and potential pests and their natural enemies and the interactions of such factors among themselves and with other processes in crop production. This strategy thus presents imposing technical problems, but it seems to offer more permanent solutions, rather than palliatives of a self-defeating nature, as may often be the case with the preventive strategy.

The integrated control strategy employs the idea of maximizing natural control forces and utilizing any other tactics with a minimum of disturbance and only when losses justifying action are threatened. The rationale is deep-rooted, primarily empirically based, yet consistent with established theory. Weather factors, while a powerful repressive force, are not consistently sufficient in suppressing major pests (or they would not be major pests), but the action of such factors is often great enough to be entered in the analysis. We do not directly modify the weather for this purpose. Natural enemies are often powerful natural control factors, commonly quite sufficient, in the absence of disturbing practices, for control of some potentially serious phytophagous species. Also, introductions of new species can solve (and have solved) many problems. We can modify this factor. Innate resistance of crop plants to insect attack is substantial. The possibilities in the exploration for and use of new germ plasm carrying resistance factors are many. Yet, the very fact that biological control of phytophagous insects is a rather general phenomenon in nature means that the natural enemies have greatly reduced selection pressure for development of plants still more resistant to those pest insects that are under a high degree of biological control. The premium in selection would be on those for which good biological control has not yet developed. Thus, the two tactics are basically compatible and supplementary in the integrated control strategy. Cultural control is a third basically compatible tactic. Cultural control commonly is used in ways to expose the pest insects to adverse weather factors, to disrupt their natural development, to increase the action of natural enemies, or to increase the crop's resistance.

Chemical control is inherently incompatible with control by natural enemies, but some chemicals are far less disruptive than others. Moreover, the more disruptive chemicals can be used selectively in ways less disruptive. However, chemicals often furnish the most reliable immediate solution to a problem. Thus, insecticides (including, hopefully, hormones and expanded use of microbials) remain a most necessary tactic of this strategy. Pests can also be avoided by growing a crop in an area lacking especially destructive ones. A number of new tools are also appearing on the horizon which offer much promise, and some of these could serve as excellent tactics in the integrated control program, or they might initiate a new strategy or revive the old era of preventive control through use of chemicals (e.g., use of hormones).

Knowledge sufficient for predicting pest status is required for the ideal employment of the integrated control strategy. Predictability is adequately met only with respect to a very limited set of factors and species at present. Determination of the degree of predation and parasitism of several aphid species (pea aphid, spotted alfalfa aphid, and walnut aphid), scale insect (olive scale), or lepidopteran (alfalfa caterpillar) populations or of predator action on mites (two-spotted mite) is a feasible means of roughly predicting pest status at a subsequent time (given reasonably predictable weather). However, we have not developed knowledge of the complex of relationships and the programming needed for proper decision-making in a single case. As Chant (1964) noted: "Watt [1963] brought a measure of science to this area. He pointed out that in determining control strategy we err by attempting to use the policy most suitable on the basis of how we want circumstances to be at the next stage in time. He showed by using data on forest insects in Germany that dynamic [or 'look-ahead'] programming . . . can assist us to rise above empiricism in the plotting of strategy. He showed in his model that the strategy of killing as many insects as possible whenever density exceeds the threshold level is invariably the most inadvisable action."

Possibilities of ecologically compatible tactics for integrated control are suggested through a variety of mechanisms and insights—biological, educational, regulatory, political, and social in nature. Thorough field and laboratory studies are needed to reveal the complex interactions of the whole agroecosystem. To implement a new technology, changes in consumer attitudes and marketing and government regulations concerning insect infestation are also needed. We need especially to alter our pattern of pest control advising which too commonly has been taken over by pesticides sales people. Entomologists have perhaps been more at fault here than the chemical companies for only materials recommended by entomologists are sold. Only the biological aspects can be treated here, but the political, social, regulatory, and educational avenues will have to be developed if the potential is to be attained. This is now under way, thanks to an aroused public. Huffaker and Smith (in press) describe a major new research program launched by the International Biological Program (IBP) under support of NSF, EPA, and USDA, and through participation of 19 universities, the ARS, CSRS, Forest Service and some other participants.

COMPONENTS OF AN ECOLOGICALLY COMPATIBLE PEST MANAGEMENT STRATEGY

Several major avenues, logically taken in step-wise fashion, serve as guidelines to the development of an integrated control program. These are summarized in Table I. The various requirements and avenues are further discussed under the following topics.

Establishing the Need to Take Action

Establishing the need for remedial measures should be the first principle of insect control. No action at all *can* be the best decision! It is a remarkable fact that we know little about the economic threshold levels for most of our common pests. We don't know the impact of our insect infestations. True, we know that many kinds of insects can cause devastating losses if they are allowed to go unchecked. But we do not know at what point remedial action is called for or could be delayed or entirely

TABLE I. *Guidelines to Development of the Strategy.**

---

1. Separate the real pests from those induced by insecticides in the different regions involved.
2. Establish realistic economic injury levels for the real pests (with all hidden costs adequately considered).
3. Separate the real pests into those which cause intolerable losses (key pests) from those which cause only light or sporadic damage (controllable by occasional use of insecticides or other measures).
4. Identify the main factors controlling or of great potential value for controlling (e.g., a resistant variety, a natural enemy, cultural method, or other selective measure) populations of the key pests, and measure their effects.
5. Design and test control systems, based upon the above guidelines, in each of the areas where the key pests and/or factors are different.
6. Modify the control systems according to conditions and new inputs as the program develops.

---

* Personal communication of guidelines used by the Staff of the USDA, ARS, Columbia, Missouri.

omitted. The ability in a crop to compensate (through growth) for insect damage is often neglected. Much has been said concerning this. However, as yet the necessary systematized, massive effort has not been made to characterize the insect densities, conditions of weather, crop growth, natural mortality, and economic factors relating density to crop damage, and the latter to economic loss, for the major insect pests in our forests and fields.

Establishing the need to take action is often complex, and the suggested measure may be counter-productive. A detailed knowledge is required of the biology and economics of the whole cropping system, of the population dynamics of each pest species, the interactions among pest species, their natural enemies and other mortality factors, the measures to be taken, and the economic externalities. We are beginning to shake old views regarding the pest status of some supposedly serious "pest" species. We should ask: "Is the 'pest' really a pest?" (*See*, e.g., the work of Doutt, 1972; Doutt et al., 1969; Flaherty and Huffaker, 1970; and Laing et al., in press, on the pests of grape in California.) Doutt reports that the key pest is the grape leafhopper, especially since treatments for it cause other problems. The density of this species, indicating need for treatment, is considerably higher than formerly thought. By use of higher indicator levels and acceptance by the growers of the integrated control philosophy, it has been possible to reduce the amount of funds spent on leafhopper control from $3,384,000 in 1961 to $576,000 in 1969 (the latest figures available). Flaherty and Huffaker, and Laing et al. found that one of the major spider mites, for which treatments were formerly made routinely, commonly does not cause economic losses at the densities it attains. They also found that the other major spider mite species, while more serious, may attain high densities in late summer and yet cause no losses although its effect may be serious if high densities are attained earlier in the year.

Only with the development of computer technology and mathematical concepts appropriate to systems analysis and structuring of decision-making for complex systems can the full potentialities become apparent. No one has developed a clear case history of the use of such a system, even on a hypothetical input basis.

Fortunately, complex systems are often highly sensitive to a few parameters. A highly efficient natural enemy of a given pest species, or a resistant variety, may render irrelevant many factors previously important in accounting for the pest status of a species. The key factors or potential factors must be discovered, their manipulatability ascertained, if any, and utilized.

Plant Resistance

In wild plant communities and perhaps in primitive agricultural communities (except for alien introduced species), phytophagous insects and mites do not commonly cause devastating mass effects on the predominant plant species. Pimentel and Soans (1971) consider that this is due to development of a balanced genetic feedback population process between the plant and insect populations, such that only the interest (not capital) is utilized by the insects. Thus, if the insects reach overly damaging numbers, the composition of the plant population in the subsequent generation will contain more resistant types and vice versa. Hairston et al. (1960), on the contrary, hypothesized that control of the phytophagous species by their natural enemies is the basis of the limited destruction of our vegetation. Huffaker (1962) agreed with Hairston et al. in their broad overview of vegetation but pointed out that there is also biological control of specific plant species among that vegetation by their phytophagous enemies. The biological control of weeds is based on this fact. Such plants exist in our vegetation, not as mass dominants, but as associates (in some instances due to such biological control), and they yield far more loss to their natural enemies than the interest. By "interest" is meant the amount that could be given up without any loss in productive capital as due to the action of the insect itself. However, we would agree with Pimentel that plants not under biological control have either achieved their own protection intrinsically through developing plant resistance, or they have not had to do so because of the protective action of natural enemies of the phytophagous species, or else adapted phytophagous species are absent in the environment. Moreover, partial resistance combined with biological control may be common.

In the long-term evolutionary sense, development of plant resistance has played a major role in greatly restricting the kinds of insects capable of attacking given plants and the damage that somewhat adapted ones can do. Many insect species have been cast off while others have followed a deepening rut of host plant specialization in the process of keeping up with the resistance being developed. This is what host plant specificity is all about. For those which have kept pace—the highly host specific ones— it is unlikely that a balanced genetic feedback commonly accounts for the fluctuating or balanced fortunes of insect and plant populations. How can the plant population remain so delicately balanced genetically as to be density governed (and the insect as well) by plant-insect genetic feedback when a complex of insects, not a single species, threatens it? Among literally millions of Klamath weed plants that I have observed under attack by *Chrysolina quadrigemina,* I have never seen a single plant that exhibited any inherent capacity whatever to resist the destruction of its foliage (to complete removal). The protection afforded the species is associated with the reciprocal density dependent host-parasite interaction at the population level. For many other examples, the protection would be associated with biological control of the plant feeder.

In any event, plants present a pool of resistance factors in great variety that can be used to select and improve cultigens resistant to insects. This built-in protection is an ideal alternative to use of pesticides. Plant pathologists have used this principle extensively; some examples are of long duration. In other cases, success has been short-lived, necessitating continuing research to develop new cultigens as resistant biotypes of pathogens have developed (Borlaug, 1965; Day, 1972).

Borlaug considered the average useful life of a wheat stem rust resistant variety to be about five years in some regions. Crown rust of oats, powdery mildew on barley, and tobacco mosaic virus on tomato are other examples where continuing research efforts and introductions of a sequence of germ plasm have been required. These "partial failures" emphasize the need to explore new resistance avenues (Day, 1972).

As Day also noted, resistance to nematodes, insects, and pathogens depends either on a general host defense mechanism or on a complex or variety of other mechanisms. The first, "vertical" resistance, allows less development of the exploiter species, is controlled by one or few genes, and is sometimes overcome by appearance of another biotype. "Horizontal" or polygenically controlled resistance is less understood, allows more development but retards outbreaks, and is often effective against all biotypes of the pest species. It thus normally lasts longer than does vertical resistance.

There have been relatively few examples of insect biotypes arising to completely nullify use of a resistant variety (Pathak, 1970) although continuing research on Hessian fly has been profitable.

Entomologists have made relatively little use of plant resistance in spite of some notable early successes, e.g., Winter Majetin apple resistant to woolly apple aphid, American grape rootstocks resistant to grape phylloxera, and wheat to Hessian fly (Painter, 1951). This inattention may have been due to: 1) the belief that resistance approaching immunity is required; 2) the length of time required to develop an acceptable resistant variety; and 3) effectiveness of insecticides. The profession is now slowly recognizing that these reasons are not tenable. Relatively low levels of resistance can be very useful (Hensley and Long, 1969; Chandler, 1968). Acceptable varieties can be developed about as quickly as chemical insecticides, e.g., alfalfa resistance to the spotted alfalfa aphid (Harvey et al., 1960). Moreover, the availability of effective, economical, and socially acceptable insecticides is rapidly declining.

Resistance to insect attack has been divided into two types, 1) nonpreference (behavioral), and 2) antibiosis (metabolic); the characteristics in either case are either physical or chemical. The research is pursued along three main approaches which have been termed: 1) the Painter approach; 2) the after-the-fact approach; and 3) the synthetic approach (Beck and Maxwell, in press). Most sustained efforts have been attended with some success. The Painter approach involves subjecting large numbers of diverse genetic lines to intense infestation, followed by selective propagation. The after-the-fact approach starts with an observed plant resistance and seeks out the genetic roots. The synthetic approach is in part a broad study of insect nutrition, culture methods, development, behavior, physiology, and metabolic control.

A balanced program will incorporate genetic factors for insect, disease, and other pest resistance in acceptable agronomic varieties. Yet, it should not be presumed that we will be able to develop, in a single cultigen, resistance to all pests of a crop. Characters conveying resistance to one pest may commonly predispose to attack by another (e.g., Beck and Maxwell, in press).

Natural Enemies

There is substantial evidence that, except in special situations, long-term suppression of a complex of pest species in agroecosystems is unlikely to be achieved unless natural enemies are made a primary agent. This is not to minimize the importance of other approaches. Natural enemies have formed a cornerstone in every satisfactory program in integrated control (*see* Huffaker, 1971). The many pesticide-induced pest outbreaks show that many, perhaps most, insects and mites in crop situations have effective natural enemies present. There is much evidence of this "hidden" natural control that does not surface until we disturb the ecosystem. Yet, this is not to say that insecticides should not be used. This would be unrealistic.

Use of natural enemies has been pursued in two significant ways: 1) introduction of exotic natural enemies, commonly from the native region of the pest; and 2) manipulation of the host, the environment, and/or the natural enemies to make resident natural enemies more effective. Even though such efforts have been only minimally researched, understaffed, and pitifully funded, introduction of exotic natural enemies has had a high degree of success. It still offers extensive untried possibilities. The manipulative approach (including use of pathogenic microorganisms and strategic releases of the natural enemy or the pest itself) has not been investigated extensively or with adequate ecological sophistication. Opportunities in these areas have been reviewed by DeBach (1964), Huffaker (1971), and Huffaker et al. (in press).

Introduction of natural enemies has resulted in about 70 completely successful examples and some 250 presenting some degree of success (DeBach, 1964), embracing 223 pest species; about half have been at least partially successful (C. P. Clausen: *See* DeBach, 1971). Especially noteworthy is the fact that little has been done on many of our most notorious pest species (e.g., codling moth and cotton boll weevil). The horizons suggested in respect to introductions of pathogens have hardly been touched, although the excellent results from the inadvertently introduced milky spore bacterium of Japanese beetle into the U.S.A., and then its deliberate spread, and that of a polyhedrosis virus of the European spruce sawfly into Canada are well known.

Possibilities with strategic or inundative releases have been little explored. While effective for certain pests (e.g., a complex of greenhouse pests [Hussey and Bravenboer, 1971] and certain species on strawberry [Huffaker and Kennett, 1956] and cabbage [Parker, 1971] in the field), it has had many failures and much study is needed before we can establish its broader potential. The logistics and economic aspects could preclude many successes. However, breakthroughs in developing artificial rearing methods (now progressing rapidly) could greatly improve the prospects (e.g., Hagen and Tassan, 1965, 1970; Hagen et al., 1970; House, 1967).

Only in the last 25 years has insect pathology made rapid strides. Identification of ca. 1,100 species of microbes associated with arthropods has been accomplished by a few specialized scientists. There have been few cases of control of major pests with pathogens. Again, perhaps the main reasons have been the effectiveness of chemical insecticides and the scarcity of trained personnel (Ignoffo, 1970).

Pathogens have unique properties as substitutes for chemical insecticides. Ones highly selective for certain species or groups of insects, and innocuous to vertebrates, probably abound in nature, but inadequate effort has been made to characterize them and develop methods for their use. Pathogens appears to have many of the advantages of conventional insecticides without most of their disadvantages. The technology for pesticides use is adaptable to them. Some are highly and quickly effective, specific in their activity, biodegradable, safe, and in some cases readily stored. Their disadvantages are their cost, lack of proven reliability for target pests, and problems of registration. Progress of regulatory officials in establishing protocols for determining safety has recently been encouraging.

There is now a sharply increased interest in microbial insecticides. Several companies are doing research on them, and some are producing *Bacillus thuringiensis, B. lentimorbus, B. popilliae,* and the nucleopolyhedrosis virus of *Heliothis zea* in commercial quantities (Briggs, 1963;

Ignoffo, 1967; Martignoni, 1970; Heimpel, 1972). This area of research and development offers a promising, safe, and ecologically-compatible control of insects as a vitally needed substitute for much of the toxic chemicals otherwise required.

Cultural and Physical Methods

Cultural and cropping schemes provided control of many pest insects for hundreds of years. Growing crops in uninfested areas, timing of planting and harvesting to escape periods of heaviest infestation, rotating crops or varieties, manuring, managing water, controlled burning and cultivation are well-known examples of such cultural and physical control of insects. Their use in general interferes with pest development through exposure to rigors of the environment and in fostering natural enemy action and plant resistance.

The development of synthetic organic insecticides in recent decades released growers from these unspectacular methods of insect control, and many of them are largely abandoned. However, in forests silvicultural methods are still widely used. These techniques seldom give complete control of the whole complex of pests on a crop, but they need to be revived as supplementary components in integrated control systems. In some situations, they can serve as the principal means of control.

We should never ignore relationships with other ecosystems, for insects may move among several ecosystems. Effects of cultural practices and the mosaic of crop plantings on the pest species itself, on parasites, predators, and pathogens or on alternate prey or hosts are of utmost importance. The addition of some habitat diversity in this connection may be most important. This is suggested by Doutt and Nakata (1965) relative to use of small blackberry patches next to grape vineyards in California, and by Stern et al. (1969) relative to strip cropping of alfalfa and cotton. Adding such diversity increased natural enemy effectiveness. A change from row cultivation to use of herbicides for weed control or from use of clean culture to a cover crop, or from age-distribution cutting to clear cutting in forests can have far-reaching effects on insect populations.

The general features and complexity of habitats convey a greater or lesser degree of conduciveness to reliable natural control of pests. Solomon (1953) wrote that monocultures are ". . . outbreaks of apple trees and brussel sprouts" and that by creating these crop outbreaks, we invite corresponding outbreaks of pests on them. Ridley (1930) hypothesized that the species diversity of plants in the wet tropics is due to biological control by insects (mainly) which disproportionately destroy the seeds of grouped plants of a given species in contrast to those of isolated plants. Suggestions from biological control of weeds (various authors) and from insect action on juvenile wild plants (Janzen, 1970a, 1971) strengthen this concept as one component in the situation. Moreover, with insects that tend to move appreciably when host plants are close together, relatively little hazard is faced, whereas when they are widely separated, great hazard is posed. Most entomologists have noted that single or isolated backyard trees or other plants or small garden patches of vegetables are not commonly as severely affected by insects as when the same plants are grown in extensive stands.

Turnbull (1969) suggested that certain outbreaks of pests on given forest species may be corrective biological control, tending to maintain a degree of species diversity in the forest consistent with overall natural vegetation or biome stability. Southwood and Way (1970) suggested that the greater diversity, continuity, and stable phenological patterns in natural vegetation present greater possibilities of stable biotic control of the phytophagous species than do crop situations. They also considered that such natural control of crop pests would be more likely in tropical and sub-tropical habitats. This view is diametrically opposed to the unsupported statement of Janzen (1970b) to the effect that biological control of phytophagous insects in lands of the wet tropics converted to agriculture could not be expected to be effective. Janzen's view is also clearly contrary to biological control experience in the tropics, through introductions.

Southwood and Way (1970) challenged the unconventional view of Watt (1964, 1968) that the concept of greater stability being associated with greater diversity is wrong. They introduced some clarification of terms and distinctions in the kinds of diversity involved. They defined trophic diversity as being based on the number of energy paths from one trophic level to another and showed that the numbers of species may be the same in two systems, but if one has more energy paths, it is the more diverse and more stable.

Having said all this, we must consider to what extent we are concerned in pest control with community diversity and stability or simply with factors contributing to stability of specific *components* of a crop system, and, also, with the practicability—or otherwise—of increasing diversity sufficiently in crop ecosystems to serve as a means of pest control. Southwood and Way state: ". . . in the practical context, any management practice affecting diversity must be assessed separately in respect of its effects on the pest and those on its natural enemies. . . . In these simplified conditions [agroecosystems] it is not justified to assume that any increase in diversity will have a stabilizing effect. Thus, the diversity conferred by hedgerows in agricultural areas may favor pests more than natural enemies or *vice versa*." Huffaker et al. (1971) also noted that we may, in fact, reduce total *faunal* agroecosystem diversity by initially increasing it and still achieve greater stability in the target species. Several examples of this are given. Each one involves introduction of a clearly-superior natural enemy of a given pest which resulted in displacement of a complex of other former directly competing natural enemies. The newcomer reduced host densities so low that only the newcomer could survive, and the pest species was then maintained at a stable low density, no longer threatening the stability of the crop stand.

Man has been growing some crops as monocultures for centuries, albeit with a variety of weeds present, but he has recently greatly increased the uniformity and extent of acreage under a given crop. Still more recently, he has taken to growing extensive cultures, not only of a single crop species, but of very restricted genetic lines of a single species. Adding to the oneness (e.g., for some Green Revolution and other massive irrigated agricultures), is the uniform use of controlled watering, fertilizers, and other agronomic technology. This technology may include "packaged" schemes, often substituting for old traditional cultural methods an over-emphasis on chemical controls for insects, mites, nematodes, plant pathogens, and weeds. Such uniform narrow-spectrum plants, under uniform irrigation and heavy use of fertilizer, often grow more dense and lush. The physical microenvironment is altered to greater favorability to a majority of pests but, conversely, to a reduced favorability to some. This applies to their natural enemies as well. Intensive managed monocultures mean greater problems, and adjustments in techniques are essential; nor can the problems be taken as static and prescribed for in static fashion. It is not surprising, therefore, that Smith (1972) warns of the risks of serious consequences that may follow the undoubted success of the Green Revolution[1] if a broad multidisciplinary pest control approach

1. Several-fold increases in yields of rice, wheat, and maize have been reported.

is not mounted to forestall the potentials of calamity inherent in some of the technology employed.

Not only is it desirable to consider the break-up of vast monocultural plantings to a single crop species, but even where this is impracticable, it may be practicable to break up such large areas into plantings of different cultigens of the same crop. Only because about 90% of the U.S. corn crop in 1970 carried a common source of cytoplasm was the southern corn blight potential so great. Smith (1972) notes that in Indonesia over 600 varieties of Bulu rice are grown, but as the Green Revolution proceeds, this threatens to be changed to only a few varieties offering vastly greater opportunity to severe and widespread devastation by pests. Much potential rests in schemes of deliberate rotation in one field and for shifting mosaics of plantings in a region of varieties offering resistance to different species of insects and other pests.

Southwood and Way (1970) note that the characteristics of cropping systems, determining the potentialities for different methods of control, depend upon four major characteristics:

1) The diversity of vegetation and associated fauna in the agroeco-system.
2) The degree of permanence of the crops.
3) The stability of the climate.
4) The extent of isolation of the crop from influencing habitats.

They also presented a chart (Fig. 1) which, along with the ideas suggested by Southwood and Way, presents graphically good points for consideration. In this figure, the lengths of the bars represent the degree of plant diversity, permanence of crop, stability of the climate, and isolation of the habitat. Yet, the types of agroecosystems, as so classified, do not necessarily present the sequences of predictability they suggest in any infallible way; many qualifications are required, or many exceptions would be obvious. They note clearly that predictions cannot be made ". . . in the absence of detailed knowledge of the density responses of the various trophic links." For example, a "developed agricultural area" could also be an "extreme annual crop monoculture." One would need to consider the specific crop and area situation with respect to the four characteristics.

Lastly, Pimentel (personal communication) has suggested that some of the loss from insect pests occasioned by greatly reduced use of insecti-

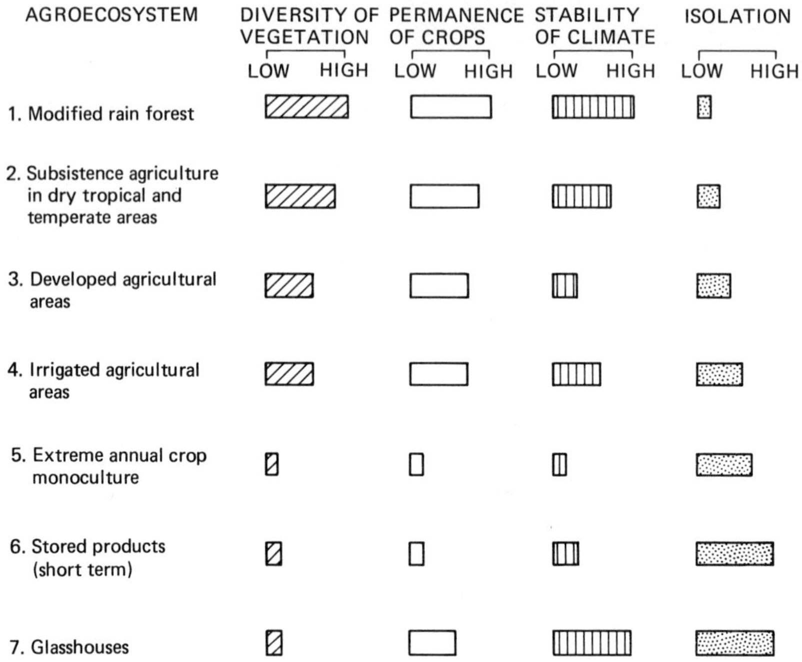

AGROECOSYSTEM	DIVERSITY OF VEGETATION		PERMANENCE OF CROPS		STABILITY OF CLIMATE		ISOLATION	
	LOW	HIGH	LOW	HIGH	LOW	HIGH	LOW	HIGH
1. Modified rain forest								
2. Subsistence agriculture in dry tropical and temperate areas								
3. Developed agricultural areas								
4. Irrigated agricultural areas								
5. Extreme annual crop monoculture								
6. Stored products (short term)								
7. Glasshouses								

FIGURE 1. The characteristics, of particular significance in pest management programs, of the main types of agroecosystems. (Modified from Southwood and Way, 1970.)

cides could be made up simply by putting more acreage into production. While there are some real constraints in this alternative, the idea is worth exploration.

Biochemical Determinants of Insect Behavior

Increased interest in insect attractants and other behavioral chemicals has also been triggered by problems associated with conventional insecticides, especially development of resistance in target species. Except in isolated cases, the practicability of attractants and repellents for field crop pest *control,* as distinct from their use in *monitoring,* remains to be explored and demonstrated. Their use in survey and detection of infestations has been invaluable in control programs using other methods. The nature of these materials and the techniques for developing them are discussed at length by Beroza (1972) and Wood et al. (1970).

Insect pheromones are compounds secreted by individuals of a species which influence the behavior and/or development of other individuals of the same species. Pheromones (sex and aggregation types) which induce an attractant response have now been isolated and identified for many important pest species (Beroza, 1970; Wood et al. 1970). They present horizons worthy of extensive investigation.

Significant advances looking toward pest control, utilizing this biochemical approach, remain slow. This is due to our primitive understanding of insect behavior as related to such biochemicals, problems associated with mass rearing and isolation and identification of significant compounds occurring in minute amounts in complex mixtures, or because of synergism and masking effects and difficulty of synthesis of the materials or suitable substitutes. Moreover, there are serious problems in developing control approaches that can utilize synthetic compounds (Wood et al., 1970).

However, we must be cautious in large-scale field programs because some pheromones could perhaps attract certain natural enemies as readily or more readily than they do target species. This could either be disastrous or perhaps turned to advantage. Such natural enemies may be crucial in control, not only of the given target species (Bedard et al., 1969), but of other species in the ecosystem, perhaps ones of equal or greater potential hazard. Also, while some claim that the target species cannot develop an unsusceptible biotype, this is by no means assured. (*See* further Atkins, 1968.)

Sterile Insect Releases and Other Genetic Tools

The genius of the sterile insect and genetic principle of insect control has attracted worldwide fascination. These methods include not only the sterilization of insects and their release as a means of interfering with natural matings in the field, but also other genetic avenues, such as chromosomal translocations, hybrid sterility (e.g., *Anopheles gambiae* [Davidson et al., 1967]), deleterious genes, and cytoplasmic incompatibility (*Culex pipiens quinquefasciatus* [Laven, 1967]). However, success has been minimal, other than with release of sterile insects, and even this technique is not viewed as a general solution of our insect problems. The method's great utility rests in its use, where feasible, for eradication, or keeping under continuous control, of a key pest species (e.g., boll weevil or codling moth), the treatments for which may lead to rapid resurgence, induced outbreaks, and pesticide addiction.

THE MECHANISMS.—The mechanisms are of two kinds: 1) eugenic development of better insects, which in pest control would mean better natural enemies, and 2) dysgenic (or autocidal).

The eugenic approach for insects is represented in improved honey bees and silkworms. Improved parasites, predators, or pathogens may be developed through selection, breeding, and heterosis. Altering a parasite species, to make it better fitted to climatic or pesticide extremes, offers possibilities. White et al. (1970) developed lines of *Aphytis lingnanensis* more resistant to both summer and winter climatic extremes in southern California. Croft (1970) incorporated gene(s) for pesticide resistance found in a Washington stock of the mite predator *Metaseiulus occidentalis* into a southern California population.

The necessary methods for using the autocidal mechanisms of dominant lethality, chromosome translocation, existing sterility barriers, and bionomics modifiers (e.g., diapause) largely remain to be developed (Craig, personal communication). Adequate mass production and distribution of appropriate genetically defined stocks is largely an engineering problem and not necessarily one which is solvable within existing economic constraints. The necessary information on when, where, how many, and in what condition releases should be made is detailed by Knipling (1964). Knipling also deals with the relevant considerations on the biologies and ecology of the target insects and the possible relevance to the program of the ecosystem in other respects. The method is highly selective, species specific, and as a disadvantage, it may even be biotype- or population-specific. It is not applicable by the individual farmer.

Chemosterilants pose hazards to non-target organisms because the most effective ones now known are mutagenic, carcinogenic, or teratogenic in acute doses and little is known about the dangers from repeated small doses (Proverbs, 1969). Until safer chemosterilants are developed, irradiation would seem to remain the principal technique.

Insect population suppression has been achieved many times by heavy releases of sterile insects. The suppression (other things equal) is dependent on the ratio of sterile to native insects. Unlike many other methods, the lower the native insect population, the more effective the given effort may be in a sterile release program (Knipling, 1966a, 1966b) unless, for example, special problems of getting the sterile insects adequately close to the last small "preserves" of the declining population(s) present increasing difficulties (density related effects—Huffaker, 1970). Moreover, a biotype of the natural females may be selected which would not mate readily with sterile, "marked" males, or the insectary-produced males could lose their competitive vigor. Berryman (1967) noted that the generation survival, which is commonly taken as a constant, may change markedly at low population densities, thus altering the actual result from that predicted by the simplified models.

Significantly, Knipling (1966a, 1966b) presented an hypothetical description of how the combination use of insecticides (or of parasites) and sterile insects might greatly speed up the desired result (suppression or eradication), and LaBrecque and Weidhaas (1970) discuss various advantages of a combined employment of insecticides and sterile insects. Proverbs (1969) noted, however, that we can only speculate on the usefulness of these integrated techniques, for they have not been tested.

Insect Hormonal Chemicals

Hormonal regulation of physiological processes (growth, development, molting, and reproduction) has been shown to occur in invertebrate phyla (Charniaux-Cotton and Kleinholz, 1964; Wigglesworth, 1964; Highnam and Hill, 1969). Robbins (1972) has noted that it may prove possible to develop selective hormonal insecticides and chemotherapeutic agents for use against invertebrate pests and that we are now ready to undertake development of hormonal pesticides only for the insects. The requisites include (from Robbins):

1) Basic information for hormone-regulated processes on how and when the hormones normally act to regulate insect growth, development, reproduction, and diapause.
2) Knowledge of the chemistry of insect hormones, gained through their isolation, characterization, and synthesis.
3) The availability of synthetic hormones, hormone analogs, and other synthetic compounds which either have hormone activity or which disrupt the hormone-mediated processes of insects.

Robbins notes that research on insect hormones in the past six years has provided many potent chemical regulators of insect development, metamorphosis, reproduction, or diapause, making it possible "to attempt to bring to realization the prior predicted applications of this horizon in insect pest control." The basis for optimism regarding these compounds has been related to: 1) They disrupt physiological and biochemical processes peculiar to insects and their near relatives, or else the mechanism in insects is quite different from that in vertebrates; 2) the known hormones that regulate processes in insects are structurally different from the hormones of vertebrates; and 3) the belief that insects could not develop resistance to their own hormones.

These three points warrant intensive study, but they are not entirely supported and are not alone an adequate basis for assessing this horizon. There is, in fact, real danger that the development of this field could follow the disastrous pattern resulting from development of, and almost exclusive reliance on, conventional insecticides with the attendant ills. Points 1) and 2) imply promise that this method should prove safe for vertebrates, whereas this does not necessarily follow, for possible toxic effects on vertebrates or other non-target species could be due to effects on processes other than those with which they are associated in insects. Benskin and Plapp (in manuscript) have recently reported that for one— a juvenile hormone analog—cross-tolerance has been exhibited with carbaryl in the housefly. This at least directly disproves the view (3) above) that insects will not be able to develop resistance to their own hormones. Moreover, the exogenous source, method of entry, timing, and dosage of application could produce a basis for natural selection not posed by the precise normal hormone release in the insect itself. Robbins (personal communication) has shown that some such hormonal chemicals, entering the insect from an exogenous source (e.g., by ingestion), may undergo chemical change to materials hormonally inactive. Development of resistance in such cases might well be expected.

Some of these chemicals have effects on development, growth, and reproduction of some invertebrates other than insects. Their influence on a wide range of invertebrates, and vertebrates as well, should receive intensive evaluation in both laboratory and field before they can be advocated. Influences on marine and other aquatic arthropods especially require thorough study because the materials applied as insecticides could reach our streams and estuaries. The extent of field testing of juvenile hormone mimics is reported by Bagley and Bauernfeind (1972). Much remains to be done.

The brain hormone activates the prothoracic glands, and this results in secretion of one or more steroids, the ecdysones, or growth and molting hormones (MH). The kind of molt is controlled by the juvenile hormones (JH) secreted by the corpora allata.

According to Robbins (1972), the JH compounds seem to offer at present the most promise as they readily penetrate insect cuticle, are highly active, and would be the least expensive to produce. However, since they only block the terminal molt, their use on a given population of larvae would not prevent their decimating the crop. Yet, in the reduction of the population density, they would protect the crop subsequently. The MH compounds do not readily penetrate insect cuticle, and they would be expensive to produce, but because they act at any immature molt, they could be used as an *immediate* solution, a main value in an insecticide.

There are also possibilities in developing chemicals that disrupt or interfere with activity of hormonal chemicals or hormonal-regulated processes—e.g., hormone antagonists or antihormones and ones that interfere with hormone biosynthesis and metabolism. Such disruptive chemicals could be used to make JH compounds effective as pesticides at the early immature stages. They might also be useful relative to the MH regulated processes, and perhaps they would be more amenable to manufacture than the hormonal chemicals themselves (Robbins, 1972).

SELECTIVE PESTICIDES AND SELECTIVE
USE OF NON-SELECTIVE ONES

Use of selective pesticides and of non-selective pesticides in a manner that produces selective effects in the ecosystem offers real possibilities of alleviating the harm that conventional use of pesticides has occasioned. Resurgence of the target species and development of secondary pest outbreaks may be much reduced if natural enemies are thus left relatively unhindered in the ecosystem. The consequent reductions in quantity of materials and their pollutive effects (by wise choice of materials) may, in fact, reduce the rate of development of resistance. In all these ways, there can be a direct reduction in the adverse environmental effects on workers in the crops, consumers of the crops, and on non-target organisms that can be affected miles away from places of application.

Of much significance is the question: "What can be done about outbreaks of secondary pests?" An obvious answer is the selective use of pesticides. All pesticides have some selectivity, but the degree of selectivity varies greatly. We have sought mainly materials of high toxicity to invertebrates and low toxicity to mammals. We must now seek differential toxicity within the insects. We do not need species-specific specificity, but specificity for groups such as thrips, aphids, lepidopterous larvae, etc. A differential effect can be obtained by using a non-selective material in a special way: 1) by selective placement on the plant; 2) by specific timing; and 3) by careful dosage and formulation selection (Smith, 1970; Adkisson, personal communication). A number of materials used in such ways have had considerable utility in various programs.

The ideal selective material is not one that eliminates all individuals of the pest species while leaving all of the natural enemies. The maintenance of low populations of pest species is, of course, essential to the continuity of predators or parasites. In Washington apple orchards, the apple rust mite, *Aculus schlechtendali,* can be tolerated at moderate populations without economic loss. These populations of apple rust mite are a good food source for mite predators which not only prevent eruptions of apple rust mite but also regulate McDaniel mite at low densities and help to control European red mite.

Gasser (1966) and Metcalf (1966, 1972) discuss the future possibilities for developing selective chemical insecticides. Metcalf considers that many materials are already known that offer real possibilities and should be developed. Gasser, however, thinks that the industry will not make extensive efforts here because of the great costs in developing a chemical which may not return much profit. This suggests government subsidization or their development by government. We cannot afford to neglect this area, for we are not likely to find adequate solutions for every problem without some supplemental use of chemicals.

SUMMARY OF TACTICS FOR USE IN DEVELOPMENT OF AN ECOLOGICAL MANAGEMENT OF INSECT PESTS

1) Establish the need for control of a pest and develop systems analysis for decision making.
2) Intensify development of biocontrol measures (here to include use of resistant varieties).
3) Revive interest in and develop the use of cultural control measures, including design of cropping mosaics and rotations.

4) Develop selective pesticides and selective use of non-selective ones (including use of entomopathogenic microbes and insect hormonal and behavioral chemicals).

5) Develop knowledge of and use other selective measures not yet broadly proved in practice (e.g., use of sterility and genetic tools, hormonal and behavioral chemicals, physical exclusion, etc.).

6) Develop essential subsidiary avenues of *implementing* the pest control system:

   a) Educate the public and marketing standards people to an informed attitude about "good" and "bad" "bugs" and minor insect "contamination" in foods.

   b) Divorce the sale of insecticides from the pest control advising systems—as are medical diagnosis and prescription of drugs separated from the sale of drugs.

   c) Develop an informed and effective new system of insect control advising, based upon objective entomological field analysis of crop situations.

   d) Develop a system for utilizing the crop subsidy and land bank systems for agriculture to promote crop and variety rotation to further profitable and ecologically compatible pest management.

7) Recognize that the insects are man's chief competitors and allocate adequate funds and skills for the needed developments.

References

Atkins, M. D. 1968. Scolytid pheromones—ready or not. *Can. Entomol.,* **100**: 1115-1117.

Bagley, R. W. and J. C. Bauernfeind. 1972. Field experiences with juvenile hormone mimics. *In*: J. J. Menn and M. Beroza (eds.). *Insect Juvenile Hormones—Chemistry and Action*. Academic Press, New York.

Beck, S. D. and F. G. Maxwell. Use of plant resistance. Chap. 25. *In*: C. B. Huffaker, P. DeBach, and P. S. Messenger (eds.). *Theory and Practice of Biological Control*. Academic Press, New York. (In press.)

Bedard, W. D., P. E. Tilden, D. L. Wood, R. M. Silverstein, R. G. Brownlee, and J. O. Rodin. 1969. Western pine beetle: Field response to its sex pheromone and a synergistic host terpene, myrcene. *Science,* **164**: 1284-1285.

Benskin, J. and F. W. Plapp. Juvenile hormone resistance in houseflies. Presented at the annual meeting of the Entomol. Soc. Amer., Nov. 29, 1971, Los Angeles, Calif. (In manuscript.)

Beroza, M. (ed.). 1970. *Chemicals Controlling Insect Behavior.* Academic Press, New York. 170 p.

————. 1972. Attractants and repellents for pest control. p. 226-253. *In*: Natl. Res. Council. *Pest Control Strategies for the Future.* Natl. Acad. Sci., Washington.

Berryman, A. A. 1967. Mathematical description of the sterile male principle. *Can. Entomol., 99*: 358-365.

Borlaug, N. E. 1965. Wheat, rust and people. *Phytopathology, 55*: 1088-1098.

Briggs, J. D. 1963. Commercial production of insect pathogens. p. 519-549. *In*: E. A. Steinhaus (ed.). Insect Pathology, an Advanced Treatise. Vol. 2. Academic Press, New York.

Chandler, R. F., Jr. 1968. The contribution of insect control to high yields of rice. *Bull. Entomol. Soc. Amer., 14*: 133-135.

Chant, D. A. 1964. Strategy and tactics of insect control. *Can. Entomol., 96*: 182-201.

Charniaux-Cotton, H. and L. H. Kleinholz. 1964. Hormones in invertebrates other than insects. *Hormones, 4*: 135-193.

Croft, B. A. 1970. Comparative studies on four strains of *Typhlodromus occidentalis.* I. Hybridization and reproductive isolation studies. *Ann. Entomol. Soc. Amer., 63*: 1158-1163.

Davidson, G., H. E. Patterson, M. Colluzzi, G. F. Mason, and D. W. Micks. 1967. The *Anopheles gambiae* complex. p. 211-225. *In*: J. W. Wright and R. Pal (eds.). *Genetics of Insect Vectors.* Elsevier Publishing Co., Amsterdam.

Day, P. R. 1972. Crop resistance to pests and pathogens. p. 257-271. *In*: Natl. Res. Council. *Pest Control Strategies for the Future.* Natl. Acad. Sci., Washington.

DeBach, P. (ed.). 1964. *Biological Control of Insect Pests and Weeds.* Reinhold Publishing Corp., New York. 844 p.

————, D. Rosen and C. E. Kennett. 1971. Biological control of coccids by introduced natural enemies. p. 165-194. *In*: C. B. Huffaker (ed.). *Biological Control.* Plenum Press, New York.

Doutt, R. L. 1972. Biological control: Parasites and predators. p. 288-297. *In*: Natl. Res. Council. *Pest Control Strategies for the Future.* Natl. Acad. Sci., Washington.

———— and J. Nakata. 1965. Overwintering refuge of *Anagrus epos* (Hymenoptera: Mymaridae). *J. Econ. Entomol., 58*: 586.

———— and R. F. Smith. 1971. The pesticide syndrome—diagnosis and suggested prophylaxis. p. 3-15. *In*: C. B. Huffaker (ed.). *Biological Control.* Plenum Press, New York.

————, J. Nakata, and F. E. Skinner. 1969. Integrated pest control in grapes. *Calif. Agric., 23*(4): 4,16.

Flaherty, D. L. and C. B. Huffaker, 1970. Biological control of Pacific mites and Willamette mites in San Joaquin Valley vineyards. *Hilgardia,* **40**: 267-330.

Gasser, R. 1966. Use of pesticides in selective manners. *Proc. FAO Symp. Integrated Pest Control,* Rome, **2**: 109-113.

Hagen, K. S. and R. L. Tassan. 1965. A method of providing artificial diets to *Chrysopa* larvae. *J. Econ. Entomol.,* **58**: 999-1000.

———— and ————. 1970. The influence of the food Wheast® and related *Saccharomyces fragilis* yeast products on the fecundity of *Chrysopa carnea* (Neuroptera: Chrysopidae). *Can. Entomol.,* **102**:806-811.

————, ————, and E. F. Sawall, Jr. 1970. Some eco-physiological relationships between certain *Chrysopa,* honeydews and yeasts. *Boll. Lab. Entomol. Agric. Portici,* **28**: 113-134.

Hairston, N. G., F. E. Smith, and L. B. Slobodkin. 1960. Community structure, population control and competition. *Amer. Natur.,* **44**(879): 421-425.

Harvey, T. L., L. H. Hackerett, E. L. Sorensen, R. H. Painter, E. E. Ortman, and D. C. Peters. 1960. The development and performance of Cody alfalfa, a spotted alfalfa aphid resistant variety. Kans. Agric. Exp. Sta. Bull. 114. 27 p.

Heimpel, A. M. 1972. Insect control by microbial agents. p. 298-316. *In:* Natl. Res. Council. *Pest Control Strategies for the Future.* Natl. Acad. Sci., Washington.

Hensley, S. D. and W. H. Long. 1969. Differential yield responses of commercial sugarcane varieties to sugarcane borer damage. *J. Econ. Entomol.,* **62**: 620-622.

Highnam, K. C. and L. Hill. 1969. *The Comparative Endocrinology of the Invertebrates.* Edward Arnold Ltd., London. 270 p.

House, H. L. 1967. Artificial diets for insects: A compilation of references with abstracts. Inform. Bull. No. 5, Can. Dept. Agric. Res. Inst., Belleville, Ontario. 163 p.

Huffaker, C. B. 1962. Some concepts on the ecological basis of biological control of weeds. *Can. Entomol.,* **94**: 507-514.

————. 1970. Summary of a pest management conference—a critique. p. 227-242. *In:* R. L. Rabb and F. E. Guthrie (eds.). *Concepts of Pest Management.* N. C. State Univ., Raleigh.

————. (ed.). 1971. *Biological Control.* Plenum Press, New York. 511 p.

———— and C. E. Kennett. 1956. Experimental studies on predation. 1. Predation and cyclamen mite populations on strawberries in California. *Hilgardia,* **26**: 191-222.

———— and R. F. Smith. The IBP program on the strategies and tactics of pest management. Proc. Tall Timbers Conf. Ecol. Anim. Control by Habitat Manage., no. 4. Tallahassee, Fla. (In press.)

————, P. S. Messenger, and P. DeBach. 1971. The natural enemy component in natural control and the theory of biological control. p. 16-67. *In*: C. B. Huffaker (ed.). *Biological Control*. Plenum Press, New York.

————, P. DeBach, and P. S. Messenger (eds.). *Theory and Practice of Biological Control*. Academic Press, New York. (In press.)

Hussey, N. W. and L. Bravenboer. 1971. Control of pests in glasshouse culture by the introduction of natural enemies. p. 195-216. *In*: C. B. Huffaker (ed.). *Biological Control*. Plenum Press, New York.

Ignoffo, C. M. 1967. Possibilities of mass-producing insect pathogens. p. 91-117. *In*: P. A. van der Laan (ed.). *Insect Pathology and Microbial Control*. North-Holland Publishing Corp., Amsterdam.

————. 1970. Microbial insecticides: No—Yes: Now—When! p. 41-57. *In*: Proc. Tall Timbers Conf. on Ecol. Anim. Control by Habitat Manage., No. 2. Tallahassee, Fla.

Janzen, D. H. 1970a. Herbivores and the number of tree species in tropical forests. *Amer. Natur.*, **104**: 501-528.

————. 1970b. The unexploited tropics. *Bull. Ecol. Soc. Amer.*, **51**: 4-7.

————. 1971. Seed predation by animals. *Ann. Rev. Ecol. and System.*, **2**: 465-492.

Knipling, E. F. 1964. The potential role of the sterility method for insect population control with special reference to combining this method with conventional methods. U. S. Dept. Agric., A.R.S. 33-98. 54 p.

————. 1966a. Plant protection in the American economy. *Bull. Entomol. Soc. Amer.*, **12**: 45-51.

————. 1966b. Further consideration of the theoretical role of predation in sterile insect release programs. *Bull. Entomol. Soc. Amer.*, **12**: 361-364.

LaBrecque, G. C. and D. W. Weidhaas. 1970. Advantages of integrating sterile-male releases with other methods of control against house flies. *J. Econ. Entomol.*, **63**: 379-382.

Laing, J. E., D. Calvert, and C. B. Huffaker. Preliminary studies of the effects of Pacific mite on yield of grapes in the San Joaquin valley. (In press.)

Laven, H. 1967. Eradication of *Culex pipiens fatigans* through cytoplasmic incompatability. *Nature*, **216**: 383-384.

Martignoni, M. E. 1970. A production control procedure for nucleopolyhedrosis virus preparations. Pac. N.W. Forest and Range Expt. Sta. Mimeo. 15 p.

Metcalf, R. L. 1966. Requirements for insecticides of the future. *Proc. FAO Symp. Integrated Pest Control*, Rome, **2**: 115-133.

————. 1972. Development of selective and biodegradable pesticides. p. 137-156. *In*: Natl. Res. Council. *Pest Control Strategies for the Future*. Natl. Acad. Sci., Washington.

National Research Council. 1972. *Pest Control Strategies for the Future*. Natl. Acad. Sci., Washington. 376 p.

Painter, R. H. 1951. *Insect Resistance in Crop Plants.* The Macmillan Co., New York. 520 p.

Parker, F. D. 1971. Management of pest populations by manipulating densities of both hosts and parasites through periodic releases. p. 365-376. *In*: C. B. Huffaker (ed.). *Biological Control.* Plenum Press, New York.

Pathak, M. D. 1970. Genetics of plants in pest management. p. 138-157.
        In: R. L. Rabb and F. E. Guthrie (eds.). *Concepts of Pest Management.* N. C. State Univ., Raleigh.

Pimentel, D. and A. B. Soans. 1971. Animal populations regulated to carrying capacity of plant host by genetic feedback. p. 313-326. *In*: P. J. den Boer and G. R. Gradwell (eds.). *Dynamics of Populations.* Centre for Agric. Publ. and Documentation, Wageningen, Holland. 611 p.

Proverbs, M. D. 1969. Induced sterilization and control of insects. *Ann. Rev. Entomol.,* **14**: 81-102.

Ridley, H. N. 1930. *The Dispersal of Plants Throughout the World.* L. Reeve and Co., Ashford, England. 744 p.

Robbins, W. E. 1972. Hormonal chemicals for invertebrate pest control. p. 172-196. *In*: Natl. Res. Council. *Pest Control Strategies for the Future.* Natl. Acad. Sci., Washington.

Smith, H. S. 1941. Racial segregation in insect populations and its significance in applied entomology. *J. Econ. Entomol.,* **34**: 1-13.

Smith, R. F. 1970. Pesticides: Their use and limitations in pest management. p. 103-118. *In*: R. L. Rabb and F. E. Guthrie (eds.). *Concepts of Pest Management.* N. C. State Univ., Raleigh.

————. 1972. The impact of the green revolution on plant protection in tropical and subtropical areas. *Bull. Entomol. Soc. Amer.,* **18**: 7-14.

Solomon, M. E. 1953. Insect population balance and chemical control of pests. *Chem. and Ind.* (Rev.) 1953: 1143-1147.

Southwood, T. R. E. and M. J. Way. 1970. Ecological background to pest management, p. 6-25. *In*: R. L. Rabb and F. E. Guthrie (eds.). *Concepts of Pest Management.* N. C. State Univ., Raleigh.

Stern, V. M., A. Mueller, V. Sevacherian, and M. Way. 1969. Lygus bug control in cotton through alfalfa interplanting. *Calif. Agric.,* **23**(2): 8-10.

Turnbull, A. L. 1969. The ecological role of pest populations. p. 219-232. *In*: Proc. Tall Timbers Conf. Ecol. Anim. Control by Habitat Manage., No. 1. Tallahassee, Fla.

Watt, K. E. F. 1963. Dynamic programming, "look ahead programming" and the strategy of insect pest control. *Can. Entomol.,* **95**: 525-536.

————. 1964. Comments on fluctuations of animal populations and measures of community stability. *Can. Entomol.,* **96**: 1434-1442.

————. 1968. *Ecology and Resource Management.* McGraw-Hill, New York.

White, E. B., P. DeBach, and M. J. Garber. 1970. Artificial selection for genetic adaptation to temperature extremes in *Aphytis linganensis* Compere (Hymenoptera: Aphelinidae). *Hilgardia,* **40**: 161-192.

Wigglesworth, V. B. 1964. The hormonal regulation of growth and reproduction in insects. *Advan. in Insect Physiol.,* **2**: 247-336.

Wood, D. L., R. M. Silverstein, and M. Nakajima (eds.). 1970. *Control of Insect Behavior by Natural Products.* Academic Press, New York. 345 p.

18 A Biologist Views the Future Climate—Social, Ethical and Economic—for the Life Sciences

ROBERT E. HUNGATE
DEPARTMENT OF BACTERIOLOGY
University of California, Davis

The future climate of biology can be considered from many standpoints. The approach in this chapter is that current trends are the best guide to future changes and that biology is and will be so inextricably woven into the rest of society, so integrally related to other aspects of human thought and activity, that its climate will be essentially that of society at large. Societal interactions, specifically involving biology, will be considered, but the main focus will be on present trends and on probable developments within the entire society. Trends within the United States will be stressed, with reference to international ramifications where they exert an effect.

There can be no "future climate" unless we assume man's survival. There is little prospect for man's imminent elimination by forces on Earth. No Earth species, except man, is a serious threat. Hazards from extra-terrestrial forces seem remote, judged by Earth's age of several billion years. One guesses that man will be here for thousands of years to come. However, the current rapid and bewildering developments in the human society suggest an increased pace of evolutionary change. An autocatalysis may be bringing Earth's senescence and death at the hands of man nearer than our knowledge of its past history implies.

Though not acute, the possibility of Earth's demise gives space exploration more significance than just "keeping up with the Russians." It is the first step in interstellar travel, now almost incredible, but in the future necessary. The earth will not be indefinitely habitable. Space exploration will continue and expand. Biological research into estivation, hibernation, low temperature preservation, and critical point drying will, with future discoveries, adapt man to travel beyond the solar system.

Food, shelter, and survival impinge so directly on all individuals and are so immediately and obviously important that they will receive adequate societal consideration and support. Human manipulative control of food sources will expand spectacularly through improved knowledge of nutrition, biochemistry, genetics, microbiology, and cell physiology. Microbial farming on biodegradable wastes will supply great quantities of protein. Microbes will be increasingly eaten, first by domestic animals, and then by man. The number of humans will increase as more food is made available. Man shares with all living forms the tendency to press into accessible habitats and to exploit for his increased numbers the maximum available from the environment.

The power of industrialized society, directing an ever-increasing fraction of Earth's bounty to the human mouth, will finally support so many humans that the increasing chronic problems of the environment will become acute, limiting human numbers and activities unless new resources and techniques are discovered.

Predictions of environmental catastrophe overlook the self-correcting tendency in ecologic imbalance. Man, damaging his environment, will decrease support resources, diminishing his numbers and lessening his damage. It is doubtful that man will so modify the Earth as to make all parts entirely uninhabitable, though the formidable supply of atomic fissionable materials may have this catastrophic capacity. Awareness of this potential will deter the use of atomic weapons.

Non-catastrophic environmental deterioration due to man will be slow enough for humans to survive, but their culture may be so disastrously affected that its power is destroyed. This sobering possibility will force continued attention to the quality of the environment.

The average life expectancy will increase as biological knowledge provides new understanding and control of body functions. Insurance and public support programs will cover medical costs for all individuals. Health-related biological disciplines will expand as medical services increase and improve.

Greater longevity must be accompanied by knowledge permitting retention of intellectual faculties or prolongation of life will become a negative asset. Society will not formulate policies as to how much effort shall be made to prolong life, but ethics will increasingly respect individual requests, made during health, for cessation of medical treatment when incapacitation will be sure and prolonged. A somewhat different, but related, question will arise in connection with severe defects in the young, detected *in utero* or at birth. Attitudes toward abortion will become more permissive. New legal, medical, economic, and ethical questions will require biological as well as societal answers.

The capacity to prolong a particular human life will be great, but resources will be inadequate to provide this same capacity to all individuals. Human life will continue to depend chiefly on its evolutionarily acquired strengths and resistances, aided by public health and medicine to the extent that resources permit. Health, with a minimum of artificial aids, will be societally valuable from both economic and esthetic standpoints.

In agriculture, engineering, and industry, there will be an increasing demand for trained biologists. Applied research projects will be supported on a scale based on their importance and need. Team research and control will expand—in industry, in the space program, in pest eradication, and in environmental and societal monitoring (chiefly through information science). Federally supported research will increase as the magnitude and extent of applications become too great for adequate funding by universities, industries, and state governments.

Large federal laboratories and teams will be established. They will be initially productive, but policies of tenure and employment in civil service will ultimately diminish their effectiveness. Bureaucracy will stall accomplishment unless stringent safeguards provide for the dismemberment of teams, retooling of members, and their redeployment in other teams. The outlook for such societal efficiency is not promising, but it must come if society is to compete successfully. Requisite governmental leadership must develop and will, either within our present system or through revolution if societal efficiency cannot be achieved in any other way.

Because of slow societal responses to inefficient bureaucracy, there will be a continuing opportunity for free enterprise with its advantage of quicker response to economic pressures to dissolve unproductive teams. Bureaucracy will be reduced and private industry will be secure if it recognizes that its promotion of the entire society is its only guarantee of long-term opportunity for profit. The profit will have to be for the great majority of the people, not a small minority, if societal strength is to be preserved. Failure of free enterprise to meet its responsibility will render it powerless to meet the challenge of totalitarianism.

Basic research will be supported, chiefly in the universities, and for some applied problems (such as cancer), industrial and governmental laboratories will engage in closely related basic research with good financial support. But overall funds for basic research will tend to remain small unless its value can be sold to the public. In the case of cancer, it will be particularly important that basic research receive support since leads to a real understanding and control will come from many aspects of biology.

In educational institutions, research will be an adjunct to teaching, minimally supported but with relative freedom. The freedom element will attract imaginative and unprogrammed minds and counteract bureaucratic tendencies, although there will be a danger that academia, too, will develop its own tunnel vision and preconceived attitudes, the latter forced on its constituency by moral suasion and professional pressures. Hopefully, scholars in their zeal will adopt the same objective attitudes demanded of others, permitting universities to foster diverse societal viewpoints and develop new and unexpected insights.

Individual scholars needing complex equipment will increasingly depend on central laboratories, but the most remarkable and valuable instrument, the human brain, will function most innovatively and effectively in individuals not part of a formal team but stimulated by the right amount of contact with thoughts of others similarly independent.

The greatest changes will come in the mechanisms for information exchange. Improvements in the filing, sorting, and distribution of information will be one of the societal phenomena most directly affecting higher education and, indeed, the entire society. Great advances in the information industry will profoundly assist the further exploration of highly specialized natural phenomena and the discovery and formulation of new biological principles. Information science will expand spectacularly, employing many professionals, including biologists. It will be essential in many types of biological research and applications and in the overall societal planning for the future course of events. The technology for this planning will be adequate, but will it be used effectively in the face of the almost insurmountable problems in integrating 200 million humans into a successful whole?

Future human changes will occur, not in the physical and mental capacity of the individual man, but in his society, culture, and outlook. The mechanism of societal evolutionary change will be a selection from random mutations. These mutations will be the bewildering diversities of behavior that only man can dream up. Selection of favorable trends (mutations) will occur through societal competition, conflict, and cooperation. The only test of societal fitness will be societal survival.

The economic prognosis for the United States is not as favorable as heretofore. Mass production and consumption, having provided great material prosperity, have seriously depleted the national resources. The emphasis on material goods and the methods for their production have been exported, together with United States capital, to other continents. U.S. profits from foreign investments, though helpful to the economy, do not strengthen domestic industry. High cost of domestic labor, imbalance of payments, and decreased efficiency will weaken the position of the U.S. in world trade, and in domestic trade foreign competition will be keen. Unless political barriers are erected, the standard of living over the world will become more uniform, at least among those participating extensively in world trade.

Taxes will increase. Inflation will continue.

The absolute standard of living in the U.S. will not diminish rapidly. More women will work to increase the family income. But this in itself will constitute a lower standard of living and is inconsistent with the concept of increased leisure as an important component of a high living standard. Actually, the oft-quoted great time savings of technology are an illusion. They fail to take account of the activities necessary to keep the total system going. Don't anticipate leisure. The resultant of the concept that we have arrived will be extinction.

The long-term future economy will be affected by the wealth productivity of societal expenditures. Heavy continued military appropriations will weaken over-all economic strength. Also, of dubious value, will be unilateral financial contributions to purchase foreign friendship. Neither will improve the U.S. internal or world position relative to foreign competition and will be replaced by bilateral or general arrangements fostering trade between countries for which it is mutually advantageous. This is likely to be preceded by a period in which severe domestic economic problems will force cooperation by U.S. labor and capital to obtain an efficiency internally more productive and internationally more competitive.

Although excessive military expenditures should decrease, as society realizes their limitations, they may increase in a desperate attempt to "protect" solely through military power. Too much peacetime military emphasis (or is it continuous war?) will be as disastrous as too little in time of real war. Most biologists will hold that the chief weapon of survival is overall understanding and that this, most readily forged into international cooperative strength during peace, is most powerful in crisis. Diminution in military emphasis will depend on success in substituting, at least partially, a different type of influence in world affairs. It will be imperative to cooperate with the world's peoples.

Race will enter into many societal problems for a long time to come, but will gradually diminish in importance. The present emphasis on race as a basis for employment will be recognized as inconsistent with societal efficiency. As justice and education provide equal opportunity to all citizens, members of minorities will be employed according to their individual merits for the work to be done rather than on the basis of the race or other group to which they can be assigned. Any other long-term societal policy will be folly. Placing of anyone but the best qualified persons in the available positions will weaken societal performance and will be selected against, either within the society, or as a result of intersocietal conflict.

The present emphasis on race, understandable in view of past submersion and injustice for minorities in the predominant culture, will become less militant. Pride in race will be expreesed more in its history, experience, contributions, and culture, less in violence. All individuals will increasingly appreciate the rich racial and cultural heritage of the United States. The exploits of the white pioneers will be leavened with the pride and lore of the native American, the labor, service and friendliness of the African and the persistence, industry, and traditions of the Asian.

The assimilation of all races into a functional multiracial society will succeed because there will be no viable alternative. Assimilation will not occur in a generation, nor will it occur completely, but it will occur to a workable extent. Impartial administration of equable laws and jealous protection of equal opportunity will hasten societal integration. The ideal sought will be individuals as members of humanity first and of their race or culture second.

The role of biology in aiding society to an understanding of racial problems will lie in bringing about an increased understanding of the nature of individual differences and an appreciation of societally-valuable individual characteristics. There is little evidence for clear-cut genetic racial differences in those traits important to human society; e.g., reliability, industry, cooperation, good will, and a societal outlook. From the fact that these traits do not correlate closely with race, it cannot be concluded that they result solely from the environment. They have a genetic basis. Environment affects the expression of these traits but operates within genetic limits.

On racial issues, biologists will provide information, yet the non-scientific and emotional attitudes engendered by existence of different races, resultants of historical, cultural, social, political and economic events, are so deeply ingrained that objective knowledge will not always be a major influence. In crises, decisions may be based, not on abstract knowledge or principle but on the nuances of personality interaction and environmentally triggered emotions. But biological knowledge, effectively and objectively presented, must have steadily increasing long-term potential influence, if adjustment by conflict is to be avoided. Will the good for the individual in a successful society be strong enough to combat the temptation toward unproductive confrontation?

Human genetics should be studied carefully by biologists. Inadequacy of our criteria for "societally important traits" should not deter a search for them. The biologist will explore and improve his understanding of those traits and suggest applications of individual and societal benefit.

In considering any societal efforts to change the population of genes underlying characteristics of societal value, the only biologically-justifiable approach will be to eliminate transmission of severe genic deficiencies by individuals exhibiting them.

Improved control of conception and modified societal atttiudes toward abortion, artificial insemination, and sperm banks will increase the potential and practicability for reducing the relative gene pool size of hereditary traits that will seriously handicap. Biological knowledge of human genetics is already extensive and will expand through applications of molecular knowledge to human metabolism, biochemistry, immunology, and pathology. Methods for diagnosis early in pregnancy will be available for detection and elimination of many serious genetic defects. Sterilization will accomplish control of traits not detectable early. Accomplishment of genetic control will be chiefly educational and advisory, but a societal authority will be needed for instances in which the individual is incapable.

Customs providing for sexual activity without reproduction will make it increasingly possible for individuals, by a non-societally-dictated choice, to change the steady state number of individuals composing a society or societal component. Reduction of numbers may better the environment, improve personal opportunities and the standard of living, and seem immediately desirable but, practiced unilaterally within one society or societal component, will ultimately diminish the strength of that society or group as compared to others, weakening it in societal competition.

This raises the question of the future competitive successes of the so-called "advantaged" as compared to the "disadvantaged" societies. On the average, a member of the former will have at his disposal a greater share of the Earth's resources. Successful competition will give him a better "standard of living." In the advantaged society, this will be regarded as essential, and to preserve and enjoy it, the advantaged individual will limit his reproduction. His total strength per individual will be greater, and through it he will be able to maintain this advantage in competition (including military) with societies containing greater numbers of individuals, each with less resources. This can persist up to a point, but too great disparity in individual resources will not be indefinitely tenable. Use of superior individual power (including military) will engender such fear and distrust among other world societies, including those in almost the same "advantaged" state, that the society with the greatest individual superiority will suffer in the competition and be brought again closer to the level at which the sheer number of individuals in the group becomes a more decisive factor. Any human society or component that fails to maintain its relative numbers will become a disadvantaged minority.

Societal approaches to population changes will continue to follow chiefly the ideas of Lamarck and Lysenko; i.e., that environment predominantly determines the course of evolution. Proposed remedies will be largely modifications of the environment. The public will waste effort and funds as it labors under the delusion that economic and cultural factors are the only ones concerned in the successful integration of individuals into a complex society capable of survival.

Resistance to societal attempts to change the genetic composition of human populations is understandable. The implementation of "Aryan superiority" policies by an "advantaged" nation has so recently shocked world opinion that future similar efforts are hardly conceivable. However, severe stresses in any society can arouse emotions against identifiable groups to the point of extreme violence. There are too many examples, some in highly "civilized," some in "underprivileged" societies, to permit future complacency in this regard, or in regard to the possibility of major violent conflicts.

Biology, more than any other field of knowledge, will continue to impinge on religious beliefs. Application of the consensus test to judge the absolute validity of religious creeds will lead the biologist to doubt most religious dogma. In this his attitude will approach that of the believer who doubts all dogma but his own. But failure to agree on creeds in no way undermines the continuing value and importance of human faith, the essential component in all religions and the one now chiefly prominent by its absence in free societies. Faith does not necessarily mean a faith in a "religion," but this is not excluded. The religious striving of humans to understand and believe in the universe and in themselves and to live out their part in it may be their trait with the greatest survival value.

Total replacement of faith by knowledge will be not only unwise but impossible. Knowledge can be expanded, extending the boundary between known and unknown, but the unknown is not eliminated. Rational "solution" of one problem introduces others. These limitations leave a domain for faith and induce a humility in the biologist, diminish his prejudice, and increase his tolerance and appreciation of the attempts of all societal components to develop a confidence in the future.

Though religious creeds and dogmas vary greatly, there are many similarities in the ethics associated with the world's great religions. Through intersocietal competition, conflict, and cooperation, ethics of societal survival value have been selected. They underlie the integration of individual humans into a functional supraindividual organization.

Authoritarian religion has in the past been the chief reinforcer of ethics. But religious support is misplaced if the ethic is incompatible with the reliable experience of secular (including biological) knowledge.

In extending the understanding of man and his society, it will be necessary for the biologist to foster human ethics, to consider the value of possible ethics, to cooperate with all societal elements able to select ethics of survival value. This will be essential to avoid anarchy. And some societies will avoid it. The regimentation of the totalitarian society is at least not anarchic.

We may ask: Are there really value differences in various possible ethics? The answer must be affirmative, more as a matter of faith than of knowledge, for the ultimate results of an ethic are unknown. If unknown, why must biologists be concerned about their formulation? The only valid answer is that striving has been, is, and will be the way of life. Each element struggles to remain viable, to maintain and extend itself. Biologists, seeking to fulfill their role in society, follow on a societal level the same burgeoning force they recognize as an elemental living characteristic. Life "tries," even without knowing. This, for humans, is faith.

The world has not yet hit upon beliefs which can unite all mankind. The United States, with its diversity in human origins and culture, has the potential to develop goals and beliefs appealing to all peoples. Its future success and that of mankind will require their formulation and implementation in a fashion that kindles the human spirit into enthusiasm for common accomplishment. This can be the non-military force with a potential for long-term societal strength. Unless some unifying peaceful force and enthusiasm can be engendered in the free world, it will not remain free.

The problem of the unskilled, by nature or inclination unqualified for employment in technical pursuits, will be met by a system of universal minimal annual salary, requiring (from those able to give it) a minimal contribution of time and effort devoted to the solution of problems of societal importance not solvable by technical means. Many environmental problems will come in this category. Such employment will be essential to long-term societal health, and through continuation of already expressed changes in mores, manual activity will be restored to societal respectability.

The minimal annual salary can be the educational vehicle by which dedicated students without other support may study intensively and extensively during their most critical period of intellectual development. Societal support of higher education will hopefully be better than this, but relief and unemployment stipends as educational fellowships will be at least a minimal solution. It could be a democratic link of the intellectual, the artist, the inventor, with the mass of his differently-motivated similarly-salaried contemporaries.

It will be uneconomical to use institutions of higher education as a means of deferring from the labor market individuals unable or uninterested in acquiring academic knowledge.

How will the biologist react in the midst of our projected economic, ethical, and other societal confusion? Should he react as an average member of society? When biologists, or any other group, similarly advantaged, react no better than the average, they will have betrayed their right to general respect. The individual, whether advantaged through education, acquisition of wealth, public recognition, or other perquisites, has an obligation to use his skills, wisdom, and advice constructively toward the welfare of society.

This is the essence of the new political awareness now encouraged so strenuously by innumerable citizens, young and old. It will persist and grow. After years of paternalistic governmental attempts to do for the people what they themselves felt they could not do alone, the citizens will realize that they are the government and that the success of their society depends on their doing more than just vote for or follow their leader. They will participate. For the first time, technology will give people a fair chance to succeed in a combined effort to influence the course of their own evolution. The mechanics will be available, the need will be obvious; only the will and the ability of our millions of individuals to mold themselves into a society, functioning for their overall benefit, will be in question. If we don't all try, a few will do it for us, but not so well, nor to our liking. If we fail, we will have no one but ourselves to hold responsible.

The need for biological knowledge in solving many societal problems will call for aggressive participation by biologists. Knowledge can be acquired, and it can be pertinent and of great societal import, but unless it is translated into a form that can be communicated to and understood by the average citizen, unless it can become part of the knowledge of the community and of its legislative and executive representatives, it will have little use. It will not be enough for biologists to know and enlarge their subject. They must extend and infuse it into the social consciousness.

One of the most difficult responsibilities will be to distinguish between knowledge and its use. Knowledge itself is amoral. The same knowledge, whether of atomic energy, laser beams, or the genetic informational system, can be used for "good" or "bad." Applications and their morality cannot be foreseen until new knowledge is acquired. Any society, ceasing the acquisition of new knowledge because it might be "badly" used, will be deprived of the potential "good." Biologists will have the responsibility for informing society of the good and bad applications it can foresee and of recommending (even very strongly) societal applications, but the unpredictability of their ultimate outcome should prevent biologists from giving an impression of infallible authority.

An important problem will be the extent to which biological organizations, including national societies, take formal positions on ethical and economic decisions in which biology is not directly involved. Official stands on controversial non-biological issues will have the hazard of weakening the effectiveness on biological matters. But opportunities for informing members on all issues must be provided.

Critical will be the education of biologists. Part of their qualifications must be an awareness of the broad problems of society, obtained perhaps by cooperation between the social sciences and biology, if not as part of biology which, after all, encompasses also the societal phenomena of life.

Biology is logically a part of the foundation for societal science. Humans are living animals. Many phenomena they display are well developed only in man, but rudiments can be observed in other animals. Objectivity by man is vastly easier when viewing other species; the phenomena they present, though rudimentary, may reveal relationships overlooked with attention focussed solely on man. Indications of a realization of this are perceptible, and on the basis that a knowledge of biology will assist sociological analysis, one predicts that it will be increasingly included in the social sciences curriculum. Societal programs and policies based on invalid biological assumptions will not be as valuable as those in harmony with the principles developed in the life sciences.

The undertaking by society of the vast problem of directing its own evolution (planning) will employ an ever-increasing portion of the available manpower, including biologists. Individuals aspiring to greater service and improved pay will move from the minimally-salaried class into more productive and remunerative activities. The size of the minimal employment class will shrink with improvements in overall societal health, and increase during societal ailments, serving as a barometer of societal health.

Organization of biologists to influence societal decisions will be essential. Biology is so large a subject, with so many ramifications, that different components will have different information to contribute on each societal problem. Only in rare instances will all aspects of biology be important. But the increased effectiveness of a united biology in bolstering its component contributions will lead to some sort of national biological organization, influencing governmental and other societal decisions at national levels.

Many biological organizations, such as the American Institute of Biological Sciences, The Federation of Societies for Experimental Biology, The American Medical Association, and the American Society for Microbiology now have headquarters in Washington, D.C., serving many functions, including advice to governmental bodies when biological knowledge is needed. Additional offices will be established as biological societies attain the financial and membership strength to support these efforts. And these efforts will be a must for biology.

Not only lobbying efforts, but continuing educational services, will be essential to insure a healthful climate for the life sciences. The biological knowledge of young and old will require continual upgrading, reorientation, and renewal. Biologists will have to contribute more dues to permit their national societies to initiate extended educational programs, supported on a continuing basis by fees from participants. Power for support of biology and biological knowledge must be generated, with the motive of service to society. This motive must permeate efforts of biologists and other societal elements if success is to be achieved.

A free society offers great opportunities for societal strength of all sorts —material prosperity, good morale, understanding cooperation with all nations, and an enduring development consistent with changing human problems. But society does not exist apart from its individuals. The challenge of future society is whether the vast number of human individuals composing it can envision their own best advantage in cooperation with, and service to, all. The extent to which this challenge is met will largely determine the future climate for the life sciences. It will not be completely met, but not to try will insure failure.

Biologists will face the question of organization as part of labor unions. The decision will not be whether to join the union or not. A simple decision not to join the union will be of no avail. In the absence of any bargaining organization to represent biologists in professional matters, individual biologists will be by majority vote incorporated into the union and subject to its decisions, including dues payments considerably higher than those they would pay to their national biological society even when it takes on a professional bargaining function. The biological societies must either themselves serve as bargaining agencies or join to support a broader-based national biological professional organization to represent their professional interests. Their dues will be increased, and part of the funds so available will be used for lobbying and in the continuing education program. Education and good public relations will be more effective in promoting a healthful climate for biology than will strikes and other forceful methods. A strong society cannot be built on a system in which internal force seriously disrupts its operation.

An important danger in organization is loss of individual freedom and of individual responsibility for efficient and capable performance. Some system for enlistment of all in a combined societal effort and awareness will be essential for success and survival of individual freedom. It may come only in response to a direct forceful external threat, and may come too late.

Out of the new awareness and interest and the new dedication to broader service will arise the pride in accomplishment, the appreciation of fellow men, and the spirit necessary to maintain individual freedom and societal health.

The overall prognosis for the future of the human society is favorable, based on past experience. But for the individual, there is no easy prospect. He must seek his way through the bewildering maze of possible pathways of action, some leading to individual and societal survival, some to extinction. The chances for finding the best paths depend on traits such as the industry, patience, tolerance, endurance, courage, and self-sacrifice that have served humans and their ancestors through millions of years. They ensure continued societal success if suitably exercised.

19 Economics As a Not Very Biological Science

KENNETH E. BOULDING
INSTITUTE OF BEHAVIORAL SCIENCE
University of Colorado

The relation of economics to the biological sciences can be described as that of "second cousins, twive removed" in the extended family of the sciences. In spite of this remoteness of genetic connection, however, there are some quite surprising family resemblances and, as the communication between them is limited, an extension of that communication might be quite fruitful.

The historical connections could not be described as extensive. Adam Smith, who might properly be regarded as the founder of scientific economics, was a contemporary of Linnaeus, although Smith's economics was much more Newtonian than Linnaean. His concern was for the perception of nature's global regularities rather than for the description of nature's diversity and speciation. This tradition has continued to the present day. The mainstream tradition in economics, and even in its Marxian underground, has been, on the whole, an attempt to find a "celestial mechanics" of prices and commodities, incomes and classes. In 1870, W. S. Jevons (1911), one of the founders of the marginal utility school, described economics as the "mechanics of utility and self-interest." Whatever taxonomy has been done in economics has been done by casual empiricism and intellectual model building. The "factors of production" of classical economics—land, labor, and capital—are heterogeneous and dimensionally confused categories. The Marxist categories of class, means, and relations of production are also heterogeneous and diffuse categories. Among the social sciences, anthropology is the only one which has had much interest in careful taxonomy. The great tradition of biological taxonomics simply passed economics by.

Nevertheless, the penchant of economists for system building was not without its impact on the biological sciences. Darwin acknowledged his debt to Malthus as the originator, or at least the popularizer, of the idea of an equilibrium population of the species, that in which birth and death rates were equal, each of them being functions of the size of the population and the nature of the environment. The basic ideas of an equilibrium population are already implicit in Adam Smith's *The Wealth of Nations,* although Malthus certainly deserves the credit for bringing the idea clearly out into the open. Implied in Malthusian theory is also a theory of ecological equilibrium which, in turn, is an essential component of the theory of evolution. The movement of the biological sciences from taxonomy into dynamic systems, therefore, has a second-cousin relationship to Malthusian economics.

A good many economists have been uneasy with the mechanical and Newtonian character of economic theory. Alfred Marshall (1961), a great English economist of the end of the nineteenth century, had at least a slightly bad conscience about the essentially mechanical substructure of his economic theory and made general libations in the direction of linking economics more closely with biology although, it must be admitted, he did not really do very much about it. Thorstein Veblen (1919), perhaps the most singular, dramatic, and stimulating figure in American social science, wrote a penetrating article on "Why is economics not an evolutionary science?" He did not do very much himself to make it so. One of the most serious attempts to link economics with the biological sciences, at least with physiology, was that of Reinhold Noyes, whose extraordinary work, *Economic Man* (1948), was an attempt to reduce economic behavior to its physiological substrata. However, the book remained largely unread and made virtually no impact on economists. In my own work, I have tried to link certain ideas in regard to biological growth to social and economic organizations, for instance, in *The Organizational Revolution* (1953). I have also been interested in the application of evolutionary theory to social and economic systems, for instance, in *A Primer on Social Dynamics* (1970). These exercises,

I suspect, have been regarded by the economics profession as an amiable eccentricity rather than a major contribution.

In spite of this not very encouraging history, I am still confident that economics has a great deal to learn from the biological sciences, and perhaps, the biological sciences have something to learn from economics. Insofar, indeed, as there are parallels or homologies between economic systems and biological systems, we would expect to find fruitful interactions. There are three major areas where these parallels may be found: One is in the theory of the organism and its behavior; the second is in the theory of the ecosystem, that is, the interaction of populations of different organisms; and the third is in the theory of evolution or the succession of ecosystems through time. In each of these three areas, each science, I believe, has something to learn from the other.

In economics the theory of the organism, or economic behavior, has two major divisions: the theory of the firm and the theory of the household. The taxonomic poverty of economics is reflected very clearly in this division. The variety of economic organizations is certainly not as enormous as that of biological species, but, nevertheless, simple categorization into households and firms is wholly inadequate. Economics has had very little to say, for instance, about foundations, semi-governmental enterprises, port or valley authorities, hybrids like Comsat or Amtrak, and all the rich variety of organizations that is found in what Etzioni has called "the third sector." Economics still, perhaps, has to find its Linnaeus who will carefully observe and classify the structure, genetics, growth, and behavior of social species. Nevertheless, the narrow taxonomy of economics has some advantages in the development of systematic formal theory and the identification of common patterns which might easily be lost in a wider perspective.

The key to the theory of economic behavior is the concept of *optimization* through choice. The organism is perceived as examining the set of images of possible futures, ordering these on a value scale—that is, a scale of better or worse—and then selecting that one which is "best," that is, first in the value order. The theory is almost formally tautological, for, almost by definition, an alternative which is actually chosen by the decision-maker must have been, in his own mind, the best at the time of the choice. If somebody chooses what he says is the worse of two alternatives, one suspects either than he is lying or that, in the language of his value system, what he calls the worse is in fact the better.

On these rather slender assumptions and on some further assumptions about what might be called the "plausible topology of value orderings," economics has built an elegant general theory of behavior under conditions of choice, from which, in spite of its formality, certain conclusions emerge. Thus, it can be deduced that, in an exchange relationship, a worsening of the "terms of trade" (the ratio of what we get per unit to what we give up) is almost certain to result in a diminution in the amount offered, and the amount of this diminution is related closely to the substitutability of the two goods being exchanged.

The theory of the firm and the theory of the household are in fact formally identical. The only difference is that, in the case of the firm, we suppose as a first approximation a simple relationship between profits and preferability, in the sense that the firm will always prefer larger profits to smaller, though even this assumption is by no means true and can easily be modified. What emerges for economics first of all is a formal theory of choice which could be applicable to all organizations. In its broadest form, the theory becomes a kind of "game tree" in which the organization comes to one decision point after another, a decision point being a point at which it perceives alternative futures. At each decision point, it selects one of these which it pursues until another decision point is reached. A theory as general as this, of course, has very little content; a richer theory is derived from its application to some rather specific cases, in which the alternative futures can be specified in terms of what is called a "possibility boundary" in the variable space of the organization. The possibility boundary, as the name suggests, divides possible combinations of variables from impossible ones. It is, thus, a reflection and a definition of "scarcity," in the broad sense of implying that not all things are possible. It frequently, however, applies to scarcity in a more restricted sense. Usually the possibility boundary has the character that an increase of one variable could only be obtained by the sacrifice of another. Along with the possibility boundary, we then postulate a preference function in the field which tells us which of any two elements in a certain field is preferred.

These concepts are illustrated in two variables in Figure 1. Here we suppose two variables, A and B; each point in the field represents a combination of the two. The possibility boundary, HKLM divides the field into a possible area and an impossible one. As drawn, the line has two sections, HK and LM, in which it has a negative slope, indicating

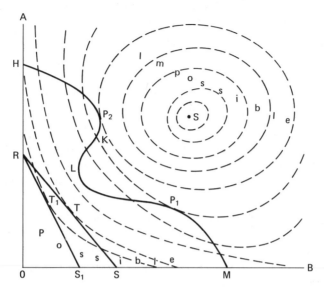

FIGURE 1. (Explanation in text.)

that from any point on the line we cannot move to any position where there is more of both A and B, but we can move to a position where there is more of one and less of the other. This is scarcity in the narrower sense. Between K and L the line has a positive slope. Here it is possible to go from a position on the possibility boundary to another where there is more of both A and B. In an economic system, this would be regarded as a very peculiar case.

We then postulate a utility or value function, which can be thought of as a surface in the third dimension, the height of which measures the "preferredness" of each point of the field. The dotted lines are contours of this surface and are known as "indifference curves." They join all those points on the field which represent combinations of A and B that have the same value, towards which, therefore, the decision-maker is indifferent. In the diagram we have supposed that the value function in the vertical is a dimension "mountain," where the summit at S represents satiety. The indifference curves will be roughly circular around S. The "value mountain" will have four quadrants; south and west of S, both A and B are "goods," that is, an increase in either of them is preferred; north and east of S, both of them are "bads," that is, an increase in them is not preferred. North and west of S, B is a good and A is a bad; south and east of S, A is a good and B is a bad.

An optimum in the small is where the indifference curve touches the possibility boundary, as at P_1 or P_2. From each of these points any small movement, either along the possibility boundary or within it, leads to lower indifference curves representing lower levels of preference. It will be noted that in the large P_2 will be preferred to P_1, although, in order to get from P_1 to P_2, the organization would have to pass through regions of lower preference than P_1. If, now, in a more restricted case, A and B are commodities which can be exchanged at a fixed exchange ratio, and the decision-maker starts with an amount of A equal to OR; the possibility boundary is a straight line RS, the slope of which is equal to the ratio of exchange, that is, the number of units of B that can be gotten for one unit of A. Under these circumstances, the optimum position is T, where RS is touched by an indifference curve. A worsening in the terms of trade will be reflected in a shift in this line, say, to RS', and a shift in the optimum point to T'. The results of the change here depend on the nature of the indifference curves, that is, of the value function.

I am not sure whether this kind of analysis has the slightest value to biologists. Man, however, is not the only animal who economizes or who makes choices. An amoeba, faced with a piece of food on the one hand or a piece of dirt on the other, will ingest food and reject the dirt. This implies that even the amoeba has a value function and, in a sense, makes choices. As we go up the scale of complexity, the role of choice and, therefore, of evaluation in the behavior of living organisms becomes more and more important. In the less complicated forms, of course, the value system is largely genetic in origin and, hence, not much subject to change during the life of the organism. With increase in complexity, however, learned values become more and more important. Even in the birds we find the phenomenon of imprinting, as in the famous goose who thought Konrad Lorenz was his mother. In the mammals there is a good deal of learning of values in infancy, and in man, of course, almost all values are learned even though they are built on a genetic substructure.

In regard to the growth, success, or failure of the organization or organism, it would not surprise me if economics has more to learn from biology than biology from economics, even though this learning process may not be much more than a hope for the future. The particularly important contribution of biology here is the concept of "allotropy," as

Bertalanffy calls it, or the principles which give any particular form of organization, whether living organism or social organization, an optimum size or, at least, an optimum range of sizes. I recall being enormously influenced as an economist by Julian Huxley's famous little essay "On Being the Right Size." The proposition, that the surface is increased as the square of the length and volume as the cube as we increase the linear dimensions of a particular structure, has very far-reaching implications in both biology and the social sciences. It explains the small size of the one-celled organism, the moderate dimensions of the exoskeletal insect, the general size range of the reptiles and mammals, and even why the whale has to live in the ocean. It explains, also, how increased size has to be compensated for by change of structure and particularly in terms of endoskeletons and convolutions of lungs, bowels, and brain in order to increase the surface area relative to the volume. Nothing can happen that is not superficial; that is, all transactions or interactions take place on surfaces. Hence, the proportion of surface to volume is one of the most important parameters of any organization. This is one of the most universal of principles. It applies, for instance, to architecture where, as long as buildings had an exoskeleton like an insect, they could not be much bigger than, shall we say, the Palace of Versailles, but once the endoskeleton, that is, the steel frame, had developed, they could be as large as the Empire State Building and even larger. Similarly, artificial lighting, plumbing, and ventilation permit the development of much larger structures than would be possible where all the inputs and outputs had to come in directly through the exterior walls.

There are similar principles in regard to social organizations, although they are harder to detect. Communications follow a linear pattern. Inputs from and outputs to the external world take place on the "surface" of organizations. It is the sales clerk who meets the customer, the infantryman who meets the enemy, the priest who meets the congregation, and the teaching assistant who meets students. The upper members of any hierarchy have to derive their information indirectly through channels of communication, and the longer these are, the more likely they are to be corrupted. What I call the "organizational revolution" came about as a result of a change mainly in the techniques of communication, such as the telephone, the telegraph, the typewriter, the mimeograph, and, perhaps, the vice president or the staff organization. All this took place around 1870 and permitted an enormous expansion of the scale of organizations, giving rise to such monsters as General Motors, the United States Department of Defense, and the Soviet Union, all of which would have been inconceivable before 1870. In economics the phenomenon is known as "decreasing returns to scale." Some economists have doubted whether this exists, using the argument that if we could change all inputs in exactly the same proportions, there seems no reason to suppose why the outputs should not be increased in the same proportion. Perhaps, if they had known a little more biology, they might have been spared this fallacy, though we can perhaps get around it formally by supposing that what "returns to scale" really means is that it is impossible to increase all inputs in the same proportion—if only because of the laws of squares and cubes.

Another phenomenon, where a little interaction between economics and biology might be helpful, is in the study of growth. This is a phenomenon which is common to all the sciences and the possibility of a general theory of growth which cuts across the disciplines is extraordinarily tempting. The growth of a baby from the fertilized egg in the womb of its mother is a process which is not wholly unlike the growth of an automobile in the womb of its factory. In both cases, there is a blueprint —the genetic code in biology or the factory plan in the case of the automobile. In both cases, there is assembly of different parts. In the biological case, the parts and the whole grow together in a way that they do not in the case of the automobile. All these processes imply some sort of destabilizing feedback. I doubt if an embryologist would learn much from studying the growth of the automobile in the factory, but I cannot help wondering whether the concept of the "payoff" might be useful in biology as it is in social sciences.

Moving now from the individual organism or organization to the larger environment or ecosystem in which it finds itself, we find striking parallels between biological and socio-economic systems, so that the sciences again might have something to learn from each other. It could be an interesting exercise to compare the work of Walras, who developed a set of equations for the general equilibrium of the price system, with the work of Volterra, who developed a model of the dynamic interaction of populations. Walras is a little weak on the dynamics of the system and, perhaps, Volterra in what an economist would call "comparative statics," that is, what difference in the position of the final equilibrium would be created by a given change in the parameters of the system. The similarity between the two systems, however, is highly significant. Both depend essentially on the simple proposition that in any system of N variables, if each variable has an equilibrium value which depends on the position of all the others, we can immediately derive a system of N equations with N unknowns, for we have one equation for each of the N variables. If this system of equations has a solution, which usually has to fulfill some limiting conditions such as that all the equilibrium values should be positive, then, at least, there is specified what might be called a "conditional equilibrium" of the whole system in the sense that a certain set of values of the variables can be specified in which the value of each variable is consistent with the value of all the others. This conditional or general equilibrium does not necessarily have to be stable, that is, the dynamics of the system could pull it away from the equilibrium rather than pulling it towards it. As Samuelson (1947) has pointed out, we have to know the dynamics of the system before we can specify the stability of any equilibrium.

The mathematical problems become increasingly difficult as we increase the number of variables. The general principle, however, is a relatively simple one that applies to biological, as well as to social, ecosystems. I have learned to think of society, indeed, as a "great pond," a pool of social species which consists of types of organizations and artifacts as well as occupations and persons. Seventh Day Adventists, corner gas stations, automobiles, international corporations, foundations, and national states all jostle each other in the environment provided by the biosphere, the geosphere, the atmosphere, and the hydrosphere, and something like an ecological equilibrium can be perceived, at least in part of the system for short periods of time. Thus, a relative price structure may persist even through large inflations. If a pound of butter is worth 10 pounds of bread before an inflation, this ratio is likely to be not very different after it. Even such things as geographical price structures have astonishing persistence. Commodities have complementary, competitive, or predatory relationships, much like biological organisms. There are food chains in economics just as there are in biology—a tractor eats gasoline, wheat eats fertilizer, flour eats wheat, bread eats flour, and people eat bread.

Biological ecosystems tend to be more cyclical than social ecosystems. In biology, nitrogen goes round and round, financing protein on the way. Economic processes are much more linear, going from mines and wells to commodities, garbage, and dumps. Nevertheless, if the doomsayers are right, nemesis is only just around the corner, and at some time or other, mankind has to come to terms with circularity and establish a "spaceship earth," in which most materials which are transformed into commodities are recycled back into the source from which they came. The dumps, in other words, have to become mines. A system of this sort needs inputs of energy to drive it, otherwise the second law of thermodynamics takes over very rapidly. This is as true of the biosphere as it is of the "sociosphere."

A very interesting question, to which I have never been able to give a satisfactory answer, is what, if anything, in the biosphere corresponds to the concept of a price system, and especially to an equilibrium price system, in economics. Prices have a parallel in the biosphere in the concept of metabolic rates or input-output ratios. The animal "exchanges" oxygen for CO_2, and must have an approximately "perfect market" for this exchange, that is, if the proportion of oxygen or even of CO_2 in the environmental air changes substantially as he breathes, the organism very soon gets into trouble. Evolution has proceeded for a very long time on the assumption that a lung full of air contains approximately the same amount of oxygen no matter when or where it is inhaled.

The economic concept of production, or a production function, also has counterparts in the biosphere. Every organism has inputs and outputs, and the relations of these to one another provide essential parameters for the ecosystem. If we have not yet developed a general theory of the ecosystem applicable to both biological and social systems, it is perhaps because biological systems have had to come to terms with circularity before this necessity has imposed itself on social systems.

Some of the complexities of these relationships can be illustrated even in the simple case of a two-population ecosystem. This is illustrated in the parts of Figure 2. Here we measure the size of one population (A) vertically and the other (B) horizontally. In Figure 2a we suppose two mutually competing populations such as lions and tigers; they are, let us say, competing for the same food. We can postulate a partial equilibrium "lion curve," LL', showing the equilibrium number of lions for each number of tigers. With no tigers, there will be OL lions, and with OL' tigers, there will be no lions at all. The curve TT' is the corresponding "tiger curve." These curves intersect at E, which is a position of equilibrium. The dynamics of the system can be represented by the dynamic

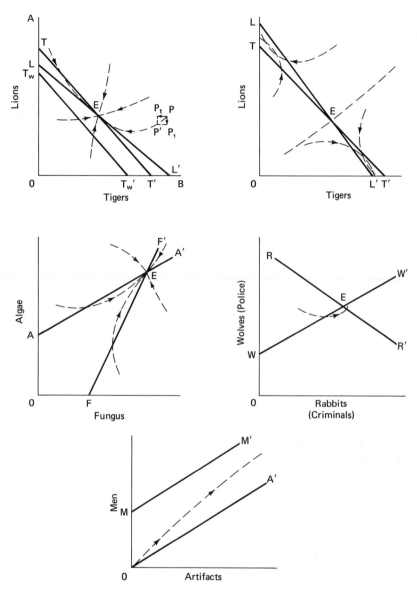

FIGURE 2. (Explanation in text.)

path lines that are shown with arrows. From each point, we can suppose that in the next time period, each population will move towards its equilibrium level, and it will move towards its own particular equilibrium curve. Thus, from point P, we can suppose that in the next time period, the number of tigers will decrease by PP_t, the number of lions by PP_1, the next point being P′, the result of these two movements. In the limiting case, these paths become the dynamic functions of Volterra. In Figure 2a we see that all the dynamic paths converge on the equilibrium point E, and the equilibrium is clearly stable. If, however, we reverse the position of the two curves, as in Figure 2b, we again may have a position of equilibrium E, but it is unstable. On the upper left-hand side of the dotted line through E, the system moves to the point T, at which the lion becomes extinct and there are OT tigers. Downward and to the right of this line, all the dynamic lines move towards L′, with OL′ lions and no tigers.

Figure 2c shows the corresponding case for two mutually cooperative or complementary species, such as the algae and the fungus which together constitute a lichen. Here, again, there may be an equilibrium point at E which, in this case, is stable. There are unstable cases that could easily be formulated. Figure 2d is a very familiar case of predation or parasitism; in this case, we suppose populations of wolves and rabbits. We have a wolf equilibrium line, WW′, suggesting that, with no rabbits, there will be some wolves (OW), but that after that point the more rabbits, the more wolves. The rabbit line, RR′, is downward sloping, indicating that the more wolves, the fewer rabbits. Here, again, there is an equilibrium point at E which is usually stable. Under some circumstances, there might be a circular equilibrium producing a constant cycle. Under other circumstances, there might be a converging cycle, or even an explosive or divergent cycle which might destroy the equilibrium.

One very interesting problem here is the sensitivity of the system; by this we mean what happens to the equilibrium position when the parameters of the equations change. When the partial equilibrium lines have the same general slope, as in Figures 2a, 2b, and 2c, the system is highly sensitive. Thus, if in Figure 2a, there is a slight worsening of the comparative position of the tigers, through the shift in the partial equilibrium line TT′ to $T_wT'_w$, tigers will become extinct and the lions will triumph. In Figure 2d, the equilibrium is much less sensitive, and it will take very large shifts in the parameters to lead to the extermination of either of the populations. This perhaps explains why the predation-parasite relationship is so popular.

Any of the above cases could be applied to social systems. Figure 2a, for instance, could be automobiles and horses or better, perhaps, two makes of automobiles. Figure 2b could be automobiles and stagecoaches; Figure 2c could be automobiles and gas stations; Figure 2d, criminals and police—the more criminals, the more police; the more police, the fewer criminals. Figure 2e is a suggested explanation for the extraordinary explosion of the human population. Man and his artifacts are mutually cooperative. The partial equilibrium line for man is MM'. There will be some men even without artifacts; thereafter, the more artifacts, the more men. The partial equilibrium line for artifacts is OA'. With no men, there would be no artifacts, but the more men, the more artifacts. If these two lines are parallel, the population of both men and artifacts will expand indefinitely. One point which is not noted in the diagrams is that, for biological populations, there is some size of the population below which reproduction is virtually impossible. A biological population with sexual reproduction cannot come down to one member, or even to a population consisting all of one sex, without dying out very rapidly. For such populations, therefore, we can postulate a band of survival roughly paralleling the other axis.

A third area where biological and social systems have a great deal in common is in evolution. Within biology, evolution is regarded as ecological succession produced by mutations in the genetic codes. The dynamics of the system is, of course, appallingly complicated. It would be nice if we could assume that at any time and place the ecological equations of interacting populations would work themselves out towards an equilibrium. A genetic mutation would then change the parameters and move the system towards a new equilibrium with perhaps some of the old species failing to survive and a new species surviving in the new ecosystem. Unfortunately, things are not this simple. Genetic mutations and environmental changes go on all the time, so that ecosystems rarely have time to achieve definite equilibrium. The dynamic paths of Figure 2 are continually being changed by genetic mutations which also change the partial equilibrium curves and the equilibrium position of the system. If these paths dip below the critical survival numbers of the species, then that species will become extinct. The unique elements of its genetic code, which distinguish it from other species, will disappear from the gene pool, and its extinction will change the equilibrium positions of the ecosystem and, therefore, the chances of other species for survival. Nevertheless, the principle that it is ecosystems rather than species that are selected is a significant one, even though it may be hard to pin it down to particular equilibrium cases. The great Darwinian vision of evolution as a process with genetic mutation and recombination, and phenotypic selection, nevertheless, holds up as a poetic vision even though it is extraordinarily hard to formulate in explicit models. Evolution is a theory without adequate mathematical models and with virtually no predictive power; nevertheless, it is one of the most profound illuminations to ever hit the human consciousness.

The mutation-selection pattern is just as characteristic of human history—that is, of the dynamics of the social system—as it is of the biosphere, but in social systems, it is harder to distinguish the genotype from the phenotype. It is tempting to regard the "noosphere," to use Teilhard de Chardin's term, that is, the sphere of all human knowledge as it is embodied in human nervous systems spread around the globe, as the social genotype. Out of this knowledge comes artifacts on the one hand, and organizations on the other. Human artifacts, indeed—automobiles, machines, airplanes, organizations, and so on—are social species, the genetic base of which is human knowledge imposing itself on the material and social world. There is a parallel here to the way in which the genetic code, which can also be regarded as knowledge—or at least, "know-how" —imposes its organizing potential on the material world in the creation of the phenotype. Organizations, likewise, require "know whom," as well as "know-how," and a complex of images and values which can be regarded as the genotype of the organization.

The parallel between biological and social evolution, however, must not be carried too far, for at some crucial points, it breaks down. The survival of human knowledge depends only loosely on the survival of the phenotypes which it creates, for it is embodied, not in artifacts or in organizations, but in human nervous systems, and it is transmitted from one human being to another by communication and learning, which again are only loosely related to the organizations within which they may take place. Nevertheless, there is some relationship between the survival of the phenotype and the survival of the genotype in social systems in the sense that if there is a general collapse of the organization of the transmission of knowledge, knowledge will simply come to an end. A good example of this was the collapse of the Mayan civilization within which the organization, whatever it was that transmitted the elaborate astronomical and technical knowledge of the Mayans, collapsed, and the knowledge itself disappeared as a result.

Another fundamental difference between biological and social evolution is that, in the biosphere, the genotype of a particular individual comes usually from two parents of opposite sexes, except in the case of asexual reproduction, whereas in social systems and in the transmission of knowledge, there are innumerable "sexes." The knowledge stock of one person is derived, not from his parents alone, but from all the people and, indeed, all the experiences with which he has had contact. The transmission of language and culture within the family have something of a genetic quality about them in the sense that languages perpetuate themselves by children growing up with parents who both speak the language, but here, again, the parallel is not close, and the analogy must not be pushed too far. Culture traits may be propagated by something that looks almost like asexual reproduction, that is, by simple imitation. The same is true of technology. Thus, the Japanese discovered Western technology after 1868 and adopted a great deal of it by sending their young men to Europe to learn the new science and the new technology, and when they returned to Japan, as most of them did, this became part of the Japanese knowledge stock. We are now witnessing a great diffusion of culture traits as a result of increased transportation and communication which have resulted from the scientific revolution. Some of these are so universally recognized to be valuable, such as the periodic table and nuclear physics, that they are almost universally adopted. Other traits are more specific to the subcultures in which they are perpetuated, so each society represents a combination of almost universal traits together with highly particular traits of particular subcultures, such as language, art, ideology, religion, nationalism, class, and so on.

In economics, evolution becomes "development," which is almost the same word. The main emphasis is on the total output of the system, at least in terms of economic goods, and especially in terms of per capita output of these goods. A number of economic models of growth have been developed, especially in the last thirty years. These models have not, as far as I know, found much application in biology. Perhaps a good reason is that the total output, or throughput, of the biosphere is not of particularly salient quantity although it is by no means devoid of interest as at least a possible quantitative measure of the evolutionary process itself.

Today, there is a sudden realization by economists that the growth process cannot go on forever and that mankind is expanding into a biological niche, the niche in this case being the whole earth. The quasi-religious manifestos of the Club of Rome may be received with some skepticism in the economics profession. Nevertheless, the problem cannot be brushed aside, and the concept of the "carrying capacity" of the earth, in terms of the human population, has suddenly become of first importance. Up to this century, man has conceived himself as expanding on a virtually infinite plane. Now, suddenly, the plane has become a sphere, and he has become acutely aware of the limitations of the tiny "spaceship earth" to which he is confined and on which he must travel towards some unknown destination. It is at this moment of truth that economics suddenly becomes ecology.

Even on the spaceship earth, however, we must beware of an overemphasis on equilibrium. The earth has not been in equilibrium, certainly as far as the biosphere is concerned, for three or four billion years, and it is certainly not going to reach equilibrium now. What we are facing is what we have always had—an evolutionary process within the limits of the terrestrial environment. The evolutionary process itself has had its moments of disaster. Each geological age, indeed, is separated from its successor by a disaster, and it is still a moot question as to the significance of these evolutionary disasters in the general evolutionary process. It can be argued that they have been necessary for evolution, for otherwise the earth would have reached an equilibrium long ago, and evolution would have come to an end. We may be coming to another evolutionary disaster as a result of the uncontrolled expansion of human population and throughput. If this is not fatal, however, it may again set the stage for a new phase of evolutionary development, although this may not be a particularly cheerful thought for mankind if we are a species that is not included in the next development.

The role of catastrophe in evolution is somewhat related to the problem of the role of dialectical processes in human history. Dialectical processes are those which involve systems-conflict, that is, the struggle of one of fairly well-defined system against another, leading to the overflow of one and its replacement by the challenger or, of course, possibly leading to the failure of the challenger and the continued existence of the challenged. This reflects itself in human history in such processes as the succession of empires, the conflict of states and classes, and revolutions. I argue that evolution is an essentially non-dialectical process in the sense that it operates, not by the conflict of systems, but by the succession of ecosystems as a result of almost continuous small changes in the parameters, either through genetic mutation or through irreversible changes in environment. Nevertheless, the role of catastrophic changes, which destroy a previously established equilibrium and hence permit a new surge of evolutionary development, is by no means to be ruled out.

The real difficulty is that neither in biological evolution nor in social evolution do we understand very much about the generation of evolutionary potential. Why was it that the vertebrates developed organized intelligence rather than the octopus? Why did it, then, develop through the simians rather than the felines? Both evolutionists and historians tend to assume too easily that what happened had to happen. Both evolution and human history are the result of a mixture of random and non-random processes. The non-random element is suggested by the fact, for instance, that the marsupials of Australia, or even the birds in the Oceanic Islands, evolved to fill the mammalian niches. This suggests that there is a potential niche structure which provides a significant non-random element in the evolutionary process. Similarly in social systems, Japan, in relative isolation, developed many of the institutions in a somewhat different form than Europe developed under feudalism. Classical Japan could almost be described as a marsupial society. Nevertheless, the random elements are also there and cannot be denied. The survival of the early examples of any major mutation has a strong random element in it. We see this very clearly in human history, especially in the foundation of the great "phyla" of religion, ideology, and culture. It is hard to believe that this is not true also in biological evolution, and I suspect biologists have paid too little attention to this problem.

There is one final area in which striking parallels exist between biological and social processes and in which, also, there seems to be very little interaction between the two sciences. This is in the phenomenon of regeneration, whether at the level of the phenotype or that of the ecosystem. Many lower organisms can regenerate a limb that is cut off. Part of the price of complexity seems to be a certain loss of regenerative power, although even man's body can heal a cut and reorganize a brain. Ecosystems, likewise, regenerate. After a forest fire, a whole succession of stages takes place until the original forest is regenerated. The necessity for regeneration may also change that which is regenerated—thus, a forest which is not subject to forest fire may end up as a very different kind of forest to one that is.

Social systems exhibit similar properties. A role occupant of an organization, if he quits, retires, or dies, is usually replaced by another. If a college loses its whole football team in an airplane accident, in a couple of years it will have another one. A country, like Germany, which loses territory in a war may do much better economically on its restricted territory rather than on its original territory. An industry may be destroyed by law, as the liquor industry in the United States was destroyed by prohibition. It may reestablish itself surreptitiously or, if the law is removed, it will grow back again just like the leg on a salamander. This "pattern persistence" phenomenon, as it might be called, is a characteristic of virtually all complex systems. As far as I know, there is very little general theory of this phenomenon. In social systems, the payoff structure is a very important element in this process. In the economic model, the "price-profit mechanism," as it is called, is an important explanatory factor explaining both the distribution of economic activity and also its regeneration. Crime will expand roughly to the point and not much beyond the point where it pays the going average wage. The liquor industry was smaller under prohibition because of the legal costs and penalties involved. Once these had been removed, it grew again to approximately its previous size, again to the point where the economic returns in it were approximately normal. It is a fascinating speculation as to whether there are any processes corresponding to this in the biosphere. In an ecosystem, each species expands up to the point where it no longer "pays"—at least in terms of birth and death rates—to expand any further. It is harder to perceive processes of this kind in the body and hard, perhaps, to conceive of a process of "payoffs" for individual cells. But the line of thought at least seems worth pursuing.

These second-cousin relationships between economics and, indeed, the social sciences generally, and the biological sciences may not be any more than suggestive of some future possibilities. Nevertheless, they are tantalizingly suggestive, and one hopes that a few family reunions might set in motion conversations and learning processes which would lead to mutual enrichment.

References

Boulding, K. E. 1953: *The Organizational Revolution*. Harper and Row, New York.
———. 1970. *A Primer on Social Dynamics*. The Free Press, New York.

Jevons, W. S. 1911. *The Theory of Political Economy*. 4th Ed. 21. Macmillan and Co., London.

Marshall, A. 1961. *Principles of Economics*. C. W. Guillebaud (ed.), 9th ed., Macmillan, New York. 50.

Noyes, C. R. 1948. *Economic Man*. Columbia University Press, New York.

Samuelson, P. A. 1947. *Foundations of Economic Analysis*. Harvard University Press, Cambridge, Mass.

Veblen, T. 1919. *The Place of Science in Modern Civilisation*. B. W. Huebsch, New York.

20 Communication in the Biological Sciences

RICHARD H. FOOTE
ENTOMOLOGY RESEARCH DIVISION
Agricultural Research Service
United States Department of Agriculture

Nothing is easier than to talk about information problems, and we have been talking about them for a long time. In doing so, we have identified many complex inter-relationships in the communication of scientific information. In this chapter, we have space to examine only a few aspects of this complexity—specifically those that appear to offer outstanding promise for the solution of our more pressing problems in the communication of biological information.

The years 1964-1967 appear to mark a transition from discussion to action for many individuals and organizations in biology. For this reason, the ensuing discussion is based largely upon descriptions of things that have been done in the recent past or are now in their formative stages. The course of many of these plans and activities already may well have determined our future.[1]

1. As far as possible, the references cited in the text of this chapter have been selected from the biological literature itself or from sources readily available to most biologists; thus, they are not necessarily the ones giving detailed and definitive information on a subject. A complete bibliography is beyond the scope of the present treatment.

The Nature of the Information Problem

SIZE AND GROWTH

Man is primarily a social animal. On the premise that he could accomplish more by establishing and working within organizations, he has created them in profusion. Within one special kind of organization—the professional society—man has indeed accomplished much. He has given himself status within his profession and in society; he has improved his material well-being; he has made possible better communication with his colleagues who have the same problems and interests; and he has created a publication outlet for the results of his scientific research. In the United States alone, in 1968, 68 national biological societies were in existence; there were 17 agricultural societies, and probably about 30 concerned with the bio-medical sciences (Frye et al., 1968). Numerous additional regional, state, and local organizations in these three broad disciplines bring the current total for North America to somewhere between 600 and 800. Whatever may be its primary role, the professional society remains by far the principal publisher of the scientific journal—the vehicle which seems so largely responsible today for the problems we face in retrieving information from the world's biological literature.

Many estimates of the magnitude of the world's scientific literature have been made, with widely varying results. The most-quoted is by de Solla Price (1961) who estimates a doubling of the number of scientific journals every 10 to 15 years since 1900 when approximately 10,000 were in existence. Estimates of a more critical nature by Gottschalk and Desmond (1963), Barr (1967), and Hutton (1967) place a total number of journals for the whole of science and technology at about 26,000. Of these, approximately 13,000 belong to the life sciences.

In 1966, Licklider estimated that the world's scientific and technical information contained about 10 trillion characters (letters, numerals, and punctuation marks). Assuming that 1/1000 of this body of information constitutes a specialty (10 billion characters), a scientist who reads 3,000 characters a minute could peruse every word of his specialty by reading 13 hours a day every day of the year for 12 years. He further pointed out that 60 years ago a specialist needed to read for only 25 minutes each day; eleven years hence (i.e., 1977) he would have to read for 24 hours a day to accomplish the same end.

The scientific journal (i.e., serial) is not the only source of trouble. The situation is seriously complicated by books, published and unpublished reports, monographic works, and by the thousands of newsletter-type publications having only parochial interest. Few of these publications ever get into the mainstream of information flow; quite probably, for this reason, very little is known about the size or present growth of this body of literature.

These figures do not reflect the steady growth in the number of articles published in individual journals. For instance, the Entomological Society of America (ESA), one of the larger AIBS adherent societies, produced the *Annals of the ESA,* one of its three major publications. During the period October 1, 1962 to September 30, 1970 (Table I), the number of published papers increased by 269%, and the total number of published pages doubled. If these figures can be taken as fairly typical of biological journals, we can understand how the increase in numbers and size of serials alone has contributed to the troubles biologists currently encounter in their searching of the literature.

INCREASING COSTS

Societies today spend an average of 75 to 80% of their total income for publishing purposes. With few exceptions, most of the money they devote to publication is spent outside the society to pay for the costs of printing and mailing. These outside costs, geared directly to current wage rates and prices of materials in the market place, have been rising steadily. The recent experience of the Entomological Society of America is fairly typical (Table I). For the *Annals* of that Society, printing costs rose nearly three-fold to produce a two-fold increase in the total number of pages printed in an 8-year period. W. P. Murdoch, Executive Secretary of ESA, has calculated that the cost to each member for 1,000 pages of his Society's journals was actually less in 1970 than in 1917, and this may be the experience of other societies as well (personal communication). However, the facts that dues in the ESA have increased almost five-fold during that time period, and a page charge of $30.00 now applies where none at all existed previously, do not augur well for the future of journal publishing. In fact, most societies and other organizations that publish scientific material by commercial press are even now confronted with a need to alter their present publication methods drastically, and more societies will be joining their ranks shortly.

TABLE I. *Growth of* Annals of the Entomological Society of America, *1962-1970* (*from Reports of the Managing Editor in the March issues of Bull. ESA for respective years*).

Year	Total No. Papers	Pages per paper[a]	Total pages	Printing Costs Total	Printing Costs Per page
Oct. 1, 1962-Sept. 30, 1963	143	6.5	872	$29,636	$34.00
" 1963 " 1964	166	5.4	850	29,574	34.79
" 1964 " 1965	160	6.6	940	33,810	35.97
" 1965 " 1966	230	6.1	1232	46,803	37.99
" 1966 " 1967	264	6.0	1432	54,899	38.34
" 1967 " 1968	313	6.0	1600	66,695	41.68
" 1968 " 1969	330	5.9	1552	68,189	43.93
" 1969 " 1970	384	5.5	1824	85,480	46.86
% increase or decrease	169	−15	109	188	38

[a] Not including scientific notes.

LACK OF CONTROL

Until quite recently, the publishers of the primary literature have never collectively assumed the responsibility for keeping an orderly record of their output, except for the traditional index at the end of a volume, or a cumulative one at regular or infrequent intervals. For years, the larger publishers even devised separate, quite unrelated indexes for each of the serials they produced, and many still do. Hence the scientist searching for material relevant to his needs, often widely scattered through the literature, had no means for finding that material through a single inquiry or search. Until secondary information services made their appearance, the classification system of a library was about the only source of help for the user. In those cases in which the secondary service is not effective, biologists still go from journal to journal and volume to volume to search indexes that define content only superficially.

Even the secondary information systems which have evolved have added to the confusion of locating pertinent literature by failing to communicate with each other. They duplicate coverage but not sufficiently to provide a single source of information to any user. They do not index information with compatible languages and systems, so an inquiry must be redefined to match each system's requirements. The user has no choice but to consult *all* services, a situation that only complicates his literature-searching problems.

Current Trends and Outlook

BROAD STUDIES

The problems of making information available to the scientist have been recognized for many years, and the urgency of these problems has continued to grow. Since 1963, a number of major studies have been conducted in an attempt to define the problems more precisely and to provide general recommendations for solving them.

The father of all broadly-based studies on information-handling in the sciences is the report of the Weinberg panel of the President's Science Advisory Committee (Weinberg, 1963). Most of the sweeping recommendations in that visionary statement are recognized as valid, and one finds them repeated time and again in subsequent reports. It was these recommendations that really awakened the scientific community to the need for concerted action to improve information handling in the sciences.

The Committee on Scientific and Technical Communication (SATCOM) was established in February 1966 by the National Academies of Sciences and Engineering to investigate the present status and future requirements of information flow and transfer in the scientific and technical communities. Its full report (SATCOM, 1969) contains not only an extensive series of recommendations but is recommended as an excellent textbook in providing background information on the subject. A recent effort to bring world-wide unification to information-handling activities in science is the publication of UNISIST (UNESCO/ICSU, 1971), a study report on the feasibility of establishing a world science information service. This study, implemented early in 1967 by a committee jointly created by UNESCO and the International Council of Scientific Unions (ICSU), recommends that there be established a fully integrated world network covering all field of knowledge. Biology has been represented by delegates from Biological Sciences Information Service (BIOSIS).

One of the most significant events in biological information handling was the formation of the Council on Biological Sciences Information

(COBSI) in 1965 as a result of a conference at Cherry Hill, New Jersey, sponsored by the Board of Trustees of Biological Abstracts. Representatives of the biological community attending this conference unanimously agreed on the critical need for a single organization that could speak with a unified voice for the information needs of biologists. Subsequent to its first meeting early in 1967, COBSI undertook several rather ambitious projects, its outstanding contribution being the so-called "COBSI report" (COBSI, 1970). Comprehensive in treating all phases of information-handling in the biological sciences, this report has already significantly influenced the course of events in this field and will continue to do so, with appropriate modifications, for years to come. This report forms the basis of the material presented in this chapter.

While many of the recommendations found in these reports seem to lack concreteness and objectivity and others fail to take us all the way down the road, taken together they chart the course for the future of information-handling in biology and should be on the bookshelf of every interested biologist.

PRIMARY PUBLICATION

Today, primary publication is the major medium for disseminating scientific information. An eloquent appeal for the published research report as a means for preserving information has been issued by Lamanna (1970) in supporting a widely held concept that "publish or perish" is good. In view of the apparently irreversible trend toward a continual increase in the world's knowledge, we can only try our best to gain better control over how it is produced and the forms in which it can best appear. As long as we use the printed word for communication, it is incumbent on us to learn to use it effectively.

Much has been said and written about improving the scientific article —to improve its overall quality, to make it more readily understood, to reduce irrelevant and sharpen relevant material, and to improve abstracting and indexing procedures so that its subject matter can be better and more quickly identified. A large number of concerned biologists, perhaps foremost among them Peter Woodford (1967, 1968), have shown us many ways to produce more effective scientific writing. Closer attention during the coming years to their guidelines is mandatory for everyone who records the results of his research for publication.

Additional guidance has been provided by the Council of Biological Editors in their publication *Style Manual for Biological Journals* (CBE, 1972). This book reflects a recent, laudable trend to stabilize and standardize the publications of biologists; thus, it promotes a "universal language" for biology that is sorely needed by an ever-growing number of scientists in the ever-diversifying fields of biology and is mandatory for use in a computer world. To remain effective, this publication must be revised regularly; we predict that the current third edition and its subsequent versions will be more and more widely adopted by editors of biological journals.

Not many guides are presently available, specifically for the biologist, concerning effective and utilitarian ways to apply indexing terms, but some excellent studies on effective abstracting (Weil et al., 1963; Weil, 1970) are available. For many reasons, brought out elsewhere in this chapter, effective abstracting must be cultivated as a continually more significant part of the information-recording process.

The present and future states-of-the-art in computer development have given rise to speculations that today's scientific journal will soon be obsolete. As early as 1938, Watson Davis predicted its demise, and Brown et al. (1967), Singer (1969), and Wooster (1970) have described the consequences of today's publishing practices.

The multitude of alternatives to traditional journal production boggles the imagination: Rather than print the full text of an article, store it in a computer memory, or in microform, or as an "unpublished" manuscript. Publish only an abstract and distribute it according to predetermined user profiles, or use a title and indexing terms in place of an abstract, or publish and distribute appropriate preprints.

In the biological literature, one of the first attempts to publish titles, indexing terms, and abstracts, holding full texts of papers for distribution on demand, was for the taxonomic literature of entomology. In the announcement of this *"Data Document"* service in *Entomological News* (Arnett, 1970a), a methodology for optional use by contributors was presented in detail. Despite the fact that many information-oriented biologists anticipated wide acceptance of this scheme, to date very few contributors to this journal have opted for its use (Arnett, 1970b). AIBS is currently investigating a similar experiment for *BioScience,* hoping to establish realistic cost estimates and determine user acceptability. Certainly, plans such as these should receive careful consideration by organizations that publish journals where such schemes would be appropriate.

When fully developed and available, the combination of optical character recognition and a very large computer storage capacity holds promise for the future never dreamed of before. The titles and full texts of manuscripts might be read into such devices automatically, to be held in storage and recalled on demand. They might be automatically indexed, so that all manuscripts containing common information elements could be recalled or a bibliography produced. In fact, such effective controls may be established that the appropriate abstracting and indexing can be relayed to secondary services automatically.

Around this kind of concept can be built an information system such as described by Koch (1971) for the American Institute of Physics (AIP), wherein it is possible to establish a secondary capability and integrate it with a primary publication program. A strong control over the primary sources of information feeding into the system is a prerequisite for total performance—such control is possible for AIP or any other organization that is primarily responsible for producing most of the publications in a discipline. Variations on this system, however, should make a small-scale beginning possible in biology.

The point to be emphasized here is the capability of the system to establish an effective connection between primary and secondary operations. But until biologists have access to such systems, the responsibilities of primary publications to secondary services must be taken much more seriously than ever before. Although secondary services will be able to supply a continually larger overall proportion of a biologist's information needs, rising costs and an ever-increasing corpus of literature may well force them to rely more and more heavily for abstracting and indexing services on journal editors and authors in order to maintain the effectiveness of the secondary service.

SECONDARY INFORMATION SOURCES

The startling growth and diversification of the primary literature in science emphasizes the important role now being played by the secondary services. Consequently, it is not surprising that a large number of relatively small services now operate to meet the pressing needs of biologists with special interests. For instance, a recent study by Patrias (1971) lists and describes 50 secondary serial literature publications containing significant amounts of entomological information, and another by Hammack (1971) lists and describes 23 secondary services likewise useful for entomologists. Some of these services and publications are restricted to the subject-matter of entomology, whereas many others include other disciplines of biology as well. There are now probably at least 75 secondary sources available, containing significant information about insects and other arthropods alone.

Studies on the use of secondary services by biologists have shown that three sources—*Biological Abstracts* and associated services of Bio-Sciences Information Service; *Chemical Abstracts* and associated services; and *Bibliography of Agriculture*—are probably best known and most widely used. Several other services are rather effectively used by biologists—*Zoological Record, Current Contents,* and other services of the Institute for Scientific Information, the abstracting series for several biological disciplines produced by Crowell, Collier and Macmillan Publishing Co., and the reporting offered by the National Technical Information Service, to name a few.

Biologists generally, recognizing the value of these information sources, are beginning to demand diversity and refinement in the output of secondary services. In response to this demand, BIOSIS, for example, has initiated the publication of *Abstracts of Mycology, Abstracts of Entomology, Abstracts on Health Effects of Environmental Pollutants,* and a new series of monthly abstract journals on a variety of subjects, *Bioresearch Today.* Additional services such as C.L.A.S.S. and others (BIOSIS, 1972) provide further direction for this refinement.

A few biologists feel that present-day secondary services can and should be improved in several other ways. The services represented, for example, by the data base from which *Biological Abstracts* is published, are structured to serve a wide spectrum of biological disciplines, and under these circumstances, depth of indexing must inevitably suffer. Deep indexing of the subject matter is expensive and time-consuming, hence, extremely difficult to accomplish effectively without the close guidance of the biological scientists who are in the forefront of their respective disciplines. A need for deeper indexing has been expressed, and BIOSIS has instituted some newer action concepts (BIOSIS, 1970) in response to this need. As an example, in a project now under way at the University of Wisconsin, subject-matter specialists are deep-indexing a specially selected segment of the biological control literature in entomology to test whether the retrieval aspects of the BIOSIS service can be improved and to provide more complete coverage of the subject matter for the BIOSIS file (Shervis et al., in press).

The successful future of the secondary information service will hinge directly on the extent to which it is sensitive to the needs of biologists. As the latter become more aware of the potentials inherent in modern information handling methods, they will continually demand more of these services. As a result, close liaison will be established between the services and their users with mutual advantages not heretofore realized. Thus, the secondary service will become one of the most effective links in the chain of communication of biological information.

OTHER SOURCES OF INFORMATION

One of the biggest problems in controlling and accessing information is determining what is available to be controlled and accessed. The difficulty is faced by the secondary services trying to decide what should be included in their systems. It is also faced by the individual user who must know what literature and what secondary and other services are available.

The curriculum of almost every well-rounded department of biology, zoology, or botany should include a course in the use of the literature. The importance of training the undergraduate and graduate student in this phase of his profession has been played down because it is a difficult subject to teach adequately and because not all biology departments have faculty that are interested or even knowledgeable in the subject. *Failure to provide such training is a major shortcoming in academia today.*

During the next 25 years, an important improvement that can be made in information handling in biology is the universal establishment of such courses. They will demonstrate to the beginning student the major sources of information in his field and the successive steps by which he may obtain specialized information. At the same time, these courses will sharpen the skills of the advanced student and increase his awareness of the possibilities offered by new information-handling methods. A large number of teaching guides have already been developed. Unfortunately, most of them have never been published for general distribution.

Descriptions of the serial literature in a given discipline are important to a secondary service in establishing a more realistic baseline for its operation. For biological serials, ICSU-AB (1967) has established a pattern worthy of emulation. Recent descriptive lists for several biological disciplines have been published as "communiques" by the Biological Science Communication Project of the George Washington University Medical Center, and one for the core literature of entomology has been prepared by Hammack (1970). More of these analyses should be undertaken for the literature of many disciplines since secondary services will be able to establish better baselines for their operations as a result.

A few concerned biologists have attempted to gain some measure of control over their widely scattered and disparate literature by writing reviews of the publishing habits and literature use of biologists in their disciplines (Alverson, 1965 for pesticides; Anderson, 1966 for ecology; Anderson and Van Gelder, 1970 for mammalogy; Baldwin and Oehlerts, 1964 for ornithology; Kull, 1965 for microbiology; Norris, 1971 and Simon, 1970 for biological control; Foote, 1969b for entomology; and Kennedy and Parkins, 1969 and Smith and Reid, 1972 for biology). Undoubtedly there are many others. Such studies should be pursued in depth by the society sector, as they can provide a large amount of information of value to secondary services which will, or should, be seeking more and more help in the years to come from the professions they serve.

In addition to requiring information on completed research, normally available through the literature, the biologist should have access to information about on-going research. Such information is difficult to obtain. However, recent emphasis on studies concerning research management have resulted in the strengthening of a major source of this kind of biological information—the Smithsonian Information Exchange (Hersey, 1970). The establishment of the Current Research Information System (CRIS) of the Agricultural Research Service within the U.S. Department of Agriculture has provided another important source of information on on-going research in biology (Turnbull, 1967). Both of these automated systems provide demand searches on their respective data bases. The usefulness of these and other similar kinds of services yet to be established makes them a big factor in information retrieval for the future. An interesting recent summary of the on-going "automated" research projects in systematic biology by Crovello and McDonald (1970) brings into focus the need for further digests of this kind. Through them, biologists are effectively apprised of on-going research in their field, and in future years, many scientists may well receive inspiration by reading about what has already been done to store and retrieve information about their specific research interests.

PARTICIPATION OF SOCIETIES AND OTHER ORGANIZATIONS

Societies and similar organizations can play a very important role in bringing order to information exchange. One of the outstanding examples lies in those services provided to the community of chemists by the American Chemical Society, which has a broad program designed to encompass all information elements of interest to this group of scientists. Likewise, the American Institute of Physics has initiated somewhat similar activities, and the mathematics community will soon be served along broad lines such as these by the American Mathematical Society.

In contrast to some of its sister sciences, biology is far from being in so fortunate a position because there is no strong centralized control over primary publication. Consequently, individual organizations must provide the necessary information services. Moving in this direction, the Entomological Society of America, by means of two grants from the National Science Foundation in 1969 and 1970 (Foote, 1967, 1969a), has designed a system concept for information handling in entomology (Graham, 1971). This concept involves the establishment of an information center which would guide entomologists in their information-seeking effort by informing them of the appropriate sources they might consult and by producing certain information aids such as mentioned elsewhere in this chapter. This concept, with appropriate changes, could well be adopted by organizations that represent other biological disciplines.

It is immediately obvious that unless there is massive coordination among such organizations, the information systems picture will become as complex as that now existing in the primary literature. In order to avoid such a danger, AIBS, during the past four years, has hosted a series of information round tables in conjunction with its annual meetings. The first of these round tables, to which adherent societies of AIBS were invited, was held in Columbus, Ohio in 1968. Gordon's (1969) summary of that conference emphasizes the importance of societies working together toward the common goal of providing over-all control of biological information. This was also the conclusion of succeeding round tables held in Burlington, Vermont; Bloomington, Indiana; and Fort Collins, Colorado. But this series of round tables has still failed to identify a central core of information activity in biology; so, the problem remains: How can a biology-wide "system" to handle information be established?

Recently, an information Task Force has been established within the AIBS to continue the effort. During the year and a half of its existence, this group has attracted 24 adherent societies; their representatives have identified these objectives:

1) to identify information needs common to all biologists, regardless of discipline;
2) to explore the ways in which various discipline-oriented societies might cooperate in their approach to solving the information problems of their members; and
3) to propose the elements of an educational program that can be effective in making biologists of all persuasions aware of the problem and means for its solution.

The Task Force has determined that there is an urgent need to fund at least one full-time information-oriented biologist who would guide the information activities of a large number of societies by providing direction for their initial information efforts, advising them on existing information sources, and devising information aids for their use. It is clear that the Task Force has potential to bring some measure of unity to the biological sciences information picture. Everything must be done to assure that this Task Force succeeds in its objective.

SYSTEMS FOR HANDLING DATA

So far in this chapter, we have emphasized the literature of biology because of the overwhelming problems it presents. Another, and very important, aspect of information handling is the need to collect, control, and make available biological data.

Data handling for the chemist and physicist by computer has been facilitated by the quantitative nature of their data and the standardization of the symbolism they use. In biology, the situation is more complicated, in part due to the failure of biologists to devise any kind of universal language that can be adapted readily for use in a computer.

Numerous attempts have been made to establish data-oriented systems in biology, some successful and others not (e.g., Wood, 1953; Denmark et al., 1958; Bean, 1969; Shenefelt, 1969; Perring, 1971; Shetler et al., 1971; *see also* Cutbill, 1971).

The Flora North America (FNA) project is today's outstanding example of a complex, well-conceived data-oriented information system, planned with substantial support from the National Science Foundation under the auspices of AIBS. Very briefly, FNA as a system comprises a standardized taxonomic data bank on North American vascular plants as a core, with appropriate programs to input, process, and output the data. This central core of information will be used, not only to publish a new Flora but also to serve as a searchable computerized data base for the future. A type-specimen register and a means for computer-assisted plant identification will be satellite "services." The system, both in concept and some detail, is described by Taylor (1971), Shetler (1971), and Shetler et al. (1971). The reader is urged to consult these references for further detail as FNA promises to be a system of the kind that the biological community should strive to maintain and develop to its highest possible level.

The data-banking operation of FNA is based on the concept of a two-dimensional matrix, the vertical axis of which comprises a taxonomic hierarchy and the horizontal axis an array of discipline-oriented information elements associated with the taxa. Substantive information can be entered in the "cell" represented by the intersection of the vertical and horizontal axes; thus, the accumulation of appropriately labeled data and bibliographic references in computer storage is a physical realization of the concept.

A logical extension of this concept would permit us, ultimately, to record in an orderly fashion everything that is known about all living things. Having established a comprehensive plan at the very beginning, we can enter data wherever in the matrix and in whatever amounts our capabilities and resources will allow. To the minds of many, this kind of matrix concept promises to provide the overall information "system" for biology deemed so essential for control of our information problems.

What must be done to make this concept a reality? Most important, the community of biologists must support the concept as a plan under which it will operate and be willing to accept its operational restrictions as well as its advantages. Biologists must agree on the essentials of the data elements to be employed. Information scientists, their hardware and software, and their ability to design information systems, must be involved, and all extant information systems must agree to make operational adjustments necessary for accommodation within the system. The experience gained by FNA during its implementation and operational phases will prove invaluable to all of the disciplines of biology.

Already progress is being made on some fronts. The question of the storage and retrieval of museum specimen data has recently been discussed by a Museum Data Bank Coordinating Committee, and a vigorous action program is currently being proposed for funding. The taxonomic community for years has concerned itself with catalog preparation as one of its primary tasks, and steps are being taken now to automate some of these catalog data—a first step in the establishment of the taxonomic file. Numerous thesaurus activities by biological specialists are beginning to provide the necessary indexing capability and standardization that will be demanded by the system.

This concept of a universal information system for biology and the activities now underway that seem to be contributing to its realization are indeed exciting developments. If the commitment of the community to this kind of plan were achieved, the future success of information handling in biology might very well be assured.

MACHINES AND METHODOLOGY

Our awareness of modern information handling methods stems not only from the problems which currently press on us. A great deal is generated by the windfall we have enjoyed in the advent of the second and third generation computer and other modern tools for information handling. Especially fortunate is the fact that they have been made available to us at a time when they are most desperately needed to help us solve our problems. As we use these modern tools, new ways to put them to use are suggested to us.

Fascinating developments in hardware and ways of using it occur every day. Optical character recognition, mini-computers, remote terminals, and networking are only a few of the elements that one day will become a way of life for us. We will eventually learn how to use all of them as they are perfected and made available to us as tools for effective information handling.

In the near and distant future, a large community of information scientists, fully knowledgeable in the use of modern information handling methods, will be available to biologists. It will be incumbent on every scientist to take full advantage of the expertise offered by this group of highly trained people, upon whom he will depend heavily for access to computers and associated software.

The use of microform by biologists is virtually nonexistent. Despite many attempts to familiarize biologists with the advantages of using microfilm or microfiche, these scientists have still not adopted what we consider today to be a valuable information tool. They complain that microfilm and microfiche readers are not only inadequate and generally unavailable but are also clumsy to work with, and their use is too time-consuming. And today's biologist was born to and brought up with the printed page, a tradition difficult to overcome. One of the most important breakthroughs to be made in information handling during the next 25 years is to establish a more universal use of microform. Part of it will be forced upon biologists by economic necessity since many already experience trouble finding storage space for documents. As more and more of our current literature is stored in large computers, computer-generated microfilm should become a well-used information tool—we need to prepare ourselves for that day.

NEED FOR EDUCATION

As expressed elsewhere in this chapter, there is an outstanding need for educating scientists at all levels in the use of modern information handling methods. First of all, a concerted effort must be mounted to increase the awareness of all scientists to available sources of information. Once a biologist has learned the advantages of using an information source in an effective way, he can very well catalyze his colleagues to become involved. As he becomes familiar with a system's shortcomings, the working biologist can suggest the ways a service might be improved for his and others' use. He should not hesitate to establish this kind of communication since it is the most important means by which the service can be improved. Furthermore, the adoption by working scientists of effective ways of obtaining the information they need will be seriously hampered until their administrators are made aware of the possibilities that exist.

A Challenge for the Future

Our examination of the literature of biology has shown that it has grown in size and cost for a long time without effective controls. We have noted several broad studies and the current efforts of a relatively few individuals and organizations during the past decade to release us from the dilemmas posed by this information explosion. We have been encouraged by plans and activities that offer promise of substantial help in:

1) making publication more effective and reducing its costs;
2) rendering the outputs of secondary information services more relevant;
3) enabling organizations and individuals to work together more meaningfully;
4) designing systems that better organize biological information; and
5) teaching us to use modern information-handling methods to a better end.

Proper emphasis in promoting these trends will surely lead us in the right direction, but there is one further element of communication activity that must become a part of our lives before we are able to make measurable progress. That is *dedication*. It is not enough to ask a few individuals or organizations for it—dedication must be embodied in the activities of every part of the community. It must take various forms because of the complexities of the problems we must solve, and it must be continually apparent and continuously applied (Foote, 1971).

One might say that a scientist first becomes committed to the overall information "system" in biology with the publication of his first paper and continues so throughout his professional life. His contribution to primary publication must commit him to organization, conciseness, and accuracy. His use of the secondary information sources must commit him not only to conform to their styles but also to help in every way possible to make their services better. His attainment of professional excellence must commit him to act as an authority on the inputs and outputs of any system designed to handle the information of his interest, while very probably not benefitting much from the system itself. His leadership in the professional community must commit him to encourage younger scientists to adopt the faith of modern information handling, with its new tools and methods. And, finally, his own commitment must encourage the organizations of which he is a part to become committed in the same ways.

Acknowledgments

I deeply appreciate the assistance of several of my colleagues, who helped me gather material and markedly improved the organization and content of this chapter: Harriet Meadow and Stanwyn Shetler, FNA; Harold Bamford, NSF; H. E. Kennedy, BIOSIS; Ross H. Arnett, Jr., Tallahassee, Florida; and Ralph W. Bunn and Wallace P. Murdoch, Entomological Society of America.

References

Alverson, R. A. 1965. An evaluation of the pesticide literature—problems, sources, and services. *J. Chem. Doc., 5*: 204-208.

Anderson, P. K. 1966. The periodical literature of ecology. *BioScience, 16*: 794-795.

Anderson, S. and R. G. Van Gelder. 1970. The history and status of the literature of mammalogy. *BioScience, 20*: 949-957.

Arnett, R. H., Jr. 1970a. Data documents: A new publication plan for systematic entomology. *Entomol. News, 81*: 1-11.

———. 1970b. Comments on data documents. *Entomol. News, 81*: 50; 78; 125-126; 208-212.

Baldwin, P. H. and D. E. Oehlerts. 1964. The status of ornithological literature. In: *Studies in Biological Literature and Communication, 4*: 1-53.

Barr, K. P. 1967. Estimates of the number of currently available scientific and technical proceedings. *J. Doc., 23*: 110-116.

Bean, J. L. 1969. An automatic data processing system for the documentation of forest-insect survey information. *J. Econ. Entomol., 63*: 1181-1184.

BioSciences Information Services of Biological Abstracts (BIOSIS). 1970. Biosciences Information Service—A Concept Plan. (Draft). BIOSIS, Philadelphia, Pa. (Mimeo.)

———. 1972. Editorial in *Biol. Abstr., 53*(2): (unnumbered p.).

Brown, W. S., J. R. Pierce, and J. F. Traub. 1967. The future of scientific journals. *Science, 158*: 1153-1159.

Committee on Scientific and Technical Communication (SATCOM). 1969. Scientific and technical communication—a pressing national problem

and recommendations for its solution. National Academy of Sciences, Washington. 322 p.

Council of Biological Editors (CBE), Committee on Form and Style. 1972. *Style Manual for Biological Journals.* 3rd ed. AIBS, Washington. 297 p.

Council on Biological Sciences Information (COBSI). 1970. *Information Handling in the Life Sciences.* W. C. Steere (ed.). Div. Biol. Agr., Nat. Res. Council, Washington. 79 p.

Crovello, T. J. and R. D. McDonald. 1970. Index of EDP–IR projects in systematics. *Taxon,* **19**: 63-76.

Cutbill, J. L. (ed.) 1971. *Data Processing in Biology and Geology.* Academic Press, New York. 346 p.

Denmark, H. A., H. V. Weemes, Jr., and C. Taylor. 1958. Taxonomic codification of biological entities. *Science,* **128**: 990-992.

Foote, R. H. 1967. Entomology looks at its mission. Information storage and retrieval for entomology. *Bull. Entomol. Soc. Amer.,* **13**: 99-104.

———. 1969a. Recent advances in bioscience information–entomology's role. *Bull. Entomol. Soc. Amer.,* **15**: 233-234.

———. 1969b. Introduction, p. 1-5; user study, p. 6-25; conclusions, p. 133-4. *In*: A system-designed entomology data center–a feasibility study. Phase I, Final Rept. Biol. Sci. Comm. Proj.–Entomol. Soc. Amer. (NTIS Document No. PB 186-470).

———. 1971. New directions for commitment. *J. Wash. Acad. Sci.,* **60**: 136-140.

Frye, R. E., W. A. Creager, W. F. Johannigsmeier, and James D. Noel. 1968. Professional scientific societies: 1968. Wolf Res. & Developm. Corp., Bladensburg, Md. (NTIS Doc. No. PB 180-907). 106 p.

Gordon, R. E. 1969. Toward an information system for biology-community activity. *BioScience,* **19**: 628-629.

Gottschalk, C. and W. F. Desmond. 1963. World centers of scientific and technical serials. *Amer. Doc.,* **14**: 188-194.

Graham, J. 1971. System design: Environment, concept, and programs. A system-designed entomological information center–a feasibility study. Vol. 1. Phase II, Final Rept. Entomol. Soc. Amer., College Park, Md. (NTIS Doc. No. PB 204-937).

Hammack, G. 1970. The serial literature of entomology–a descriptive study. Unnumbered Pub., Entomol. Soc. Amer., College Park, Md. 85 p.

———. 1971. ESAID–Entomological Society of America Information Directory. *In*: J. Graham and R. H. Foote (eds.). A system-designed entomological information center–a feasibility study. Phase II, Final Rept. Entomol. Soc. Amer., College Park, Md. (NTIS Doc. No. PB 204-937).

Hersey, D. F. 1970. Society and the research dollar. *J. Wash. Acad. Sci.,* **60**: 10-15.

Hutton, R. S. 1967. ASLIB, past and future. *ASLIB Proc.,* **19**: 19-28.

International Council of Scientific Unions Abstracting Board (ICSU-AB). 1967. Some characteristics of primary periodicals in the domain of the biological sciences. ICSU-AB, Paris, France. 79 p.

Kennedy, H. E. and Phyllis V. Parkins. 1969. Biological literature. p. 537-551. In: *Encyclopedia of Library and Information Science*, Vol. 2. Marcel Dekker, Inc., New York.

Koch, H. W. 1971. Current physics information. *Science,* **174**: 918-922.

Kull, F. C. 1965. Publication trends in microbiology. *Bacteriol. Rev.,* **29**: 534-543.

Lamanna, C. 1970. In favor of publish or perish. *J. Wash. Acad. Sci.,* **60**: 129-135.

Licklider, J. C. R. 1966. A Crux in Scientific and Technical Communication. *Amer. Psychol.,* **21**(10): 1044-1051.

Norris, J. R. 1971. Information sources and literature searching in biological control. Append. 2. p. 717-722. *In:* H. D. Burges and N. W. Hussey (eds.). *Microbial Control of Insects and Mites.* Academic Press, New York. 861 p.

Patrias, K. J. 1971. Analysis of secondary serial literature publications of interest to entomologists. *In:* J. Graham and R. H. Foote (eds.). A system-designed entomological information center—a feasibility study. Phase II, Final Rept. Entomol. Soc. Amer., College Park, Md. (NTIS Doc. No. PB 204-937).

Perring, F. 1971. The Biological Records Centre—a data center. *Bull. J. Linn. Soc.,* **3**: 237-243.

Price, D. de S. 1961. *Science since Babylon.* Yale University Press, New Haven, Conn.

Shenefelt, R. D. 1969. Storage and retrieval of entomological information as applied to Braconidae. *Bull. Entomol. Soc. Amer.,* **15**: 246-250.

Shervis, L. J., R. D. Shenefelt, and R. H. Foote. Species-level analysis of biological literature for storage and retrieval. *BioScience.* (In press.)

Shetler, S. G. 1971. Flora North America as an information system. *Bio-Science,* **21**: 14-18.

————, J. H. Beaman, M. E. Hale, L. E. Morse, J. J. Crockett, and R. A. Creighton. 1971. Pilot data processing systems for floristic information. p. 275-310. *In:* J. L. Cutbill (ed.). *Data Processing in Biology and Geology.* Academic Press, New York. 346 p.

Simon, H. R. 1970. Analyses of bibliographies on biocontrol. *J. Doc.,* **26**: 337-339.

Singer, S. F. 1969. Publication savings and shortcuts. *Science,* **166**: 43-44.

Smith, R. C. and M. Reid. 1972. *Guide to the Literature of the Life Sciences.* Burgess Publishing Co., Minneapolis, Minn.

Taylor, R. L. 1971. The Flora North America project. *BioScience,* **21**: 11-13.

Turnbull, J. 1967. Current research information system. *Agr. Sci. Rev.,* **5**: 30-33.

United Nations Educational, Scientific and Cultural Organization; International Council of Scientific Unions (UNESCO/ICSU). 1971. UNISIST: Study report on the feasibility of a world science information system. UNESCO, Paris, France. 161 p.

Weil, B. H. 1970. Standards for writing abstracts. *J. Amer. Soc. Inform. Sci.*, **21**: 351-357.

————, I. Zarember, and H. Owen. 1963. Technical abstracting fundamentals. *J. Chem. Doc.*, **3**: 86-89; 125-132; 132-136.

Weinberg, A. M. 1963. Science, government, and information: The responsibilities of the technical community and the government in the transfer of information. A Report of the President's Science Advisory Committee. U.S. Government Printing Office, Washington.

Wood, G. C. 1953. Chemical-biological documentation: A new approach. *AIBS Bull.*, Oct.

Woodford, F. P. 1967. Sounder thinking through clearer writing. *Science*, **156**: 743-745.

————. 1968. *Scientific Writing for Graduate Students. A Manual on the Teaching of Scientific Writing.* Rockefeller Univ. Press, New York. 190 p.

Wooster, H. 1970. The future of scientific publishing—or, what will scientists be doing for brownie points? *J. Wash. Acad. Sci.*, **60**: 41-45.

21 Graduate Education— The Need for More Options and More Diversity

MICHAEL J. PELCZAR, JR.
OFFICE OF VICE PRESIDENT FOR GRADUATE STUDIES AND RESEARCH
University of Maryland

The National Climate of Graduate Education

In the steady flow of conference reports and press releases on the health of higher education, graduate education has not been slighted. Indeed, the current "popularity" of graduate education has perhaps never been greater. But this newly acquired "public" notoriety comes more from criticisms of our practices than from an acknowledgment of our successes.

The questions, the criticisms, and the suggested recommendations for change come through with increasing regularity. The claim of a so-called surplus of doctorates, perhaps, heads the list. Headlines like "Ph.D. Glut Created a Jobless U.S. Elite," or "Ph.D.'s for What?" or "The Degree that has Become a Glut on the Market"—and other similar headlines, frequently grossly exaggerating actual conditions, have confused the public.

Numerous conferences have focused attention on the current health of graduate education. One such high level meeting took place a few years ago at Woods Hole (August of 1969) with support from the Carnegie Commission of New York and the National Academy of Sciences. Thirty-nine selected persons, each possessing special expertise in graduate education in the broad view, attended this session; they represented universities, industry, government, and private foundations. An informal report of the meeting is summarized in part in the following cryptic tone:

"The conference met at Woods Hole on August 24-27, 1969, in an atmosphere of deep concern, if not one of crisis. The months immediately preceding it had brought disturbing reports of trends and actions affecting the stability of graduate education in this country. Reductions in the federal support of advanced education and academic science were beginning to press hard on the universities, and the outlook for the immediate future promised little relief. Fiscal year 1969, which had witnessed the granting of the largest number of Ph.D.'s in the nation's history, had closed amid reports from placement officers, prospective employers, and doctorate recipients themselves that jobs in some fields of specialization were becoming increasingly scarce. The development of what some viewed as an oversupply of Ph.D.'s was accompanied by complaints from certain sectors of employment that Ph.D.'s were overspecialized, overpriced, and undermotivated. Finally, student unrest and dissatisfaction with many aspects of education, the claims of militant minority groups, and distrust of the rational approach to problems, which were active on many campuses at the undergraduate level, were beginning to spill over into graduate education. The underlying problems of which these were symptoms were complex, persistent, and intertwined. The storm signals were flying."

One of the recommendations developed during this meeting called for the establishment of a national committee or board that might provide a global assessment of our stature in graduate education. Only recently was this accomplished by the formation of the *National Board on Graduate Education* headed by President Emeritus David D. Henry of the University of Illinois. The Board expects to direct its attention first to problems of manpower supply and demand and ways that graduate schools can and should adjust to the changing employment situation. Additional topics on their priority list for early consideration are determination of the unit costs of graduate education, aims of graduate education, and access to graduate education for women and minority groups.

Those of us close to formal graduate education know, in fact, that during the past 20 years, world leadership in graduate education has passed from Europe to the United States. Graduate study has been characterized as the example of a "brilliant success" in higher education.

Graduates from our advanced programs of study provide the leadership for industry, government, and the private sector enterprises. They are likely to be at every strategic decision-making center in our society. Why should graduate education be subject to a barrage of criticism if this is our record of performance? In part, it is because we have remained relatively silent while the voices of our critics became louder and frequently went unchallenged. In spite of the successes, we have not done a good job of either explaining our purpose or publicizing our accomplishments. It is also due, in part, to the escalation of changes in societal mores and attitudes, some of which are in conflict with traditional values in graduate education. In our day, change has permeated all segments of society; it is "the new equilibrium, the new stability." But how should we change, and how much should we change from traditional programs and practices to meet the expectations of graduate education voiced from many sectors of the public as well as state and federal agencies? Whatever the answers, these questions must be dealt with more expeditiously than we have dealt with them in the past. At the same time, we need to maintain the criteria of "academic" quality associated with higher education and learning.

Enrollments, Dollars, and Degrees

Current studies of graduate education have resulted in many statistical analyses such as: the past, present, and projected enrollments; degrees awarded and projections of degrees to be awarded; and sources and level of funding for support of research and graduate students. These data have been analyzed in various ways; extrapolations have been made, using a variety of base line assumptions. For present purposes, it will suffice to select a few examples to illustrate past and present experiences and future trends. Table I presents data from the period 1960-61 to 1969-70, showing full-time graduate enrollment in the major academic areas together with the number of full-time NIH trainees in each area. In 1960-61, the biological sciences enrollment was approximately 12,000; in 1966-67, it had doubled; and by 1969-70, it exceeded 30,000. As one illustration of graduate student support, the number of NIH full-time traineeships, for the same periods, were 680, 2,542, and 3,140. This means that the NIH trainees, expressed as a percentage of full-time graduate enrollment, were 5.4% in 1960-61 and 10.2% in 1969-70.

TABLE I. *NIH Full-Time Predoctoral Trainees Compared to Full-Time*

Field	1960-61		1962-63		1964-65	
	Full-time graduate enrollment	NIH full-time predoctoral trainees	Full-time graduate enrollment	NIH full-time predoctoral trainees	Full-time graduate enrollment	NIH full-time predoctoral trainees
Mathematics	5,104	71	6,496	125	8,860	202
Physical Sciences	15,045	14	17,666	24	21,223	40
Engineering	15,124	14	18,050	24	22,415	39
Biological Sciences	12,504	680	15,051	1,191	19,362	1,934
Social Sciences	26,219	66	32,399	115	42,377	187
Arts and Humanities	20,471	—	23,934	—	30,880	—
Education	16,085	—	19,050	—	26,631	--
Health	4,312	502	4,929	881	6,232	1,430
Other	9,825	49	10,851	86	18,840	139
TOTAL	124,689	1,396	148,426	2,446	196,820	3,971

* From: "Report on Federal Predoctoral Student Support, Part II—Students Sup-
Institute of Mental Health, The Federal Interagency Committee on Education,
(Data available for each year in original report.)

On a broader scale, federal funding for fellowships and traineeships increased from approximately 25 million dollars in 1960 to 250 million
in 1968, the peak year. A recent informal survey of the major doctorate-
awarding universities reveals that they are currently experiencing something like a 30% reduction in fellowship support when compared to
1969; by 1975 the cutback is projected to be more than 60%. We are
now seeing the other side of the mountain and asking "How far is
down?"

The most recent poll on graduate student enrollment (fall 1971),
conducted jointly by the Council of Graduate Schools in the United
States and the Graduate Record Examinations Board, shows very little
increase in the total graduate school enrollment in 1971 over 1970 (see
Table II). More significant differences are noted when comparing types
of institutions. For example, the public institutions awarding the doctorate reported a 1.6% increase; the private counterpart institutions, a
1.3% decrease. This poll did not provide information by disciplines.
However, an earlier study by the National Science Foundation (Surveys

Advanced Degree Enrollment, 1960-61—1969-70.*

1966-67		1968-69		1969-70	
Full-time graduate enrollment	NIH full-time pre-doctoral trainees	Full-time graduate enrollment	NIH full-time pre-doctoral trainees	Full-time graduate enrollment	NIH full-time pre-doctoral trainees
11,899	236	13,506	229	14,123	238
25,492	46	29,333	39	27,737	40
26,829	68	30,994	17	31,654	19
24,628	2,542	29,402	2,996	30,646	3,140
55,333	330	68,875	582	73,822	611
42,874	—	56,317	—	56,594	—
37,541	—	54,900	—	60,702	—
7,459	1,847	8,752	2,018	9,961	2,117
26,110	189	30,857	259	35,821	270
258,165	5,258	322,936	6,140	340,960	6,435

ported Under Training Grants of the National Institutes of Health and the National Student Support Study Group, April 1971."

of Science Resources Series, National Science Foundation NSF 71-27) showed life sciences enrollment in doctoral departments increasing by a few percentage points during the years 1967-68 and 1969-70.

Allan Cartter's assessment of doctoral degree production, reported in the American Council of Education publication in 1966, pointed up the growing disparity between available positions in the teaching professions and the number of doctorates produced nationally. Further documentation of this discrepancy appeared in the American Council of Education's follow-up publication by Roose and Anderson in 1970. It needs to be emphasized that these reports addressed themselves to opportunities in the teaching profession and to employment in the traditional professional concept.

On April 2, 1971, under the sponsorship of the Association of American Universities, a meeting was held at which most of the persons (and agencies) involved in making projections of doctoral output participated. (A full report of the meeting was made by Wolfle and Kidd under the title of "The Future Market for Ph.D.'s," published in *Science, 1971.*)

TABLE II. *Total Graduate School Enrollment by Type of Institution. Fall 1970 and 1971.*[1]

Graduate Schools[2] (Type of Institutions)	Number	%[3]	1970	1971	% Change
Public—Master's Highest	36	86%	65,731	67,559	2.8% increase
Private—Master's Highest	31	91%	19,094	20,778	9.2% increase
Public—Ph.D. Highest	131	93%	346,252	351,686	1.6% increase
Private—Ph.D. Highest	76	94%	118,528	116,996	1.3% decrease
Master's Highest	67	88%	84,825	88,337	4.1% increase
Ph.D. Highest	207	93%	464,780	468,682	0.8% increase
Public—Master's and Ph.D.	167	91%	411,983	419,245	1.8% increase
Private—Master's and Ph.D.	107	93%	137,622	137,774	0.1% increase
Total	274	92%	549,605	557,019	1.4% increase

[1] Source: Joint survey by Council of Graduate Schools in the United States and Graduate Record Examinations Board.

[2] For purposes of this survey, "graduate school" is defined as those parts of the institutions under the administrative control of the graduate dean.

[3] Percentage figures are percent of the number responding of the number available in the total group. For example, 36 Public Master's Highest Degree institutions responded out of a possible 42 such institutions in the CGS membership for an 86% response rate for that group of institutions.

Most of the discussion centered upon the estimates of the number of doctorates that would be graduated in 1979-80. The numbers ranged from a low of 45,200 to a high of 77,700 with several intermediate projections. The number of doctorate degrees conferred in 1969-70 is given at 29,872; the number projected for the current year's graduation (1972) is placed at approximately 32,000.

Projections which are as far apart as those cited above (e.g., 45,200 and 77,700) raise some questions about the credibility of the claims of overproduction by the graduate schools. Even more significant are the results of a survey conducted by the Council of Graduate Schools in the United States and reported by President J. Boyd Page on May 3, 1972. A survey was conducted during the spring of 1972 designed to elicit information about current trends of doctoral production; 204 member graduate schools received the questionnaire, and responses were obtained from 120 institutions. The deans were asked to give "their best individual projections of how many doctorates their graduate schools would confer in 1975-76. This year was selected because students who will earn their degrees in that academic year must be currently enrolled or readily identifiable in doctorate programs." Results of this most recent survey of individual deans revealed only a 5% increase in doctorates above the reported production in 1969-70. This assessment provides information quite contrary to a popular concept of uninhibited growth and expansion of graduate programs. The phenomenon of supply and demand in a free enterprise system may already have initiated a "steady-state" condition.

The literature on the subject of doctoral degree holders vis-à-vis employment opportunities documents very clearly that traditional career opportunities (teaching and research) will not accommodate the number of new doctorates expected to be graduated. The fact is that all graduate fields surveyed by an NSF study (1971) reported increasing difficulties between 1968 and 1970 in placing new Ph.D.'s in suitable fields. But it needs to be emphasized that these observations are made on the basis of traditional employment expectations.

As an example, I heard a story from the director of research from a major chemical manufacturing company that went something like this: A recent Ph.D. was interviewed for a position in their laboratories. He possessed extremely attractive academic credentials and was offered the position of research chemist. In the process of discussing the position, he was asked to identify his research interests; he indicated that he desired to study the active site of the enzyme chymotrypsin—an extension of his doctoral dissertation. When told that the position being offered would engage him in other areas of research, he declined the position! An exaggerated example, perhaps, but it does surface some of the "built-in" incompatibilities—namely, attitudes in some graduate education programs that contribute to false expectations.

National Science Policy

It is clearly evident that the national science policy now emerging places heavy emphasis on the coupling of science and social concerns. On March 16, 1972, the President of the United States sent a message to Congress on science and technology; this was the first Presidential message on science and technology in the nation's history. After reference to past achievements by researchers and engineers, the President went on to say: ". . . I am, therefore, calling today for a strong new effort to marshall science and technology in the work of strengthening our economy and improving the quality of our life. And I am outlining ways in which the Federal Government can work as a more effective partner in this great task."

The former Director of the National Science Foundation, Dr. W. D. McElroy, just prior to assuming the position of Chancellor of the University of California at San Diego, stated in an editorial in *Science:*

> Historically, the National Science Foundation has devoted a large proportion of its resources to the pursuit of disciplinary science—research and science education motivated solely by the intrinsic needs of a discipline or the creative needs of individual scientists. This kind of programming has been highly successful and must continue, for it is the bedrock of all scientific enterprise. However, there must also be a heightened awareness of the requirements placed on all science, and for this reason a significant share of the total resources available to NSF in the future must be devoted to the social and technological needs of the nation.

> And he continued: The social milieu within which the NSF finds itself has changed so markedly and so rapidly that we must not fail to accept the challenges offered by these new and pressing opportunities. We should recognize that, although science is one of the great cultural accomplishments of man, public support on the scale required for man's survival can be justified only as the needs of the larger society are recognized. (McElroy, 1972.)

Not only our nation, but the whole world, has been alerted to environmental phenomena that must be brought under control to maintain, let alone improve, our quality of living. Major voids in our knowledge need to be closed. We need to have a much better understanding of many biological phenomena, such as: interactions among organisms and particularly microorganisms in various natural habitats; the impact of thermal pollution on a given ecology; availability of biological agents for use as pesticides and insecticides; the selective action of plant fertilizers as plant nutrients but not pollutants. These and a myriad collection of other problems must be dealt with. Many require that new fundamental knowledge be discovered before they can be resolved. Others require a translation of the academic information into a new sophisticated technology. Most, if not all, of these problems require the talents of many disciplines, e.g., the biologist, the chemist, the engineer. These are problems of national and global dimensions. It is of more than passing interest to note that the world's first comprehensive attempt to respond to global environmental conditions will be held in Stockholm, Sweden, on June 5, 1972, when the United Nations will convene a Conference on the Human Environment. Coincident with this development, there should be a major, long-range, coherent national educational program that would promote the development of the necessary talent and skills required for the job. Biology programs need to be re-structured to provide options that will educate graduates for careers at a new high level of environmental science. But there needs to be a commitment at the national level to encourage the development of significant innovations by way of educational experiences and opportunities.

Program Options

RESEARCH, TEACHING, AND PRACTITIONER DEGREE PROGRAMS

Graduate education has experienced very little innovation since its inception. Graduate programs, particularly at the doctoral level, have adhered rather rigidly to traditional format. They have grown in size, and we have developed a capacity to educate large numbers of graduate students in essentially the same mold. The times call for the development of new thrusts in our programs, a reorientation of some graduate study away from "pure science" in specific disciplines toward studies germane to societal affairs. At the same time we will need to "strip away much of the snobbery about pure research untainted by mundane practical applications."

Our graduate schools will need to educate not only individuals with the competency to work on the problems referred to earlier but will also need to impart an attitude to the graduate student population that a career in applied science, i.e., a practitioner of the discipline, is an intellectually satisfying and rewarding occupation and that this kind of employment has stature equal to that of teaching or the pursuit of basic research. Many of the societal problems, all of which are intimately associated with biological phenomena, are intellectually demanding and require a degree of creativity which rivals that required for research. Our need for exceptionally qualified graduates to devote their careers to

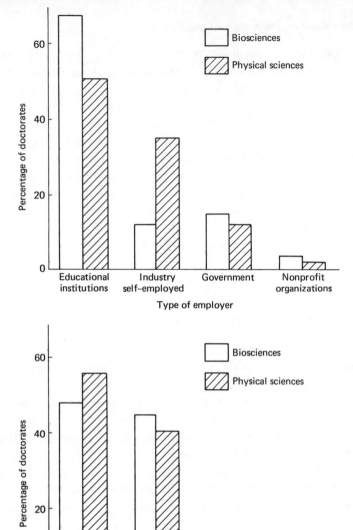

FIGURE 1. Type of employer and type or primary work activity for employed doctorate bioscientists and physical scientists in 1968 National Register of Scientific and Technical Personnel. From "Education and Employment Patterns of Bioscientists, a Statistical Report," Office of Scientific Personnel of National Research Council under the sponsorship of The National Institute of General Medical Sciences, National Institutes of Health, 1971.

this type of professional occupation is likely to increase beyond present expectations. Indeed, within this decade, we may experience a shortage of persons educated to the doctoral level who are needed to translate the highest level of scientific achievement to technological implementation and to public understanding and acceptability. It is, therefore, a matter of urgent business that graduate schools provide options beyond the traditional teaching and research goals. Much of this could be achieved if graduate faculties promoted higher regard for careers as practitioners of science and technology—a regard *no less* than that associated with a career in teaching or research. Equal prestige and reward must be associated with all of these options. Parity among these options will provide a much better match between the graduate student's talents and expectations and the present and potential needs of employers and society.

The pattern of employment for doctorate scientists which we have experienced in the past is shown in Figure 1. These data illustrate that bioscientists, in comparison to physical scientists, are more likely to be employed by educational institutions; a larger percentage of physical scientists are employed by industry. There is little difference between the two groups in terms of their primary work activity—approximately one-half are engaged in research and development, and roughly one-half are employed as teachers.

A significant fact to observe from these data is that, of the graduates from a program which places emphasis on research (the Ph.D. program), approximately one-half are engaged in teaching. In addition, a very high percentage of Ph.D. holders do not pursue a significant research enterprise beyond their doctoral dissertation. Among the many specific criticisms made of the Ph.D. program is that, while it "professes to educate for research, in reality it trains for it." Students become "armed with approved methods, skills, and techniques"; they are not prepared to think innovatively, holistically, and intellectually in the broad meaning of these terms.

New Degree Programs vs. Multiple Options Within the Ph.D.

Recommendations for improvement of graduate education stress the need for more diversity and options within programs. This criticism is, of course, directed at the major emphasis placed on research in the Ph.D. degree which is, indeed, recognized as a research degree. Should we introduce new programs at the doctoral level which would prepare the student for a career other than research? Or, is it to be assumed that a graduate program built around a research program is the best preparation for any and all careers? There are, of course, professional doctoral degrees such as the D.S.W. (Doctor of Social Work), the D.B.A. (Doctor of Business Administration), the D.M.A. (Doctor of Musical Arts), and the D. Engr. (Doctor of Engineering). More recently, the D.A. (Doctor of Arts) was introduced to provide a program equally as demanding as the Ph.D. but with an emphasis on preparing the student for a profession of teaching. This degree program has been endorsed by the Council of Graduate Schools in the United States. However, it has not been adopted by a large number of doctoral degree granting institutions; a variety of reservations are shared by many graduate deans.

A more acceptable plan might be to re-define the purpose of the Ph.D. degree program to include other components in addition to *research,* namely, *scholarly teaching* and implementation of new knowledge at the highest level, i.e., a *practitioner* of the discipline. Each of these three options within the Ph.D. would need to be of the same order of academic quality; each needs to be equally demanding in terms of expectations of student performance; each must be equally prestigious. This is not a new idea; it has been talked about before. However, it needs to be surfaced again and given serious consideration as a reasonable response to our present dilemma. This approach offers a means whereby graduate schools could meet many criticisms and implement suggested recommendations for change with very minimal administrative effort.

Non-degree Graduate Education—Continuing Education

Graduate schools have exhibited a passive attitude in the area of non-degree, continuing education needs at the graduate level. In an era of knowledge-explosion, coupled with the fact that the half-life of information grows progressively shorter, the need for more frequent and intermittent up-grading in academic subjects is self-evident. One of the big problems in graduate education is that a clear distinction has not been developed between *graduate program (degree) education* and *post-baccalaureate (non-degree) education.* The tendency exists to consider everything in terms of conventional degree programs. Attention needs to be directed toward developing "packages" of information which can be offered in various ways, other than conventional semester course sequences (e.g., workshops, seminars, and conferences) in a time frame necessary to convey this information. Concomitantly, an acceptable system of acknowledging satisfactory achievement in such offerings needs to be formulated by the academic community, and this system needs to be honored by employing agencies.

Student Attitudes

A few months ago, the American Council on Education, in connection with its Continuing Institutional Research Program and in cooperation with the Carnegie Commission on Higher Education, published the report entitled: "The American Graduate Student: A Normative Description." The survey included responses from a sample of 33,119 graduate students from 153 institutions. The questionnaire used in this survey was designed to provide information about the students' attitudes, perception, and evaluation of a host of academic, social, and political matters. It may be of interest to note that replies to several statements in the questionnaire reflect, in part, students' attitudes to programs.

Listed below are a few examples:

"The doctorate is mainly a 'union card,' enabling one to get the job he wants."

Response:

Strongly agree	17.0%
Agree with reservations	36.0%
Disagree with reservations	31.0%
Strongly disagree	16.1%

"In graduate school to serve mankind better."

Response:

Strongly agree	32.2%
Agree with reservations	43.5%
Disagree with reservations	14.5%
Strongly disagree	9.8%

"In graduate school to contribute to ability to change society."

Response:

Strongly agree	21.1%
Agree with reservations	38.6%
Disagree with reservations	20.8%
Strongly disagree	19.4%

"In graduate school to increase earning power."
Response:

Strongly agree	41.5%
Agree with reservations	39.9%
Disagree with reservations	9.3%
Strongly disagree	9.3%

There are those who argue that if, as a nation, our priorities were re-ordered and we devoted our resources and talents to improve the quality of life for mankind, his personal well-being, and his physical environment, we would indeed create a large demand for more highly educated and trained talent.

Public pressures and public expectations for assistance from those who have benefited from our highest level of education are likely to increase. A new order of demands is likely to be addressed to scientists and technologists to provide solutions to social-engineering problems such as a viable plan for urban development; a clean, rapid transportation system; control of pollution; elimination of poverty; improved health care delivery; and acceptable developments in gene therapy. This will require attacking problems that are intricately more complex and sensitive than those dramatic accomplishments we have witnessed in the physical sciences. These are problems that are intertwined with the life styles of people, their behavioral patterns, and their expectations and ambitions. There is need for more fundamental knowledge; there is need to develop ways of implementing the new as well as the already extant sophisticated technology.

A high level of educated man and woman power is required for engagement with these topics—all of which demand multi-disciplinary collaboration. Indeed, it is precisely in such areas of investigation that we need more, better prepared, and more appropriately educated graduates. We need specialists, but we also need generalists. We need researchers and teachers, but we also need practitioners—practitioners educated to the point that enables them to translate the highest level of academic knowledge into applicable technology. Certainly one could not conclude, at least at this point in time, that our intellectual capacity and capability is "in surplus" of the needs required to resolve societal problems.

References

Carnegie Commission on Higher Education. 1971. *Less Time, More Options.* McGraw-Hill Book Company, New York.

Cartter, A. M. 1966. An assessment of quality in graduate education. American Council on Education.

———. 1971. Scientific manpower for 1970-1985. *Science,* **172**: 132-140.

Craeger, J. A. October, 1971. The American graduate student: A normative description. American Council on Education, Research Reports. Vol. 6, No. 5. 190 p.

Federal Interagency Committee on Education, Department of Health, Education, and Welfare. April, 1971. Report on Federal Predoctoral Student Support, Part II, Students Supported Under Training Grants of the National Institutes of Health and the National Institute of Mental Health.

Heiss, A. F. 1970. *Challenges to Graduate Schools.* Jossey-Bass, Inc., San Francisco.

Huther, J. W. 1972. Small market for Ph.D.'s, the public two-year college. *AAUP Bulletin,* **58**: 17-20.

McElroy, W. D. 1972. NSF: A look ahead. *Science,* **175**: 361.

Office of Scientific Personnel, National Research Council. February, 1971. Education and employment patterns of bioscientists. 18 p.

Roose, K. D. and C. J. Anderson. 1970. A rating of graduate programs. American Council on Education. 115 p.

Surveys of Science Resources Series, National Science Foundation. NSF 71-27. July, 1971. Graduate student support and manpower resources in graduate science education. 105 p.

Whaley, W. G. 1971. In these times—A look at graduate education with proposals for the future. The Graduate Journal, Vol. 8, No. 2. 488 p.

Wolfle, D. and C. V. Kidd. 1971. The future market for Ph.D.'s. *Science,* **173**: 784-793.

Student Chapters

22 A Tree Survey of the South Slope of Brushy Mountain at Carvins Cove Area, Virginia

MIKE SLAUGHTER
LANCE HUNT
SOPHOMORES
Virginia Western Community College

History

The area surveyed is located in the Carvins Cove Reservoir area, owned by the Water Department of the City of Roanoke. In the early thirties, a government representative of the Civilian Conservation Corps received permission from the Water Department to build a fire trail across the top of Brushy Mountain. The forest ranger that supervised the construction of the trail confirmed the fact that all the forest on the mountain was second growth. There was absolutely no original timber on Brushy Mountain. Knowledge of the area since 1923 assures the authors that this land has not been cut over since that time.

Location and Description of the Area

For this tree survey, an area was chosen at the southwestern tip of the Carvins Cove Reservoir on the southeastern slope of Brushy Mountain. The location is accessible from Salem by traveling north on State Route 419 and turning right on County Road 1404 five-tenths of a mile from the entrance ramp of Interstate 81. The transect begins at a point on this road two and six-tenths miles from its entrance. Its beginning point is approximately 1,240 feet above sea level. It runs sixty degrees northwest to the fire trail across Brushy Mountain. It ends at approximately 2,180 feet above sea level. Each end of the transect is marked with orange tape.

On the topography map (Roanoke Quadrangle, 7.5 Minute Series, U.S. Geological Survey, Rev. Ed. 1968), the area is in the northwest corner. County Road 1404 is the restricted road running from the tip of the reservoir along Horse Pen Branch. The transect runs from the letter "d" in the word "restricted" to the fire trail, also labeled "restricted" on the map.

In general, the transect is on the south-southeastern slope where there are intermittent small ravines and ridges. The ravines and slopes are often quite steep, and the presence of shale in the soil makes possible many xeric habitats in the area studied.

Purpose

The purpose of this survey was to determine certain facts about the forest of the area. For example: What species are dominant in the area now? What species will be dominant in the future? Also, on completion of the project, we hoped to be able to see indications of successional stages as the forest moves toward the climax stage. Since there was selective cutting in the area, it is impossible to determine which were the pioneer trees.

Herein we have attempted to answer these and other questions by analyzing the data gathered in our study of the area.

Method of Study

The method of study used, called the quarter method (Phillips, 1959), is very similar to that used by original Federal surveyors. Sampling points are set up at equal distances along a pre-determined compass line through the study area. These points were at 25-yard intervals for this project. Each point is considered the center of four quarters. The quarters are designated I, II, III, and IV, moving clockwise from the left forward quarter. From each quarter, the tree closest to the center point is chosen (Fig. 1). Only those trees at or above 4 inches d.b.h. (diameter at breast height) are considered. Each tree is identified and recorded. For each tree, the distance to the center point and actual d.b.h. are recorded.

The trees surveyed were divided into five categories according to size:

1) 4.0 to 6.0 inches d.b.h.   4) 10.1 to 12.0 inches d.b.h.
2) 6.1 to 8.0 inches d.b.h.   5) 12.1 plus inches d.b.h.
3) 8.1 to 10.0 inches d.b.h.

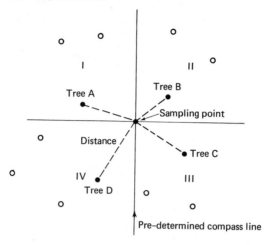

FIGURE 1. The symbols I, II, III, and IV indicate the four successive quarters. A, B, C, and D are the nearest trees to the sampling point in each quarter. (Nearest trees—black circles; other trees—open circles.) The distance between each tree and the sampling point is recorded. (Phillips, 1959)

The following information was determined in each size category for each species studied:

1) Relative density—the proportion of the density of a species to that of the stand as a whole.
2) Relative dominance—the proportion of the basal area of a species to that of the stand as a whole.
3) Relative frequency—the proportion of the frequency of a species to the frequency of all species in the stand. (Frequency may be calculated by dividing the total number of points in which a species occurs by the total number of points sampled.)

The above information was calculated by means of the following formulas:

Relative density $\dfrac{\text{Number individuals of the species}}{\text{Number individuals of all species}} \times 100$

Relative dominance $\dfrac{\text{Total basal area of the species} \times 100}{\text{Total basal area of all species}}$

Relative frequency $\dfrac{\text{Number of points of occurrence of the species}}{\text{Number of points of occurrence of all species}} \times 100$

The relative density, relative dominance, and relative frequency were then totaled for each size category for each species to obtain the Importance Value Index (IVI).

TABLE I. *Relative Values for a Tree Survey of the South Slope of Brushy*

| | Relative Frequency, Relative Dominance, | | | | | | | |
| | 4.0–6.0 | | | | 6.1–8.0 | | | |
	Rel. Freq.	Rel. Dom.	Rel. Den.	IVI	Rel. Freq.	Rel. Dom.	Rel. Den.	IVI
Quercus coccinea	19.4	20.6	20.5	60.5	22.2	25.1	24.6	71.9
Quercus prinus	17.3	20.0	18.9	56.2	31.5	32.1	32.8	96.4
Pinus rigida	55.1	7.8	7.9	20.8	9.3	9.7	9.8	28.8
Quercus velutina	10.2	10.3	9.4	29.9	9.2	8.1	8.2	25.5
Pinus virginiana	3.1	3.1	3.1	9.3	11.1	10.5	9.8	31.4
Quercus marilandica	13.3	11.7	13.4	38.4	33.7	2.7	3.3	9.7
Quercus borealis	8.2	9.4	8.6	26.2	3.7	3.3	3.3	10.3
Oxydendron arboreum	10.2	8.1	8.6	26.9	1.9	1.4	1.6	4.9
Quercus alba	3.1	1.9	2.4	7.4	7.4	7.1	6.6	21.1
Carya glabra	4.1	2.5	2.4	9.0				
Amelanchier arborea	2.0	1.7	1.6	5.3				
Acer rubrum	2.0	1.2	1.6	4.8				
Quercus ilicifolia	2.0	1.7	1.6	5.3				
TOTAL	100	100	100	300	100	100	100	300

The mean distance, average distance from the sampling points of all trees surveyed, was determined for the entire group. This was calculated by dividing the sum of all distances by the total number of distances taken. (14.32 ft).

The identification of the species follows that of Petride's *A Field Guide to Trees and Shrubs* with references to other taxonomy books listed in the bibliography. Voucher specimens have been deposited in the herbarium at Virginia Western Community College.

Analysis of Data

Quercus coccinea and *Quercus prinus* are the most important species of this forest, usually ranking first or second in the IVI column in all size categories (Table I). Also, in the totals (Tables II & III), *Q. coccinea* was the most numerous while *Q. prinus* had the highest total basal area. The other 11 species were considerably below *Q. coccinea* and *Q. prinus* in both characteristics. Both of these species are not only the current dominants but also seem destined to continue to be since they are reproducing (Table I).

Mountain at Carvins Cove Area, Virginia.

Relative Density, and Importance Value Index for each size category.

8.1–10.0				10.1–12.0				12.1+			
Rel. Freq.	Rel. Dom.	Rel. Den.	IVI	Rel. Freq.	Rel. Dom.	Rel. Den.	IVI	Rel. Freq.	Rel. Dom.	Rel. Den.	IVI
37.2	41.1	42.2	120.5	43.5	44.8	43.5	131.8	11.8	8.2	10.0	30.0
23.3	22.0	20.0	65.3	21.7	20.9	21.7	64.3	29.4	30.3	30.0	89.7
9.3	8.6	8.9	26.8					29.4	34.3	35.0	98.7
7.0	6.5	6.7	20.2	8.7	9.7	8.7	27.1	5.8	4.0	5.0	14.8
13.9	13.4	13.3	40.6	17.4	16.5	17.4	51.3	11.8	8.9	10.0	30.7
7.0	6.5	6.7	20.2	8.7	8.1	8.7	25.5				
								11.8	14.3	10.0	36.1
2.3	1.9	2.2	6.4								
100	100	100	300	100	100	100	300	100	100	100	300

Pinus rigida and *Pinus virginiana* usually rank third and fourth in the IVI column in most of the size categories. *P. rigida* has the highest IVI of all species in the 12.1^+ d.b.h. category. The presence of these species and their location—xeric ridges and South-facing slopes—goes along quite well with Whittaker's findings (1956. map, p. 77). The IVI of both species decreases as the size categories become smaller, indication that both are having difficulty reproducing. This is to be expected as both are to a degree shade intolerant. These species will probably become less important components of the future forest since their reproduction is limited.

Quercus velutina and *Quercus borealis* would probably rank fifth and sixth in importance as shown by their IVI's (Table I). Both of these species are reproducing, as indicated in the IVI's of the smaller size categories. However, it is not expected that either of these will become dominants in this forest. The *Q. borealis* tends to be located at higher elevations, and *Q. velutina* does not dominate in any specific habitat (Whittaker, 1956. map, p. 79). Therefore, these will probably remain important as secondary species.

Quercus marilandica, Quercus alba, and *Carya glabra* do give indica-

TABLE II. *Numerical Breakdown of Identified Species.*

1.	*Q. coccinea*	72
2.	*Q. prinus*	64
3.	*P. rigida*	27
4.	*Q. velutina*	23
5.	*P. virginiana*	22
6.	*Q. marilandica*	19
7.	*Q. borealis*	18
8.	*O. arboreum*	12
9.	*Q. alba*	9
10.	*C. glabra*	4
11.	*Am. arborea*	2
12.	*A. rubrum*	2
13.	*Q. ilicifolia*	2
	TOTAL	276

TABLE III. *Total Basal Area of Individual Species.*

1.	*Q. coccinea*	3206.01 sq ft
2.	*Q. prinus*	3300.38
3.	*P. rigida*	1770.90
4.	*Q. velutina*	895.40
5.	*P. virginiana*	1340.14
6.	*Q. marilandica*	352.76
7.	*Q. borealis*	666.20
8.	*O. arboreum*	230.54
9.	*Q. alba*	676.85
10.	*C. glabra*	113.31
11.	*Am. arborea*	42.53
12.	*A. rubrum*	29.92
13.	*Q. ilicifolia*	42.48

tions of some reproduction. However, since these tend to be found in xeric habitats; e.g., ridges, shady South slopes, and sheltered ravines, it is doubtful that the IVI of these species will increase much in this forest. Also, the shade intolerance factor could be important in limiting these species.

Acer rubrum does not give any indication of becoming more important (Table I). However, according to Whittaker (1956. map. p. 70), it can be expected that this species will become more important, especially in the coves and lower elevations as the forest progresses toward the climax stage.

The other species, *Oxydendron arboreum, Amelanchier arborea,* and *Quercus ilicifolia* are all understory trees and will not become important components of the canopy. They are reproducing and will remain important understory species along with the *Cornus florida* and *Hamamelis virginiana.*

As for the future of this forest, our data indicate that *Q. coccinea* and *Q. prinus* will continue to be the most important and may increase their dominance. The two pine species will probably become less important, except in selected habitats where they will hold their own.

Acknowledgements

The authors wish to express their appreciation to the following persons for their assistance in this project: Mr. Richard Crites and Mr. Ronald

Sower of the Biology Department of Virginia Western Community College; Mr. Kit B. Kiser, Supervisor of the Roanoke City Water Department; Mr. Charles Moore, retired Supervisor of the Roanoke City Water Department.

References

Archbald, D. 1958. *Quick Key Guide to Trees: Northeastern And Central North America.* Doubleday, New York.

Collingwood, G. H. and W. D. Brush. 1964. *Knowing Your Trees.* The American Forestry Association. Washington.

Curtis, C. C. and S. C. Bausor. 1963. *The Complete Guide to North American Trees.* Collier Books, New York.

Mazzeo, P. M. 1967. *Trees of Shenandoah National Park in the Blue Ridge Mountains of Virginia.* Virginia: the Shenandoah Natural History Association. Luray, Virginia.

Petrides, G. A. 1958. *A Field Guide to Trees and Shrubs.* Houghton-Mifflin Co., Boston.

Phillips, E. A. 1959. *Methods of Vegetation Study.* Holt, Rinehart, & Winston, New York.

Smith, R. L. 1966. *Ecology and Field Biology.* Harper and Row, New York.

Whittaker, R. H. 1956. Vegetation of the Great Smoky Mountains. *Ecol. Monogr.,* **26**: 1-81.

23 Seed Dispersal Methods in Hawaiian "Metrosideros"

CAROLYN A. CORN
GRADUATE STUDENT
University of Hawaii

Long distance dispersal has been discussed by Guppy (1906) and Ridley (1930). Birds have been described as hypothetical and active agents in transporting seeds over long distances by such authors as Cruden (1966) and deVlaming and Proctor (1968); wind as an active agent of long distance dispersal has been illustrated in insects by Yoshimoto and Gressitt (1961); and water dispersal and rafting have been reported by Powers (1911) and Zimmerman (1948).

The Hawaiian flora and fauna are living proof that long distance dispersal is effective. Since the Hawaiian Islands are oceanic islands built in the last 20 million years by volcanism (Macdonald and Abbott, 1970) and isolated from other land masses by wind and water currents (Gressitt, 1961; Visher, 1925) by distances of 2000 miles or more (except for Johnston Island, a small atoll some 600 miles to the southwest), plants and animals found on the islands must have ancestors that survived the long trip to the islands. The biota of these islands is considered to be most remarkable in terms of long-distance dispersal. Carlquist (1965, 1966a, 1966b, 1966c, 1967a, 1967b, 1970), Fosberg (1963), and Zim-

This work was supported in part by the National Aeronautics and Space Administration grant NGL 12-001-042 and National Science Foundation grant GB 23230.

merman (1948) have indicated actual and hypothetical methods of dispersal for some of the native Hawaiian plants and animals. However, little experimental work has been done on seeds of native plants to see if they can survive transport by air, water, or bird.

Metrosideros seeds are numerous and small, but no data has been published on the wind velocities necessary to disperse the seeds. Guppy (1906) did try to float the seeds in sea water but reported that they sank within a few days. A series of experiments were undertaken to determine the potential dispersal mechanisms which could have been involved.

Hawaiian *Metrosideros* seed material is variable in size, shape, color, and weight. The small seeds may be straight, slightly curved, or curved as much as 90 degrees, with the widest portion at the middle or curved part of the seed (Fig. 1). Upon cursory examination of the anatomical seed characteristics, the author believes that the Hawaiian seed material is similar to *Metrosideros* from New Zealand described by Dawson (1970). The embryo is surrounded by a seed coat of no more than a few cells in thickness; the outermost layer is lignified. Young mature seeds appear to be almost translucent, and seeds that have been stored become darker in color.

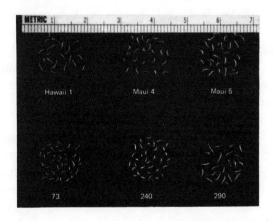

FIGURE 1. Variation of Hawaiian *Metrosideros* seed from Hawaii, Maui, and Oahu.

The genus is not only highly variable in seed characteristics but also in vegetative and flotal characters. This places the taxonomist in a difficult position. Rock (1917) described the genus as having five species —*M. tremuloides, M. Waialealae, M. rugosa, M. macropus,* and *M. collina.* The first four species are in small areas on the oldest islands of Kauai and Oahu, with the fifth species, *M. collina* subspecies *polymorpha,* occurring throughout all the main islands. He further divided this widespread subspecies into 15 varieties and forms. All of the seed material used in this study are from trees that would be classified according to Rock (1917) as this subspecies. It occurs from sea level to almost 8,300 feet elevation in areas with annual average rainfall ranging from 30 to 450 inches. Where *Metrosideros* colonizes open lava fields, it occurs as a small tree or shrub; in wet fern forests it occurs as a tree 50 feet or more tall; and in bogs it occurs as a prostrate shrub blooming when only a few centimeters tall. It is the most common tree of the native forests.

Methods and Results

Experiment 1.

Seeds from various elevations and diverse tree varieties were gathered from the islands of Kauai, Oahu, Maui, and Hawaii. Those seed samples that exhibited the largest diversity in size, shape, and weight were used in this experiment to obtain seed measurements of maximum variability. Each seed sample was composed of 200 seeds from a single tree. These samples were weighed, and lengths and diameters measured before they were subjected to wind velocity experimentation. Seed weight was measured by weighing the 200 seed sample, then dividing by 200 to obtain the average individual seed weight.

Wind velocity measurements were obtained by placing the seed sample on the lower cheesecloth of an air-blast seed separator machine (Fig. 2), placing a glass tubing over it, starting the motor, increasing the wind velocity from 0 to 15 miles per hour, and recording when the first and last seeds of the sample were lifted into the upper part of the machine. The midpoint between the maximum and minimum wind velocity readings was obtained for each sample.

When the velocity of the wind upward was equal to the gravitational

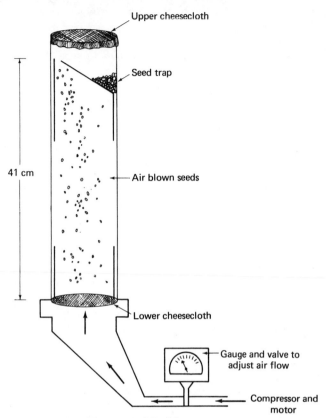

FIGURE 2. Air-blast Seed Separator Machine.

force pulling downward upon the seeds, the seeds remained suspended in mid-air. This flow rate was between 3.5 and 11.5 miles per hour, and at this wind velocity the seeds could be suspended indefinitely in air. This technique bypassed the necessity to compute theoretically the seed's surface area and mass to derive its floatability.

The 25 samples of seed show a range of seed size and weight. Individual seeds varied as much as .5 to 4.5 mm in length and .1 to .7 mm in width. However, the average length and width values computed for each 200 seed sample has less variation with the median of seed length between 1.0 and 3.0 mm and width between .1 and .5 mm. Table I gives these average values with standard deviations. The average individual seed weights of the 25 samples ranged from 0.0400 to 0.1367 mg. with the median weight of all samples 0.0697 mg.

TABLE I. *Seed Sources, Sizes, and Wind Velocities Necessary to Negate Gravitational Force.*

Sample No.	Locality	Elevation (ft)	Seed length (mm)	Seed width (mm)	Seed weight (mg)	Wind velocity to suspend seeds (mi/hr)		
						Minimum	Maximum	Median
H-1	Hawaii: Volcano House	4100	2.71±.54	.23±.05	.0530	3.5	9.5	6.5
H-2	Hawaii: Puu Huluhulu	3200	2.60±.51	.25±.06	.0705	4.5	11.5	8.0
H-3	Hawaii: Waldron Ridge	3800	2.21±.64	.24±.05	.0500	3.5	9.5	6.5
H-4	Hawaii: Halemaumau	3700	2.16±.42	.22±.04	.0400	3.5	9.5	6.5
M-4	Maui: Waikomoi Lower Pipeline Trail	3000	1.84±.32	.39±.09	.0895	3.5	11.5	7.5
M-5	Maui: Fleming Mt. House West Maui	2980	2.26±.47	.32±.07	.0535	3.5	10.5	7.0
K-289	Kauai: Kokee	3300	1.90±.44	.23±.08	.0715	5.5	11.0	8.5
73	Oahu: Kipapa Trail	2500	1.64±.42	.19±.06	.0320	4.5	10.5	7.5
78	Oahu: Kipapa Trail	2500	1.74±.37	.22±.07	.0430	3.5	10.5	7.0
211	Oahu: Palikea	2500	1.72±.31	.24±.05	.0450	4.5	9.5	7.0
214	Oahu: Palikea	2600	1.66±.35	.36±.09	.1367	3.5	11.5	7.5
215	Oahu: Palikea	2700	1.65±.39	.36±.10	.0850	6.5	11.5	9.0
216	Oahu: Palikea	2800	2.06±.56	.43±.09	.1340	3.5	11.5	7.5
224	Oahu: Palikea	2600	1.49±.41	.25±.07	.0555	5.5	10.0	8.0
225	Oahu: Palikea	2800	1.91±.45	.34±.10	.0735	5.5	10.5	8.0
239	Oahu: Palikea	2600	1.70±.34	.23±.06	.0500	3.5	10.0	7.5
240	Oahu: Palikea	2600	1.72±.32	.30±.06	.0610	4.5	10.5	7.5
263	Oahu: Laie Trail	1000	1.88±.57	.39±.08	.1090	3.5	11.5	7.5
268	Oahu: Laie Trail	1125	2.12±.36	.26±.06	.0525	5.5	10.5	8.0
273	Oahu: Laie Trail	1350	1.49±.23	.36±.07	.0640	5.5	10.5	8.0
275	Oahu: Laie Trail	1350	1.84±.36	.41±.07	.0785	5.5	10.0	8.0
279	Oahu: Laie Trail	1400	1.58±.47	.30±.07	.0505	5.5	10.0	8.0
280	Oahu: Laie Trail	—	2.62±.52	.20±.07	.0500	5.5	10.0	8.0
287	Oahu: Palikea	2600	2.17±.47	.36±.09	.1315	5.5	10.5	8.5
290	Oahu: University of Hawaii	250	2.77±.57	.22±.06	.0625	5.5	10.0	8.0

Experiment 2.

This experiment was initiated to demonstrate whether the seeds could withstand the freezing temperatures of the upper atmosphere. A seed sample from a tree at Halemaumau on the island of Hawaii was chosen since it had good viability (8 to 12%). The seeds were separated into samples of approximately 200 each and placed at 25°C (room temperature), 2°C (refrigerator), −22°C (freezer), −33°C (freezer), and −192°C (liquid nitrogen). At the end of 1½ hours, one half of each sample was removed, and at 6 hours the rest were removed, allowed to thaw at room temperature, placed on moist paper in petri dishes and watered.

Figure 3 graphs the results of the experiment. The seeds can survive these freezing temperatures without causing damage to the seed embryo, with the −30°C temperature comparable to temperatures found in the jet stream and upper air masses.

Experiment 3.

This experiment demonstrated the seed's ability to be dispersed in fresh and salt water. Six seed samples from Oahu (4 samples from 600 feet and 2 samples from 2600 feet) were used to determine tolerances

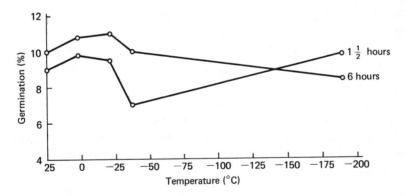

FIGURE 3. Germination of seeds after subjection to low temperatures.

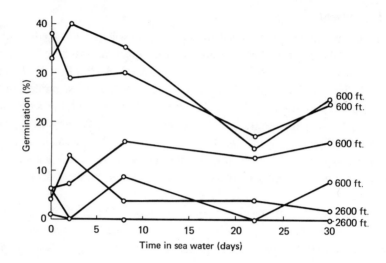

FIGURE 4. Seed germination after soaking in sea water. Numbers on the right hand side of figure refer to the elevation in feet at which the seeds were collected.

to salt water. Twelve 800 ml plastic containers were used, of which 6 containers had 400 ml each of fresh water and 6 containers had 400 ml each of salt water. Salt water of 32 °/00 salinity was collected from the reef outside Kewalo Basin, Oahu. Approximately 1,000 seeds were placed in each container, and the containers were covered and agitated several times a week. Between 50 and 100 seeds were removed after 2, 8, 22, and 30 days from the salt water, placed in petri dishes and watered.

Those seeds placed in fresh water germinated in 4 to 6 days, with seeds and seedlings remaining on the surface or below the surface of the water. In contrast, those seeds placed in salt water did not germinate. However, when the seeds in salt water were removed and given fresh water, they germinated as well as their controls.

Approximately one half of the seeds placed in salt water remained suspended on the surface of the salt water, in spite of agitation. (Surface tension may be an important factor in their ability to float, although trapped air inside the seed may also contribute to their ability to remain buoyant.) Both the seeds that floated and those that sank germinated after 30 days, although a higher percentage of germination was recorded

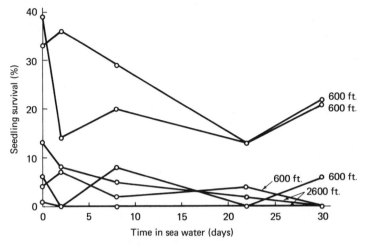

FIGURE 5. Survival one month after germination from seeds soaked in sea water. Numbers on the right hand side of figure refer to the elevation in feet at which the seeds were collected.

in the floating seeds. Figure 4 illustrates graphically that the seeds can germinate after being in salt water for at least 30 days.

Figure 5 records the amount of seedling survival from seeds left in the salt water for varying lengths of time. These figures were obtained one month after seed germination. It is interesting to note that the two samples from 2,600 feet elevation have no seedling survival while the seeds from 600 feet elevation are still healthy. There may be two explanations for these differences. There may be an actual difference in the ability of the two sets of seed to produce viable seedlings after a month of sea water emersion. However, the two samples from 2,600 feet elevation were from low germinating seed samples and are too small a sample for extrapolation to actual field populations. Further seed from other trees at 2,600 feet elevation should be tested in the same manner to see if there is actually a trend toward loss (or absence) of dispersibility of upland populations after prolonged seed soakings in sea water.

A second explanation of the data would be that further sampling would provide germinating seedlings after 1 month in sea water for those seeds from 2,600 feet elevation. What can be seen in Figure 5 is a decrease of seedling survival with time in sea water. Most of the 6 seed samples in Figures 4 and 5 showed less germination and viability after

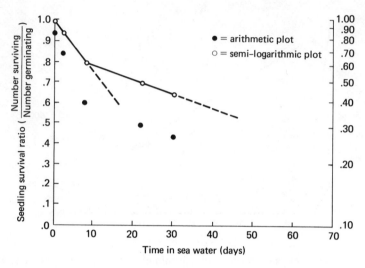

FIGURE 6. Arithmetic and semi-logarithmic plot of the seedling survival ratio after seeds were soaked for 0, 2, 8, 22, and 30 days in sea water.

30 days of sea water exposure. If the number of seedlings surviving (Fig. 5) is divided by the number of seeds that germinated (Fig. 4), an index for seedling survival can be obtained as follows:

$$\text{seedling survival index} = \frac{\text{Number of seedlings surviving after 30 days}}{\text{Number of seeds that germinated}}$$

If these data are plotted on graph paper (Fig. 6) with time along the x-axis and the seedling survival index as the y-axis, a series of points is obtained. These may be interpreted as a curve; however, if these same data are presented on a semi-logarithmic scale, the points, although approaching a straight line, fit better as two straight lines. It may be possible that several factors may be influencing their survival rate.

It is interesting to note that if one projects the maximum line drawn in Figure 6, the point where it crosses the x-axis is approximately 130 days, which is less than half the survival time of these same seeds in air when they are stored in containers at 25°C and 60% humidity. Although the test was terminated after 30 days, this decrease in seedling. viability with increased exposure of the seeds to sea water indicates that the seeds could not withstand prolonged sea-water emersion for more than a few months in duration. This would exclude sea water dispersal over long distances, but such dispersal would be plausible for short distances; for example, between islands of the same island chain.

Experiment 4.

This experiment was planned to see if the seeds that remained in salt water for a month could be desiccated for a period of time and still germinate. The seed sample with the highest germination (15 to 40%) from Experiment 3 was used in this experiment. About 400 seeds that had been soaking in salt water for 30 days were removed and placed in 4 open petri dishes. The dishes with about 100 seeds apiece were allowed to dry at room temperature and humidity for 6 hours, 1, 4, and 7 days before water was added. These "mighty midgets" survived a drying period up to 7 days at room humidity and 25°C temperature (Fig. 7).

Bird transportation of the seeds to the Hawaiian Islands seems highly unlikely. The fruit is a dry brownish capsule with dry seeds that are unattractive to birds. Field observations by the author failed to find any birds that visit the seed capsules. Efforts to feed these seeds (without their capsules) to two tame barred doves, *Geopelia striata striata*, that normally eat grass seeds of a similar size resulted in failure. If the seeds are soaked, no sticky substance is produced, and microscopic examination of the seed coat reveals no spikes, barbs, or projections on the seed coat that might adhere to bird feathers. Birds could have carried the seeds caked in mud on their feet; however, the seeds required light to germinate and do not tolerate soil burial.

Discussion and Conclusions

Wind dispersal, as shown in Experiment 1, is probably the chief seed dispersal mechanism of this genus, especially since the plant grows at many elevations on many Pacific Islands within the trade wind belt. These trade winds average 5 to 15 miles per hour and have a drying effect upon the vegetation. The seed capsules on *Metrosideros* plants, although mature, will not split open until there is a dry spell. Once the capsules split, they remain open (Corn, unpublished observations). Some of the stronger trade winds undoubtedly carry these seeds far from the parent plant, especially where the plants are on the windward side of an uphill slope. However, there is an inversion layer above which the trades do not blow (at approximately 8,000 feet elevation, and incidently, the upper level that *Metrosideros* is found in the Hawaiian Islands). This inversion above Hawaii and other high Pacific Islands is disrupted by some of the strong winter storms and there is air exchange into the upper atmosphere. These same seeds if caught in an updraft could enter the upper atmosphere and might come into contact with the jet stream and get carried great distances within a few hours before they were caught in a wind eddy and drifted back toward earth. Experiment 2 indicates that such seeds could withstand the upper atmospheric temperatures.

However, once these seeds drop back down to earth, what are their chances of landing in a suitable habitat? When one considers the amount of available land in the Pacific versus the open ocean, one could say small, very small. However, if we go back to Experiment 3, we find that the seeds also survive at least for short periods in fresh and salt water. This means that the seeds might still survive even though they did not settle on a small high island. This gives the seeds another method of arrival to a new habitat to establish themselves. They could wash down fresh water streams for several days, or float around or in between the islands for at least a month. If and when they arrived at a new location, they would be on an unsuitable, wave-washed surface where *Metrosideros* do not grow.

However, Experiment 4 indicates that these seeds can survive desiccation after floating in salt water, which could give them a chance of survival by allowing the sea breezes to blow the seeds inland to a more suitable habitat. Although this may sound far-fetched, Figure 7 illustrates that this could have happened on Oahu, where seeds from a plant collected at 600 feet elevation have survived 30 days in sea water followed by 7 days of desiccation to produce viable seedlings one month old. If the results with the few viable seeds from 2,600 feet elevation in the Waianae Range that were unable to survive this same treatment (Figure 6) can be substantiated with a larger sample, there may be at least two seed types on one island that show two methods of arrival, or admittedly, some higher elevation plants may have lost this ability to withstand salt water.

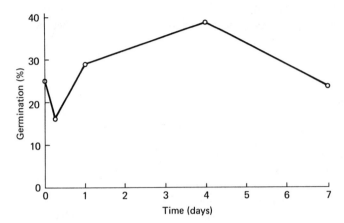

FIGURE 7. Seed germination after 30 days in sea water followed by desiccation periods shown below.

These results have some far-reaching implications. *Metrosideros* seeds could have arrived in the Hawaiian Islands by several methods at several times. Also, within the Hawaiian Islands, there may have been multiple introductions between the islands, resulting in the restocking of isolated genepools, giving new gene combinations to the established population.

The author gives a higher priority to air dispersal than to sea dispersal over long distances, because: (1) the seeds remain viable for only 9 months when stored at room temperatures; (2) data in Figure 5 indicate that these same seeds give reduced seedling survival and viability after a month or more in sea water; (3) oceanic drift is a slower method of dispersal, especially where long distances are involved, allowing more time for destructive forces to take over; for example, a fish eating a floating object, marine microbes attacking the seed coat and/or embryo, or the seed's surface being affected by hatching larvae, such as barnacles.

Acknowledgements

A special thanks to Dr. Ronald C. Taylor, Geosciences Department, for his invaluable ideas and help on methods of obtaining meteorological data; to Dr. Joel Fox, Mechanical Engineering, who helped solve some of the thermodynamic problems that arise with wind tunnel measurements; to Mr. Bernard Shinbara, Federal and State Weed Analyst, who so willingly let me modify his air-blast seed separator machine for these studies and to Dr. Stanford Siegel for his valuable suggestions. Also, thanks to Dr. Charles Lamoureux for generously letting me beg and borrow many reprints!

References

Carlquist, S. 1965. *Island Life.* Natural History Press, Garden City, New York.

————. 1966a. The biota of long-distance dispersal. I. Principles of dispersal and evolution. *Quart. Rev. Biol.,* **41**: 247-270.

————. 1966b. The biota of long-distance dispersal. II. Loss of dispersibility in Pacific Compositae. *Evolution,* **20**: 30-48.

————. 1966c. The biota of long-distance dispersal. IV. Genetic systems in the floras of oceanic islands. *Evolution,* **20**: 433-455.

————. 1967a. The biota of long-distance dispersal. III. Loss of dispersibility in the Hawaiian flora. *Brittonia,* **18**: 310-335.

————. 1967b. The biota of long-distance dispersal. V. Plant dispersal to Pacific Islands. *Bull. Torrey Bot. Club,* **94**(3): 129-162.

————. 1970. *Hawaii: A Natural History; Geology, Climate, Native Flora and Fauna Above the Shoreline.* Natural History Press, Garden City, New York.

Cruden, R. 1966. Birds as agents of long-distance dispersal for disjunct plant groups of the temperate Western Hemisphere. *Evolution,* **20**: 517-532.

Dawson, J. W. 1970. Pacific capsular Myrtaceae. *Blumea,* **18**: 431-452.

DeVlaming, V. L. and V. W. Proctor. 1968. Dispersal of aquatic organisms: viability of seeds recovered from the droppings of captive killdeer and mallard ducks. *Amer. J. Bot.,* **55**(1): 20-26.

Fosberg, F. R. 1963. Plant dispersal in the Pacific. *In*: J. L. Gressitt (ed.). *Pacific Basin Biogeography.* University of Hawaii Press, Honolulu. 273-282.

Gressitt, J. L. 1961. Problems in the zoogeography of Pacific and Antarctic insects. *Pac. Insects Monogr.,* **2**: 1-94.

Guppy, H. B. 1906. *Observations of a Naturalist in the Pacific 1896-1899.* Vol. 2. Plant Dispersal: 1-627. Macmillan & Co., London.

MacDonald, G. A. and A. T. Abbott. 1970. *Volcanoes in the Sea; the Geology of Hawaii.* University of Hawaii Press, Honolulu.

Powers, S. 1911. Floating islands. *Pop. Sci. Monogr.,* **79**: 303-307.

Ridley, H. N. 1930. *The Dispersal of Plants throughout the World.* L. Reeve & Co., Ashford, England.

Rock, J. F. 1917. The Ohia Lehua Trees of Hawaii. Board of Agriculture and Forestry Botanical Bulletin No. 4, Honolulu, Hawaii.

Visher, S. S. 1925. Tropical cyclones and the dispersal of life from island to island in the Pacific. *Amer. Nat.,* **59**: 70-78.

Yoshimoto, C. M. and J. L. Gressitt. 1961. Trapping of air-borne insects on the Pacific. *Pacific Insects,* **3**(4): 556-558.

Zimmerman, E. C. 1948. *Insects of Hawaii.* I. Introduction. University of Hawaii Press, Honolulu.

24 Plant-Insect Interactions, Tall Larkspur, and Biological Control

FRANKLIN FITZ
GRADUATE STUDENT
DEPARTMENT OF BOTANY AND ECOLOGY CENTER
Utah State University

> "for nature is to be commanded only by obeying her."
> Lord Francis Bacon, *Novum Organum*

Introduction

The regulation of plant and animal species conflicting with mankind's interests is a problem nearly as old as man himself. With the dawn of agriculture and the domestication of animals, man became engaged with insects and plants in a never-ending competitive struggle. While man has enjoyed temporary advantages and plant or insect pests have had their successes, he has neither permanently conquered his foes nor surrendered in defeat. As the early American pioneers moved west to the Rocky Mountains and beyond, they found themselves in conflict with yet another species—tall larkspur. Man's struggle with tall larkspur typifies a changing philosophy that is important for the regulation of pest species.

TALL LARKSPUR—THE NATURE OF THE PROBLEM

Two species of tall larkspur, *Delphinium barbeyi* Huth and *Delphinium occidentale* S. Wats. (buttercup family-Ranunculaceae), inhabit the Intermountain West (Fig. 1) as members of wooded aspen and open sub-alpine rangeland communities at higher elevations. These long-lived perennial forbs exist on their preferred moist, but well-drained, sites in sufficiently dense local populations for range cattle grazing on them to be poisoned by secondary plant products, eleven noxious diterpenoid alkaloids. These two plant species are responsible for more cattle poisoning

436

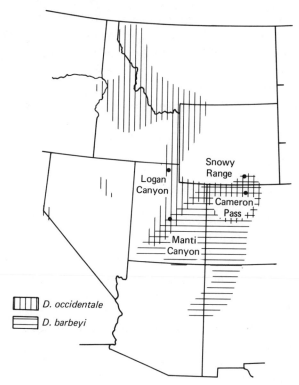

FIGURE 1. Distribution of two species of tall larkspur.

than any other range plant, including locoweed (Williams and Cronin, 1966), with annual losses of 2 to 12%, usually about 3 to 5%, but reaching a record high of 20% (Torell and Higgins, 1963). Such serious losses have stimulated over a half-century of effort to eradicate tall larkspur from national forest and rangelands (Marsh et al., 1929; Binns et al., 1971).

Eradication measures attempted to date include hand-grubbing, selective grazing, and the use of excess nitrogen fertilizer and herbicides. While hand-grubbing appeared "entirely feasible and economically possible" early in the century (Marsh et al., 1929), in modern times it seems too "slow and expensive" to be practical (Torell and Higgins, 1963). Horses are seldom affected by tall larkspur, but sheep thrive on it; thus, it would seem advantageous to selectively graze sheep instead of cattle on range where larkspur is a potential threat. No widespread effort for such controlled grazing has been made. Several researchers have measured some degree of control using 2,4,5-T herbicidal treatment, alone (Torell and Higgins, 1963) or in combination with excess nitrogen fertilizer (Binns et al., 1971), but the results have been either inconclusive or temporary and have served to increase the alkaloid content of stems and leaves (Williams and Cronin, 1963), making the rangeland even more deadly for a short time. In spite of these efforts, tall larkspur has persisted in its role as an eminently poisonous range plant (Cronin, 1971); however, there have been no investigations into possible mechanisms of biological control.

ECOLOGICAL CONSIDERATIONS

Civilized man has entered an era of heightened awareness of the values of biological control of pest species, as summarized by Huffaker (1970):

> Biological control, where effective, is cheap, usually persistent without need for recurrent expense, entails no significant genetic counterattack in the pests, usually does not occasion the rise to pest status of forms normally innocuous, does not add to the ever-growing problem of man's pollution of his environment, and is not attendant with the serious toxic hazards to the workers using the method, to consumers of the products, or to our cherished and declining wildlife.

Beirne's notion that "we may eventually be able to eradicate from producing areas all forms of life other than the ones involved in production" (Huffaker, 1970) has given way to the more realistic understanding that efforts should be made merely to control pests at levels below the "economic threshold" (Stern et al., 1959) through an integrated utilization of all available means—competition, predators, parasites, pathogens, mutants, etc., as well as selective chemicals judiciously applied.

Competition has been consistently regarded by plant ecologists to be the major force molding community structure (McIntosh, 1970). Succession can be attributed primarily to interspecific competition for environmental requisites under changing regimes of temperature, moisture, light and nutrition (Daubenmire, 1968), while spacing and numbers in plant populations are at least partly determined by allelopathic interactions (McPherson and Muller, 1969; Whittaker and Feeny, 1971). Germination in proper microsites ("safe-sites") in a heterogeneous soil environment is important to consequent seedling survival, and plant population densities may be partly regulated by the frequency of such "safe-sites" (Harper et al., 1965). Competitive exclusion of "safe-sites" by one species may seriously affect numbers of another species, and plant competitive relationships may be used as a biological control mechanism (McLaughlin et al., 1970).

For those interested in community relationships, however, emphasis on the role of plant competition has obscured another fundamental and potent force—herbivores. The role of phytophagous insects as limiting factors for native plant populations has been discounted by earlier workers (Williams, 1954) who concluded that for ecological reasons the biological control of weeds must remain limited. Herbivores, "limited by predation rather than food supply" (Hairston et al., 1960), have been considered unimportant in regulating plant populations. And in some cases the herbivores themselves have been limited by the distribution of their host plants (Dethier, 1959). The role that insects might play in determining both the diversity and abundance of plant species has been virtually ignored (Huffaker, 1959; Janzen, 1969). Until recently, this role has been poorly understood due to a paucity of experimentation (Harper, 1969).

Most plants, however, have an associated insect fauna that is "intrinsically capable of greatly reducing the population densities of their host-plants" (Wilson, 1964), and more often than not, many of these insects are host-specific (Wilson, 1964; Janzen, 1970) or at most restricted to a few plants either of the same genus or having similar biochemical composition (Andres and Goeden, 1971). The high degree of specificity between insects and plants, resulting from the diverse secondary plant compounds that guide host selection (Fraenkel, 1959, 1969; Schoonhoven, 1969), has been shown to regulate spacing, numbers and diversity of tropical tree species (Janzen, 1970) and pasture or range plants (Harper, 1969) and to reduce effective seed production in lupines (Breedlove and Ehrlich, 1968) and trees (Janzen, 1969, 1971a). Mutual host-specific plant-herbivore interactions have co-evolved through a self-intensifying process resulting from the biochemical differentiation of higher plants and the metabolic adaptation of herbivores to accommodate the plant substances (Whittaker, 1969; Harper, 1969). The net effect is a radiative increase in specialization of both flora and fauna, with a resultant increase in community diversity and corresponding decrease in host-plant density (Harper, 1969). Such natural control results in a low-density equilibrium between insect and host, with the result that often the regulation of the plant by predators may be exceptionally diffi-cult to recognize (Harper, 1969; Ehrlich and Birch, 1967; Ehrlich and Raven, 1965) unless compared with a former outbreak as in the case of St. Johnswort in California and Oregon (Huffaker, 1970).

In the many cases of the outbreak of infestations of introduced alien weeds throughout the world, partial-to-complete control has been achieved through the use of host-specific insects (Huffaker, 1959, 1970; Wilson, 1964; Andres and Goeden, 1971). Eradication is not achieved by biological control, nor is it intended; rather, a simulation of a natural equilibrium is achieved through the introduction of necessary biotic components. Because the premise of this approach is based on the host-specificity of any insect capable of controlling the plant, it can be effective for both alien and native plants (Huffaker, 1959).

The most effective biological weed control agents used to date have been host-specific phytophagous insects, usually plant-sucking or foliage-feeding types. Some authors disclaim any role of seed-eaters in affecting plant populations (Wilson, 1964; Slobodkin et al., 1967). Wilson (1964) states that "as plants tend to produce seed in great excess, the destruction of even fairly high percentages seems unlikely to control a perennial weed," but Janzen maintains (1969):

> To dismiss a priori the destruction of seeds as unimportant in regu-lation or limitation of adult plant population density is to regard the mortality of young animals as unimportant in density regulation of adult animals. Mature seeds are functionally identical to eggs and juveniles of vertebrates and invertebrates.

Seeds should not, therefore, be regarded as "plant products" (Murdoch, 1966), in a class with pollen and nectar, but as propagules which main-tain plant populations through their dispersal, germination, and establish-ment capabilities. Population recruitment will be determined by the in-tensity of the "seed shadow" and the probability of seedling establishment which involves in part escape from host-specific predators (Janzen, 1970, 1971 b,c). Destruction of seeds and seedlings can be important in regu-lation or limitation of adult plant populations by diminishing population recruitment and obscuring competitive effects. In a botanical analog to Paine's (1966) conclusion from intertidal zone studies that "local species diversity is directly related to the efficiency with which predators prevent the monopolization of the major environmental requisites by one species," seed and seedling predation may prevent any one species from becoming common enough to exclude its competitors.

The inadequacy of the role formerly assigned in plant ecology to insects as factors determining species diversity, plant-host distribution and density, and community structure, has been noted by many ecologists (Andres and Goeden, 1971; Ehrlich and Raven, 1965; Ehrlich and Birch, 1967; Harper, 1969; Janzen, 1971a; Whittaker, 1969; Wilson, 1964). Increasing recognition of the importance of this role has both theoretical and practical implications for tall larkspur. Examination of the herbivorous fauna of tall larkspur might contribute to our understanding of plant community relationships and, also might lead the way to mechanisms of biological control.

PURPOSES OF THE RESEARCH

The foregoing discussion shows that some degree of natural regulation of tall larkspur may already be operative and unrecognized. It also seems

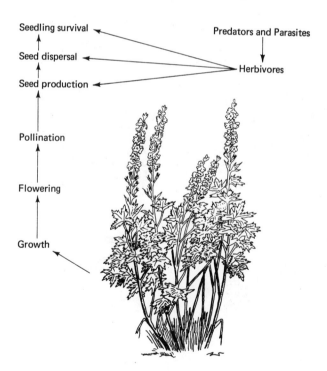

FIGURE 2. Ecological interactions with tall larkspur.

very probable that host-specific phytophagous insects, adapted to metabo-
lize the alkaloids of tall larkspur, may be found. This study was designed
to evaluate the ecological interactions with the two species of tall larkspur (Fig. 2). Primarily a field-oriented observation and descriptive
study, the importance of which has recently been emphasized (Southern,
1970), this work attempted to assess the role of herbivores, with their
predators and parasites, on vegetative growth and seed production as
factors affecting the success of tall larkspur populations.

Procedure

DESCRIPTION OF THE STUDY SITES

The two species studied are for the most part allopatric (Fig. 1) and,
within the area of geographic sympatry, are not found in the same plant
communities, probably because of altitudinal differences in preferred
habitat. Two main study sites were chosen, one in the Logan Canyon
of northeastern Utah (Fig. 3) where *D. occidentale* is found, and the

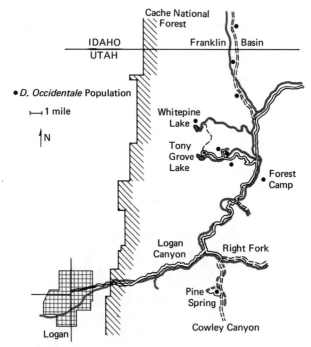

FIGURE 3. Logan Canyon area.

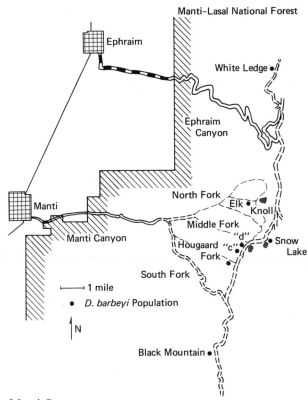

FIGURE 4. Manti Canyon area.

other in the Manti Canyon of the Manti-Lasal National Forest of central Utah (Fig. 4) within the range of *D. barbeyi*. Plant populations were located in each of these major areas. In addition, populations of *D. barbeyi* in the Snowy Range, Wyoming, and at Cameron Pass, Colorado (Fig. 1) were visited for reference to the insect fauna present.

IDENTIFICATION OF THE PHYTOPHAGOUS INSECT FAUNA

Plant-sucking, flower- or foliage-feeding, and seed-eating insects were captured with a sweep net or aspirator and preserved for identification. Other plants in the communities were thoroughly checked for the same insects and literature consulted to assist in determining host-specificity. Preliminary visual assessment of the damage to vegetation and seed crop was made to determine which of these insects might warrant additional study. Four insects were found to be apparently host-specific and of significance: the green-bronze larkspur aphid (*Kakimia wahinkae* [Hottes]), the russet-colored larkspur aphid (*Aphis rociadae* Cockerell), the larkspur mirid bug (*Hoplomachus affiguratus* Uhler), and the larkspur maggot, a seed-eating larva of an anthomyiid fly (*Hylemya laxifrons* Huckett).

PHYTOPHAGOUS INSECTS AND VEGETATIVE GROWTH

Insects feeding on tall larkspur were rated according to relative abundance in the field based on absolute frequency of collection at the various sites. Using a scheme modified from Goeden (1971), ratings were "abundant" (found commonly in small-to-high numbers in most populations), "frequent" (found commonly, but never in high numbers), and "rare" (found occasionally, but most often absent). Qualitative estimates of insect damage to larkspur vegetation were rated—severe, significant, or negligible. To assist in determining identity of immature forms, time spent in various life stages, and feeding capacities of various insects found on larkspur, insectaries were constructed which allowed fresh bouquets of larkspur to be regularly changed within screen cages. A water-filled flask held the bouquet, on which the insects developed, and was surrounded with litter-covered soil to provide burrowing sites for pupation when necessary.

NORMAL SEED PRODUCTION

As snowdrifts melt in spring, larkspur stalks emerge from overwintering buds on woody rootstalks. Mature plants produce an indefinite number of such stalks in spring, and these elongate into racemes of numerous purplish-blue spur-bearing flowers. Fruits of both species are normally triplets of follicles which dehisce at maturity in fall, yielding large quantities of small, shriveled black seeds. Since the number of racemes per plant is highly variable in both species, the individual raceme was taken as the reproductive unit. It was necessary to determine the normal seed production as the total number of seeds per raceme. This was accomplished by sampling racemes at random in populations of both species and counting both the number of follicles per raceme as well as the number of seeds per follicle.

INSECTS AND SEED PREDATION

Host-specific insects

The larkspur aphids on *Delphinium occidentale*.—The life cycle was determined by field observation and collection within aphid populations. Population growth potential under outbreak conditions at Pine Spring (Fig. 3) in a *D. occidentale* population was determined by absolute count early in the season and by calculated estimates (Bradley, 1952) of the number of aphids per raceme later in the season when densities were very high.

The larkspur mirid bug on *Delphinium barbeyi*.—The timing of the life cycle and development of the mirid bug with the growth and development of tall larkspur was determined by field observations of emergence from over-wintering eggs, behavioral habits, time of mating, egg-laying, and death. Sequential samples (Morris, 1960) were taken for counting of instars and adults to determine time spent in each stage of the life cycle.

To compare seed set between infested and uninfested plants, 10 of each were chosen at random within infested and relatively uninfested populations. Since bugs may kill a stalk on emergence from the ground, kill it in the bud, or severely stunt a flowering raceme and inhibit seed set, causing a "generally unappreciated seed destruction" (Janzen, 1969), it is possible to measure seed destruction with the relation:

$$D_m = \frac{1}{X} \left\{ K_e + K_b + S \left(1 - \frac{N_s}{N_h}\right) \right\} \times 100$$

where D_m = Seed destruction by the larkspur mirid bug
X = Total potentially reproductive stalks emerging
K_e = Total number of racemes killed on emergence
K_b = Total number of racemes killed on budding
S = Total number of racemes stunted while flowering
N_s = Number of seeds per stunted raceme
N_h = Number of seeds per healthy normal raceme

Because normal plants do not set all potential seed, due to pollination failure and abortion, a necessary reference determination of "realized" seed production under normal conditions was made by counting the number of follicles that developed seed and the number of follicles that failed.

The larkspur maggot on both *Delphinium spp*.—Field observations of the presence, distribution and abundance of various life stages of the fly were made throughout the season for life cycle and development determinations. Distribution of eggs on larkspur racemes was determined by counting egg-laying sites and the number of eggs per site on follicles of racemes of *D. barbeyi*. The preliminary observation that one larva consumes the entire seed contents of one and only one follicle during the pre-pupation development suggested that estimates of seed destruction could be made by counting the number of infested follicles and the total number of follicles on a raceme. The seed destruction on a given raceme may then be expressed:

$$D_f = \frac{N_i}{N_h} \times 100$$

where D_f = Seed destruction by the larkspur maggot
N_i = Number of follicles infested by fly larvae
N_h = Total number of follicles on the raceme

Seven populations of *D. barbeyi* in the Manti Area, one in Colorado and one in Wyoming were chosen for sampling; three populations of *D. occidentale* in the Logan Canyon were chosen. Within each population, racemes were picked and counts made of fly larval infestation in follicles and fruits (triplets of follicles).

PREDATORS AND PARASITES

Since in natural communities most phytophagous insects have enemies normally responsible for regulating their numbers (Hagen et al., 1971) and are, therefore, of significance in overall distribution and abundance of the host plants, an attempt was made to determine the predators and parasites as they were discovered in the field or in the laboratory-reared host insects. The effect of these predators and parasites on their host populations is the subject of future studies.

Results and Discussion

PHYTOPHAGOUS INSECTS AND VEGETATIVE GROWTH

Non-host-specific phytophagous insects

Lepidopteran larvae.—Four species of lepidopteran larvae were found consuming foliage of tall larkspur. Of these four, none are host-specific

a) A Plant Bug
   Plagiognathus obscurus (Miridae)

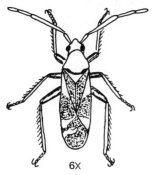

6X

b) Alfalfa Plant Bug
   Lygus hesperus (Miridae)

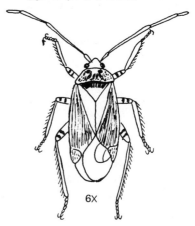

6X

c) A Looper
   (Geometridae)

3X

d) Alfalfa Semi–Looper
   Autographa californica (Noctuidae)

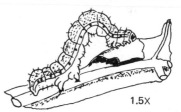

1.5X

e) A Leaf Roller
   (Noctuidae)

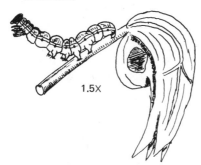

1.5X

f) ——
   Pyrrhia sp. (Noctuidae)

3X

FIGURE 5. Non-host-specific phytophagous insects on tall larkspur.

(Fig. 5). An unidentified geometrid larva was found in small numbers, and because of its scarcity, the insect was considered insignificant. Found more commonly in populations throughout the Logan Canyon were larvae of two noctuid moths, a leaf-roller and a species of *Pyrrhia*, probably *exprimens*. Although the leaf-rollers (and some of its parasites) were successfully reared in the laboratory insectaries to adulthood, identification has not been confirmed beyond family. *Pyrrhia sp.* is a general feeder and has been previously reported on *Delphinium*, feeding on blossoms and unopened buds (Hardwick, 1970). Neither of these noctuids, because of low population levels and generalized feeding habits, can be considered significant in foliage consumption of tall larkspur.

More frequently and with regularity, another noctuid was found in almost every population of *D. occidentale* or *D. barbeyi*. This moth was successfully reared in laboratory insectaries from larval stages to adulthood and identified as the alfalfa semi-looper (*Autographa californica* [Speyer]). The moth is widely distributed throughout the upper intermountain region and feeds on a variety of plants. Vegetative predation on tall larkspur by the semi-looper is low, but regular, and could represent a potential threat to larkspur populations in the absence of predators and parasites.

Other insects.—The alfalfa plant bug, *Lygus hesperus* Knight, and another mirid bug, *Plagiognathus obscurus* Uhler, found regularly in *D. occidentale* populations throughout Logan Canyon. Both were "frequent," but in small numbers, and cause no significant damage to vegetation. The polyphagous *Lygus hesperus* is common throughout the Rocky Mountains and Pacific States and is a pest of some agricultural crops, but both bugs very likely pose no serious threat to larkspur.

Host-specific phytophagous insects

The larkspur mirid bug.—Uhler (1895) first described the larkspur mirid bug from specimens collected on *D. occidentale* near Steamboat Springs in Colorado. The insect has never before been recorded on *D. barbeyi*, "probably because of the high elevations where few collectors have taken bugs" (H. H. Knight, personal communication). Specimens were found regularly in small numbers on both larkspur species, but an outbreak bug population on *D. barbeyi* in a Manti Canyon exclosure at Hougaard Fork (Fig. 4) afforded an opportunity to study the potential impact of this bug on its host plant. The plant-sucking bug in large numbers can virtually kill or prevent the entire season's growth (inhibiting seed production, discussed below), but no method could be devised to measure this quantitatively. It is suspected that a few years' outbreak infestation on mature plants could inhibit photosynthetic recharging of the plant-root reserves and ultimately result in the exhaustion of stored food and the death of the mature plant in addition to the stifling of its reproductive effort.

NORMAL SEED PRODUCTION

The results of the seed counts on both species are presented in Table I. It can be seen from these estimates that the lower number of seeds per follicle in *D. occidentale* is compensated for by a higher number of follicles per raceme, to give approximately equal reproductive output in both species.

TABLE I. *Potential Seed Production in Normal* Delphinium occidentale *and* D. barbeyi *Plants.*

Larkspur species	Mean #seeds per follicle	Mean #follicles per raceme	Mean #seeds per raceme
D. occidentale	12 ± 1	131 ± 10	1582 ± 261
D. barbeyi	17 ± 1	96 ± 7	1632 ± 222

$$p < .05 \text{ (t test)}$$

INSECTS AND SEED PREDATION

Non-host-specific insects

Of the six non-host-specific phytophagous insects found on tall larkspur, only the alfalfa semi-looper and *Pyrrhia sp.* were found consuming small developing follicles or eating the soft white maturing seeds within larger but immature follicles. These two insects occurred frequently, but damage to the seed crop appeared minimal. In the absence of predators and parasites, these two lepidopteran larvae could become a more serious factor in the consumption of tall larkspur seeds.

Host-specific insects

The larkspur aphids on *Delphinium occidentale.*—Palmer (1952) has previously recorded both aphid species on tall larkspur, and the green-

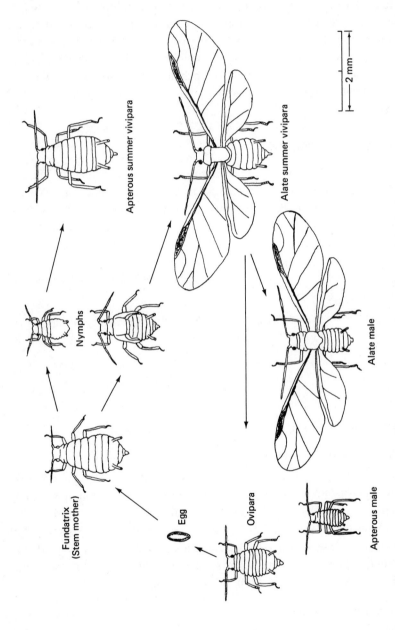

Apterous summer vivipara

Alate summer vivipara

2 mm

Nymphs

Alate male

Fundatrix
(Stem mother)

Egg

Ovipara

Apterous male

FIGURE 6. Life stages of the green-bronze larkspur aphid (*Kakimia wahinkae*).

bronze larkspur aphid also on monkshood (*Aconitum columbianum* Nutt.), a close relative of tall larkspur. Aphids were found only once on *D. barbeyi* but scattered at relatively low densities throughout the range of *D. occidentale*. A peculiarly dense local population at the Pine Spring site afforded an opportunity for observation of the life cycle, seasonal abundance and seed destruction capability. Because of rapid multiplication through parthenogenesis, viviparity, telescoping of generations, and the production of winged forms (Kennedy and Stroyan, 1959), these parasitic, sap-sucking colonial insects are particularly suited to the exploitation of ephemerally suitable plants (Way, 1968) and can cause stunting and deformation in larkspur plants by robbing them of sap, by the toxic action of their salivary secretions, and by acting as vectors of plant viruses.

From field collections, various life forms of the green-bronze larkspur aphid were sorted, and the life cycle was constructed (Fig. 6). This pattern of alternation of a sexual generation in fall with a parthenogenetic generation during the favorable season is common in aphids. Some species migrate to an alternate host during the winter, but larkspur aphids probably pass the winter in the egg stage since the first aphids found in early June were wingless stem mothers.

The phenomenal population growth of these aphids is illustrated in Figure 7 which shows the development of a colony of aphids on a single raceme of *D. occidentale*. The aphids first appear in early June as stalks of *D. occidentale* are beginning to develop. By early July, as racemes are elongating and beginning to flower, aphid populations have grown to over 500 per raceme (Fig. 7) with the production of a high proportion of winged forms which allow migration from the original host, relieving competition and effecting rapid spread throughout the host population as migrants settle on new hosts and begin new colonies.

The aphids occupied sites on the follicles in preference to leaves, moving to the latter only after follicles became very crowded. Aphid-free plants in the Pine Spring population could not be found by mid-August. Populations waned by mid-September as the current year's plant growth began dying, and by October 1 no aphids could be found. By robbing the plant of sap, shunting it away from the developing seeds, the summer peak aphid densities took a serious toll on seed production. Attempts to measure seed destruction failed to yield any consistent result throughout the larkspur population. Racemes that had produced no seed at all were

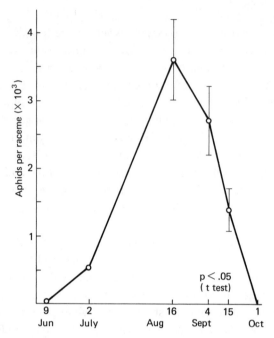

FIGURE 7. Population growth in a larkspur aphid colony.

found, while others produced many seeds. Seed destruction could not be related to aphid population density because of rapid changes in aphid populations. It was found that aphids are able to cause up to 100% seed destruction if the population density becomes extreme.

The larkspur mirid bug on *Delphinium barbeyi*.—The life cycle of the bug was found to coincide very closely with the growth season of tall larkspur. By the first of July, as larkspur shoots begin to emerge, the overwintering eggs of the mirid bug begin to hatch. The tiny nymphs seek the young succulent stalks where they spend their entire lives sucking plant sap, going through five instar stages to reach winged adulthood. Relative proportions of each life stage present in the population through the season are shown in Figure 8. The insects pass rapidly through the first three instars, less rapidly through the fourth and fifth stages, requiring about three weeks to develop from egg to adult. The entire population had reached adulthood by mid-August as the larkspur plants began to mature. In the next few weeks mating, egg-laying, and death occurred. The eggs were laid in the hollow stalks of the larkspur plant, and by mid-

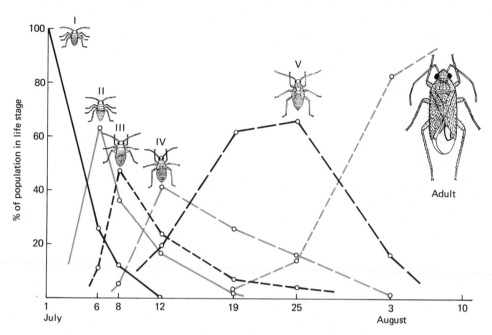

FIGURE 8. Development of the larkspur mirid bug (*Hoplomachus affiguratus*).

September the population had returned to the egg stage to pass the winter. This very brief two-and-a-half month season allows only one generation per year.

The effects of these higher bug densities are severe stunting of growth, as previously discussed, and almost complete inhibition of seed set. Infested and control plants were compared for the number of emergent stalks budding, flowering, and producing seed. The results of this comparison clearly demonstrated that nearly 20% of the newly-emergent stalks can be killed by the bugs, almost 50% were killed prior to flowering, and only 1.7% of maximum potential seed development was realized (Table II and Fig. 9). Since the normal plants showed only 85% potential seed production, the effect of the bug was essentially to cause 98% seed destruction by virtue of their plant-sucking habit, allowing only 2% of this "realized" seed production. It should be emphasized that these seemed to be abnormally high bug densities and that this effect is not widespread at the present time.

TABLE II. *Destruction of Seed of* Delphinium barbeyi *by the Larkspur Mirid Bug* (Hoplomachus affiguratus).

	Mean % stalks emerging	Mean % stalks budding	Mean % stalks flowering	Mean % seed production
Control Plants (uninfested)	100	100	100	85 ± 7.7
Experimental Plants (infested)	100	81.8 ± 6.3	50.8 ± 15.6	1.7 ± 1.5
			$p < .05$ (t test)	

The larkspur maggot on both *Delphinium spp.*—Maggots have not been previously reported from tall larkspur, though Pelton (1961) mentions a *Hylemya sp.* adult visiting flowers of *Mertensia ciliata* in Colorado and an "unidentified diptera larva feeding on anthers, corolla and ovary within

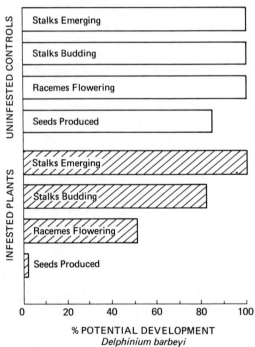

FIGURE 9. Destruction of seed of *Delphinium barbeyi* by the larkspur mirid bug (*Hoplomachus affiguratus*).

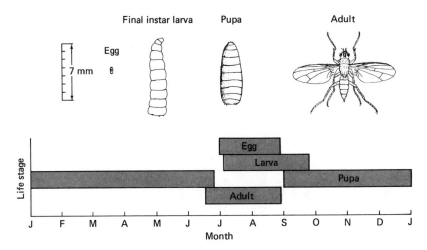

FIGURE 10. Life stages of the larkspur maggot (*Hylemya sp.*).

unopened buds." The genus *Hylemya* is large and complex and shows a high degree of host-specificity and Pelton's larvae may quite probably be of a different species.

Larkspur maggots are abundant on both larkspur species, within the spur of the corolla early in the flowering season and moving into the follicles as they develop. Although larvae are found as early as mid-July, there is a burst of egg-laying on all parts of the flowering and fruiting racemes in mid-August as the main attack on larkspur seeds coincides with maximum availability of fruit. Each larva develops within one and only one follicle, consuming all the seeds therein, and is ready for pupation by the season's end, spending the winter in the ground litter as a pupa. The adults emerge the following spring by mid-July to repeat the univoltine life cycle (Fig. 10).

TABLE III. *Destruction of Seed of* Delphinium occidentale *by the Larkspur Maggot* (Hylemya laxifrons).

Population	# Racemes Examined	Mean # Fruits Infested	Mean # Follicles Infested
Franklin Basin, Idaho	5	36.9∓8.3	14.3∓3.1
Pine Spring, Cowley Canyon	5	86.3∓9.4	54.0∓11.1
Tony Grove, Logan Canyon	5	29.6∓11.5	11.2∓4.0

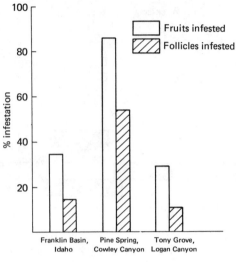

FIGURE 11. Destruction of seed of *Delphinium occidentale* by the larkspur maggot (*Hylemya laxifrons*).

The seed destruction by the fly larvae proved to be very significant and rather uniformly widespread throughout the four states where populations were sampled. The infestation of *D. occidentale* was variable. Of

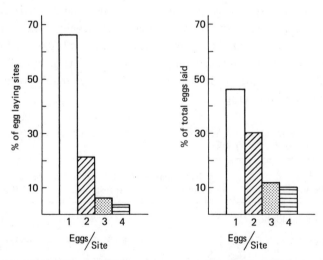

FIGURE 12. Distribution of *Hylemya* eggs on tall larkspur follicles.

the three populations examined in the Logan Canyon drainage, the seed destruction was highest in the Pine Spring population (54%) and lower at the two higher elevation sites (Table III and Fig. 11). No explanation for this variability can be advanced. The fly is rather widespread and abundant, however, and exerts considerable pressure on seed production.

In the *D. barbeyi* populations of the Manti region, it was found that at least one egg was laid on each of 91% of the fruits (clusters of follicles), with the eggs laid mostly singly or in pairs (Fig. 12) and rather uniformly spread throughout the raceme. Survival to the larval state was high, and 85% of these same fruits subsequently became infested with at least one larva, while the actual number of individual follicles infested with larvae averaged 49%. In thousands of follicles examined, never did a single follicle contain more than one larva. Seven populations examined in the Manti Canyon area showed similar infestations (Table IV and Fig. 13), and analysis of the variance between the mean numbers of infested fruits and follicles in these seven infested populations showed no significant differences. The effect of seed destruction was found to be uniformly widespread throughout the Manti Canyon area, taking a toll of 49% of the entire seed crop during the summer of 1971. Measurements for 1970 and previous years are not available, but the larvae were seen in abundance in 1970, probably taking a serious toll in seed crop.

TABLE IV. *Destruction of Seed of* Delphinium barbeyi *by the Larkspur Maggot* (Hylemya laxifrons).

Population	# Racemes Examined	Mean # Fruits Infested	Mean # Follicles Infested
UTAH, Manti Canyon			
Black Mountain	5	90.3 ∓ 8.6	52.0 ∓ 12.7
Elk Knoll	7	83.2 ∓ 13.6	49.7 ∓ 10.9
Hougaard Fork	8	83.6 ∓ 8.0	46.0 ∓ 3.2
Middle Fork (C)	8	85.5 ∓ 4.4	49.7 ∓ 3.6
Middle Fork (D)	10	82.0 ∓ 5.8	48.0 ∓ 6.5
White Fork Ledge	8	86.1 ∓ 6.4	50.6 ∓ 4.2
Snow Lake	3	87.4 ∓ 20.3	43.2 ∓ 6.0
Average		84.9 ∓ 8.3	48.7 ∓ 2.2
COLORADO			
Cameron Pass	3	75.0 ∓ 5.9	34.1 ∓ 4.8
WYOMING			
Snowy Ran.e	3	67.8 ∓ 17.2	31.1 ∓ 4.8

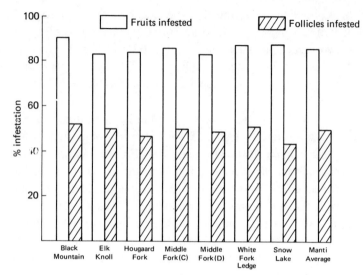

FIGURE 13. Destruction of seed of *Delphinium barbeyi* in seven populations in the Manti Canyon area by the larkspur maggot (*Hylemya laxifrons*).

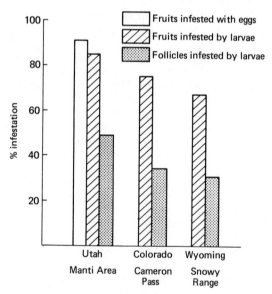

FIGURE 14. Destruction of seed of *Delphinium barbeyi* in populations from Utah, Colorado, and Wyoming by the larkspur maggot (*Hylemya laxifrons*).

Comparisons with fly infestation in *D. barbeyi* populations from Colorado and Wyoming showed a somewhat lesser, but considerable, seed destruction in these parts of the range (Table IV and Fig. 14).

PREDATORS AND PARASITES

Only those predators and parasites actually encountered in the field are reported here. Many others are referred to in the literature (Puttarudriah, 1953; Clancy, 1968; Hyslop, 1912; Borror and DeLong, 1954) and should be looked for in subsequent studies, especially *Aphelinus sp.* or *Aphidius sp.*, host-specific wasps parasitic on aphids.

Non-specific predators of aphids, larvae of the syrphid fly (probably *Syrphus ribesii* L.) are encountered frequently in larkspur aphid colonies (Fig. 15a). The adults can be seen hovering before the flowers. With chewing mouth parts, the syrphid larva rasps a hole through the exoskeleton of the aphid body and sucks out the body fluids. On several occasions it was observed that about 15 minutes were required for the larva to consume one aphid.

The damsel bug (*Nabis alternatus*) is also a general predator of aphids, and this hemipteran (Fig. 15g) can be found in aphid colonies. Passing through several wingless nymphal stages prior to winged adulthood, it is predatory in all stages of its life cycle. Generally found in very small numbers within aphid colonies, the bugs apparently disperse themselves throughout host populations. With semi-raptorial forelegs, the predator grasps the aphid and with piercing, sucking mouthparts withdraws the body fluids.

The braconid wasp (*Apanteles sp.*) is an internal parasite of caterpillars and was found parasitizing both the alfalfa semi-looper and the leaf-rolling noctuid. The adult (Fig. 15b) lays eggs on the caterpillar, and the hatching larvae burrow within the bodies of their host, feed internally, and later emerge to spin cocoons externally on the caterpillar (Fig. 15b), which is almost always killed by such parasites. Thirty-five adult braconids emerged from cocoons on a single parasitized leaf-roller reared in an insectary, and similar numbers of parasites were reared from alfalfa semi-looper caterpillars. The species is probably *Apanteles hyslopi* Vier. and is quite effective in controlling noctuid populations (Hyslop, 1912).

The rather widespread paper wasp (*Polistes fuscatus*, Fig. 15d) is a non-specific predator of lepidopteran larvae. The wasp locates prey feed-

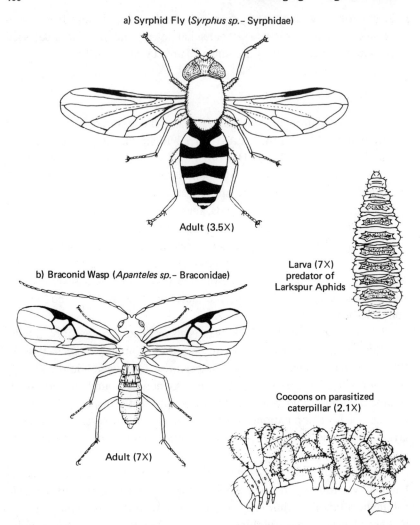

a) Syrphid Fly (*Syrphus sp.*– Syrphidae)

Adult (3.5×)

Larva (7×)
predator of
Larkspur Aphids

b) Braconid Wasp (*Apanteles sp.*– Braconidae)

Adult (7×)

Cocoons on parasitized
caterpillar (2.1×)

FIGURE 15. Predators and parasites of the phytophagous insect fauna of tall larkspur.

ing on plants and may either feed for its own use on body fluids or carry the caterpillar to its nest, where it is paralyzed with a sting and placed in chambers as food for developing wasp larvae. The wasp was seen preying on the alfalfa semi-looper on several occasions.

Internal tachinid parasites (Fig. 15c) of *Autographa californica* were found in late summer emerging from their hosts for pupation. In all cases,

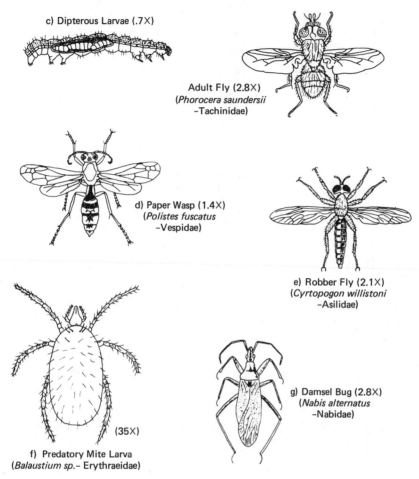

c) Dipterous Larvae (.7X)

Adult Fly (2.8X)
(*Phorocera saundersii*
–Tachinidae)

d) Paper Wasp (1.4X)
(*Polistes fuscatus*
–Vespidae)

e) Robber Fly (2.1X)
(*Cyrtopogon willistoni*
–Asilidae)

(35X)

f) Predatory Mite Larva
(*Balaustium sp.*- Erythraeidae)

g) Damsel Bug (2.8X)
(*Nabis alternatus*
–Nabidae)

from four to six mature fly larvae emerged from host-caterpillars and pupated within hours. Efforts to rear adult flies from the puparia were unsuccessful, and the identity of the fly remains unknown. Tachinid flies are generally host-specific, but host-parasite relations have not been carefully established. Hyslop (1912) found *Phorocera saundersii* parasitizing the alfalfa semi-looper and Puttarudriah (1953) reports parasitization by *Voria ruralis*. The latter is common in the Intermountain region and could very well be the species encountered at Manti.

The robber fly (*Cyrtopogon willistoni*), a general predator (Fig. 15e), was occasionally observed preying on the larkspur mirid bug. Lack of

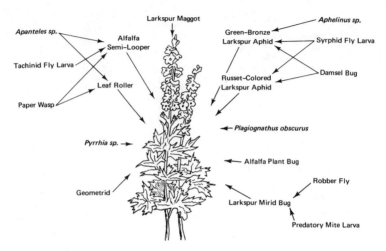

FIGURE 16. The plant-insect interactions on tall larkspur, with predators and parasites.

specificity reduces the probability of this insect representing a serious threat to bug populations.

The larva of the predatory mite (*Balaustium sp.*) was found parasitizing instars and adults of the larkspur mirid bug at Manti. Larvae are normally non-specifically parasitic on other arthropods and were also found on leaf-hoppers in the area.

A diagram summarizing the plant-herbivore interactions on tall larkspur, together with the predators and parasites of the phytophagous insect fauna, is presented in Figure 16.

Summary and Conclusions

NORMAL SEED SHADOW AND POPULATION RECRUITMENT

In the absence of insect seed predation, seed set by a single raceme of either species of tall larkspur is approximately 1,500 seeds. The seeds are dispersed by the wind or by parental collapse. The seed shadow of a mature tall larkspur plant may be considered primarily to be a set of dense aggregations where racemes are bent to the ground by early fall snow with release of seeds. These seed clusters lie about the parent plant within a circle of a radius equal to the length of the parent stalks. Also, in this circle is a random sprinkling of points where seeds fell, dispersed by stalks shaking in the wind. Beyond the circle of parentally dispersed seed, the shadow fades rapidly to zero. Seeds are also blown by the wind over crusted snow in late fall and reach points where winter snow accumulates. Population recruitment within existing larkspur stands and migration to areas where successful seedling establishment can occur is effected by normal seed production and these mechanisms of dispersal.

THE ROLE OF HERBIVORES AND THEIR PREDATORS AND PARASITES

The phytophagous insect fauna of tall larkspur in part consists of non-host-specific lepidopteran larvae and mirid bugs exerting little pressure on vegetative growth and seed production. Of greater significance are four host-specific insects capable of extensive foliar damage and reduction in seed crop size, which results in decreased intensity of seed shadow and diminished population recruitment. The larkspur aphids under outbreak conditions were found to reduce seed crop size to zero while causing little foliar damage, a result of the aphid's habit of locating colonies within the fruiting raceme instead of on the leaves. The larkspur mirid bug was not generally found in numbers sufficient to cause extensive damage to the plant but, under high bug densities, can stunt and kill emerging stalks and fruiting racemes, reducing seed crop size nearly to zero while at the same time severely damaging vegetative growth. The last host-specific insect, the larkspur maggot, is widespread throughout the range of both larkspur species and, under normal conditions, was found to take a high percentage of seed crop, up to nearly 50% in some parts of the range.

Many predators and parasites of the phytophagous insect fauna were identified, and future study may indicate the degree to which the insects are kept in check by their natural enemies.

POSSIBLE BIOLOGICAL CONTROL MECHANISMS

The use of the larkspur mirid bug and maggot seems to offer the most promising possibility for biological control. Both seemingly have few predators and parasites and can build up to great numbers, causing significant damage to both vegetation and seed crop. Inhibiting population recruitment, while stifling plant growth and development by the use of these two agents, may curtail the increase in larkspur while gradually eliminating currently-mature plants.

Long-term experiments involving herbivore withdrawal or controlled herbivore activity on tall larkspur populations could further elucidate the question of how much natural control is already operative. Detailed life history studies of all the herbivorous fauna and their natural enemies, with consideration of population dynamics under differing physical regimes, may lead to the eventual field application of successful biological control, and may contribute, as well, to our overall understanding of the natural world.

A FINAL THOUGHT

The right of special interest groups to modify public land to suit their own needs is seriously questioned, especially as rising human population pressure creates increasing and unresolvable conflict between the "multiple uses" of the land (Douglas, 1971; Hagenstein, 1971). Priorities of use will undoubtedly be determined in the near future, and it is probable that grazing values may rank below interest in watershed and recreational use in the National Forests. Such future values should be considered when defining a plant as a weed (Huffaker, 1959). Tall larkspur may some day be considered to be an aesthetically-pleasing mountain wild flower, a desirable component of the plant community, rather than a "noxious range weed" as it is often viewed by cattlemen and poisonous plant researchers. Should this occur, practical biological control will be of little interest, but the plant-insect interactions will retain theoretical ecological import.

References

Andres, L. A. and R. D. Goeden. 1971. The biological control of weeds by introduced natural enemies. p. 143-164. *In*: C. B. Huffaker (ed.). *Biological Control*. Plenum Press, New York.
Binns, W., L. F. James, and A. E. Johnson. 1971. Control of larkspur with herbicides plus nitrogen fertilizer. *J. Range Manage.*, **24**: 110-113.
Borror, D. J. and D. M. DeLong. 1954. *An Introduction to the Study of Insects*. Holt, Rinehart and Winston, New York. 819 p.
Bradley, R. H. E. 1952. Methods of recording aphid (Homoptera: Aphididae)

populations on potatoes and the distribution of species on the plant. *Can. Entomol.*, **84**: 93-102.

Breedlove, D. E. and P. R. Ehrlich. 1968. Plant-herbivore co-evolution: Lupines and lycaenids. *Science,* **162**: 671-672.

Clancy, D. W. 1968. Distribution and parasitization of some *Lygus spp.* in western United States and central Mexico. *J. Econ. Entomol.,* **61**: 443-445.

Cronin, E. H. 1971. Tall larkspur: Some reasons for its continuing preeminence as a poisonous plant. *J. Range Manage.,* **24**: 258-263.

Daubenmire, R. 1968. *Plant Communities.* Harper and Row, New York. 300 p.

Dethier, V. B. 1959. Food-plant distribution and larval dispersal as factors affecting insect populations. *Can. Entomol.,* **41**: 581-596.

Douglas, P. A. 1971. The limits of multiple use in natural areas. 2nd National Biological Congress, Miami. October 23. 15 p.

Ehrlich, P. R. and L. C. Birch. 1967. The "balance of nature" and "population control." *Am. Nat.,* **101**: 97-107.

—————— and P. H. Raven. 1965. Butterflies and plants: A study in co-evolution. *Evolution,* **18**: 586-608.

Fraenkel, G. S. 1959. The raison d'être of secondary plant products. *Science,* **129**: 1466-1470.

——————. 1969. Evaluation of our thoughts on secondary plant substances. *Entomol. Exp. Appl.,* **12**: 473-486.

Goeden, R. D. 1971. The phytophagous insect fauna of milk thistle in southern California. *J. Econ. Entomol.,* **64**: 1101-1104.

Hagen, K. S., R. van den Bosch, and D. L. Dahlsten. 1971. The importance of naturally-occurring biological control in the western United States. p. 253-293. *In*: C. B. Huffaker (ed.). *Biological Control.* Plenum Press, New York.

Hagenstein, P. 1971. Multiple use and environmental decisions on the public lands. *J. For.,* **69**: 21-24.

Hairston, N. B., F. E. Smith, and L. B. Slobodkin. 1960. Community structure, population control, and competition. *Am. Nat.,* **94**: 421-425.

Hardwick, D. F. 1970. The life history of *Pyrrhia exprimens* (Noctuidae). *J. Lepid. Soc.,* **24**: 234-239.

Harper, J. L. 1969. The role of predation in vegetational diversity. p. 48-62. In: *Diversity and Stability in Ecological Systems.* Brookhaven Symposia in Biology, No. 22. Brookhaven National Laboratory, Upton, New York.

——————, J. T. Williams, and G. R. Sagar. 1965. The behaviour of seeds in soil. I. The heterogeneity of soil surfaces and its role in determining the establishment of plants from seed. *J. Ecol.,* **53**: 273-286.

Huffaker, C. B. 1959. Biological control of weeds with insects. *Ann. Rev. Entomol.,* **4**: 251-276.

————. 1970. Life against life—Nature's pest control scheme. *Environ. Res.,* **3**: 162-175.

Hyslop, J. 1912. The alfalfa looper. U. S. D. A. Entomological Bull. No. 95, Part VII, p. 109-118.

Janzen, D. H. 1969. Seed-eaters versus seed size, number, toxicity, and dispersal. *Evolution,* **23**: 1-27.

————. 1970. Herbivores and the number of tree species in tropical forests. *Am. Nat.,* **104**: 501-528.

————. 1971a. Seed predation by animals. *Ann. Rev. Ecol. Syst.,* **2**: 465-492.

————. 1971b. Escape of juvenile *Dioclea megacarpa* (Leguminosae) vines from predators in a deciduous tropical forest. *Am. Nat.,* **105**: 97-112.

————. 1971c. Escape of *Cassia grandis* L. beans from predators in time and space. *Ecology,* **52**: 964-979.

Kenedy, J. S., and H. L. G. Stroyan. 1959. Biology of aphids. *Ann. Rev. Entomol.,* **4**: 139-160.

MacLaughlin, R. S., H. W. Miller, and O. K. Hoglund. 1970. Lana vetch for medusahead control. *J. Range Manage.,* **23**: 351-353.

Marsh, C. D., A. B. Clawson, and H. Marsh. 1929. Larkspur or "poison weed." U. S. D. A. Farmer's Bull. No. 988. 12 p.

McIntosh, R. P. 1970. Community, competition, and adaptation. *Q. Rev. Biol.,* **45**: 259-280.

McPherson, J. K. and C. H. Muller. 1969. Allelopathic effects of *Adenostoma fasciculatum,* "chamise," in the California chaparral. *Ecol. Monogr.,* **39**: 177-198.

Morris, R. F. 1960. Sampling insect populations. *Ann. Rev. Entomol.,* **5**: 234-264.

Murdoch, W. W. 1966. Community structure, population control, and competition—a critique. *Am. Nat.,* **100**: 219-226.

Paine, R. T. 1966. Food complexity and species diversity. *Am. Nat.,* **100**: 65-75.

Palmer, M. A. 1952. Aphids of the Rocky Mountain region. Thomas Say Foundation, Vol. V. 452 p.

Pelton, J. 1961. An investigation of the ecology of *Mertensia ciliata* in Colorado. *Ecology,* **42**: 38-52.

Puttarudriah, M. 1953. The natural control of the alfalfa looper in central California. *J. Econ. Entomol.,* **46**: 723.

Schoonhoven, L. M. 1969. Gustation and foodplant selection in some lepidopterous larvae. *Entomol. Exp. Appl.,* **12**: 555-564.

Slobodkin, L. B., F. E. Smith, and N. B. Hairston. 1967. Regulation in terrestrial ecosystems and the implied balance of nature. *Am. Nat.,* **101**: 109-124.

Southern, H. N. 1970. Ecology at the cross-roads. *J. Anim. Ecol.,* **39**: 1-11.

Stern, V. M., R. F. Smith, R. van den Bosch, and K. S. Hagen. 1959. The integrated control concept. *Hilgardia,* **29**: 81-101.

Torell, P. J. and R. E. Higgins. 1963. Tall larkspur and its control. Idaho Agricultural Extension Service, Bull. No. 407. 8 p.

Uhler, P. R. 1895. Descriptions of new species. p. 1-37. *In*: C. P. Gillette and Carl. F. Baker (eds.). *A Preliminary List of the Hemiptera of Colorado*. Colorado Agricultural Experiment Station, Bull. No. 31.

Way, M. J. 1968. Intra-specific mechanisms with special reference to aphid populations. p. 18-36. *In*: T. R. E. Southwood (ed.). *Insect Abundance*. Symposium No. 4 of the Royal Entomological Society. Blackwell Scientific Publications, Oxford, England.

Whittaker, R. H. 1969. Evolution of diversity in plant communities. p. 178-196. In: *Diversity and Stability in Ecological Systems*. Brookhaven Symposia in Biology, No. 22. Brookhaven National Laboratory, Upton, New York.

———— and P. P. Feeny. 1971. Allelochemics: Chemical interactions between species. *Science,* **171**: 757-770.

Williams, J. R. 1954. The biological control of weeds. Report of the 6th Commonwealth Entomological Conference, London, England. p. 95-98. (Quoted by Wilson, 1964.)

Williams, M. C. and E. H. Cronin. 1963. Effect of silvex and 2,4,5-T on alkaloid content of tall larkspur. *Weeds,* **11**: 317-319.

———— and ————. 1966. Five poisonous range weeds—When and why they are dangerous. *J. Range Manage.,* **19**: 274-279.

Wilson, F. 1964. The biological control of weeds. *Ann. Rev. Entomol.,* **9**: 225-244.

Index

ACTH, 240, 243
  circadian rhythm of, 241
  injection inhibits ovarian function, 241
    varies in mouse species, 241
  affects kidneys, 241
    mice & woodchucks, 241
AIBS
  round tables, 387
  information task force, 388
    objectives; identity needs; society co-operation; educational program, 388
    advise & develop aids, 388
ablation
  of nerve tissue, 30
abortion, 14, 15 (Table I), 19, 25, 248, 345
abstracting & indexing
  improvement in procedures, 381
  studies on effective, 382
  must be improved, 382
  & manuscripts replace journal articles, 382
  rely more on editors & authors, 383
  need for deeper, 384
  liaison between services & users, 385
α-bungarotoxin, 68
Acacia, 230
acacia-ants, 283
accidents, 135
Acer, 227
  rubrum, 420
Acetabularia, 149
acetylcholine, 37
Acmopyle, 229
Aconitum columbianum Nutt., 451
acoustical
  communicative signals, 204
  characters, 204
    vocalization, 204
  data, 205
actin, 92
actinic light (U.V.), 137
actinomycin, 90
actinomycin D, 87, 160, 183, 184
action potential, 29, 62, 67
  in muscle, 63
action spectra, 154
"activation energy," 142

  lower in neural function than aging, 142
"activation"–"inhibition" in circadian control, 161
  no true inhibitors found, 161
activators, 83
Aculus schlechtendali, 336
Adam Smith
  economics more Newtonian than Linnaean, 357
  seeking global regularities, not nature's diversity, 357
adaptation
  for selective competition, 171
adaptive
  mechanisms, 203
adrenal (*see pituitary*), 246
  androgens, 241
    block gonadotropins, 241
adrenocorticol, 246
adult state, 51
  advantaged & disadvantaged societies, 350
  maintain numbers, to retain or gain power, 350
    include military, 350
Aesculus, 227
Africa, 221, 223, 224, 225, 230, 243
aggression, (*see* pituitary) 185, 186, 240
  emphasis on evolutionary & physiological, 169
  ethological approaches not highlighted, 169
  and familiarity, 179
  forms of, 168
    fear-induced, 168
    inter-male confrontations, 168
    learned attacks, 168
    maternal, 168
    pain, 168
    predatory, 168
    territorial defense, 168
  future advances, 169
    competition & gene flow, 169
    gene expression in development of, 169
    physiological control of, 169, 185-189
  & gene expression, 181-185